# Island Biogeography of Mammals

### Edited by L. R. Heaney and
### B. D. Patterson

Reprinted from the Biological Journal of the Linnean Society
Volume 28, Numbers 1 & 2, 1986

Published for the Linnean Society of London

## ACADEMIC PRESS

Harcourt Brace Jovanovich, Publishers

London   Orlando   San Diego   New York
Austin   Boston   Sydney   Tokyo   Toronto

ACADEMIC PRESS INC. (LONDON) LIMITED
24/28 Oval Road
London NW1
(Registered Office)


US edition published by
ACADEMIC PRESS INC.
Orlando
Florida 32887

© 1986 The Linnean Society of London
ISBN 0 12 335735 7

Printed in Great Britain by
The Whitefriars Press Ltd., Tonbridge

# Contents

*Biological Journal of the Linnean Society* (1986), *28:* i–iii

# Introduction

LAWRENCE R. HEANEY

*Museum of Zoology, University of Michigan, Ann Arbor, Michigan 48109, U.S.A.*

AND

BRUCE D. PATTERSON

*Division of Mammals, Field Museum of Natural History, Chicago, Illinois 60605, U.S.A.*

Studies of the island biogeography of organisms have played a prominent role in the development and maturation of evolutionary biology since the time of Charles Darwin and Alfred R. Wallace; indeed, scarcely a textbook on general biology or evolution is published that does not comment on the historical importance of these studies. This prominence is based on the fact that island faunas serve as simpler and more tractable models for the more complex interactions among organisms on continents. By studying a world in miniature, we can come to recognize patterns and processes in the world at large.

A second, very striking aspect of island biogeography is that its importance to theoretical biology has not diminished in the 125 years since Darwin and Wallace made their seminal contributions. Early studies by Darwin and Wallace falsified many of the claims of the creationists of that day, paving the way for the tremendous expansion of evolutionary biology that followed. At the turn of the century, island studies helped to document the ubiquity of variation among populations, which ultimately led to the abandonment of typology and the acceptance of polytypic species. In the 1930s and 1940s, studies of insular variation contributed to development of the biological species concept and to the 'Modern Synthesis'. In the 1960s and 1970s, the equilibrium model of MacArthur and Wilson brought about a revolution in the way discontinuously distributed (insular) faunas were viewed, by synthesizing the current ecological theory with island biogeography. Beginning in the 1970s, vicariance biogeography combined plate tectonics with rigorous methodologies for investigating higher-level phylogenetic relationships, thus adding greater resolution to the time component of biogeographic analysis.

Throughout this period, studies of mammals have figured prominently, perhaps because their enormous range in vagility make mammals particularly apt subjects for biogeographic research. Wallace based many of his conclusions

i

on independent and parallel radiations of mammals in different parts of the Malaysian and Australasian regions; Matthew considered only mammals in his classic studies; Simpson wrote extensively on the mammal faunas of island-continents; several very prominent early studies of the equilibrium model utilized mammals; and many of the best examples of vicariance biogeography are based on studies of mammals.

In spite of the continuing contribution of studies of mammals to island biogeography, there has been no attempt at a synthesis of recent research; most symposia and published volumes on island biogeography have focused on given groups of islands (e.g. the California Channel Islands (Power, 1980), the Galápagos (Berry, 1984), and the Gulf of California islands (Case & Cody, 1983)), or have taken a very broad, and often generalized perspective (Williamson, 1982; *Oikos* special issue, 1983). Few recent studies have dealt comprehensively with a limited taxonomic group (but see the classic book on the birds of Jamaica by Lack, 1976).

In 1983, one of us (Heaney) was invited to organize a symposium on island biogeography of mammals for the International Theriological Congress to be held at the University of Alberta in August 1985. This was gladly accepted as a perfect opportunity to assemble a group of people who could provide a broad synthesis of the current state of mammalian island biogeography. Plans began immediately for publication of the papers from the symposium, with Patterson enlisted as co-editor. Astonishingly, we have been able to keep to the schedule we set for ourselves, but only with great assistance from the editors of the *Biological Journal of the Linnean Society* and Academic Press. All but two of the papers in this volume were presented at the symposium; those two were added to round out our coverage. Thus, most of the authors have had many opportunities to discuss and refer to each others' papers, and the result is a volume that is much more fully integrated than is typical for collections of papers.

The organization of the volume follows a flow from papers emphasizing short-term, primarily ecological perspectives to those with long-term, systematic and genetic perspectives. The final paper provides a summary and synthesis for the entire volume, and also includes comments on how the principles developed here can be extended to global phenomena.

In organizing the symposium and this volume, we have encouraged the contributors to combine theoretical and empirical approaches, with an emphasis on thorough documentation and empirical demonstration of patterns and processes. We believe that this has led to new insights by leading us to ask questions that have been previously unrecognized or glossed over. It has also caused us to search for new methods and techniques for measuring phenomena that we have found to be of importance. Examples of these new methods are Lomolino's procedure for determining the influence of interactive effects of extinction and immigration, Patterson and Atmar's procedure for determining 'nestedness' of faunas within archipelagos, and Heaney's use of middle Pleistocene landbridge and oceanic islands to derive quantitative estimates for very long-term rates of colonization, extinction and speciation.

Some of the results of these studies are worthy of emphasis. Demonstrations by Lomolino and Hanski of the frequency of colonization of non-volant mammals to near-shore islands provide dramatic documentation of the colonization potential of seemingly poor dispersers under ideal conditions. These provide the background for Crowell's unique measures of turnover rates, based on his 20-year studies along the coast of Maine. Patterson and Atmar demonstrate that mammal faunas in landbridge archipelagos are very rarely random assemblages, arguing that constituent faunas are typically nested subsets of the source fauna that are produced by selective extinction. Newmark evaluates area and habitat diversity as correlates of species richness in western North American parks, and concludes that area itself is the best predictor of the success of a reserve in protecting mammal populations. In an important contribution to a long-standing debate, Lawlor demonstrates empirically the biological significance of species–area slopes, correctly predicting variation in slopes among numerous archipelagos and taxa. Heaney's measurements of long-term rates of colonization and extinction are the first such estimates for mammals, and his demonstration of the importance of speciation invites a synthesis of equilibrium and vicariance biogeography. Morgan and Woods use a superb fossil record to demonstrate the fluctuation in the rate of extinction among West Indian mammals that has occurred as a result, first, of changing sea level and climate at the end of the Pleistocene, followed by the arrival of Amerindians, and finally by the arrival of Europeans and *Rattus rattus*. Berry reviews population genetic studies which indicate that founder effects contribute importantly to insular evolution. Finally, in his summary paper, Brown argues for continued use of the equilibrium model as a heuristic tool *because* of its simplicity and limitations, rather than *in spite of* them; he also argues that, on the basis of data presented in this volume, the major processes of island biogeography are highly deterministic, and therefore amenable both to further study and to prediction.

All of the authors recognize that we have raised more questions than we have answered; we take this as evidence of the fertility of the field in which we are working, and the promise of future returns on these research efforts. We expect some of our conclusions to be controversial, and we welcome the increased level of interest and research that we hope will follow.

## REFERENCES

BERRY, R. J. (Ed.), 1984. Evolution in the Galapagos Islands. *Biological Journal of the Linnean Society, 21:* 1–270.
CASE, T. J. & CODY, M. L. (Eds), 1984, *Island Biogeography in the Sea of Cortéz.* Berkeley: University of California Press.
LACK, D., 1976. *Island Biology, Illustrated by the Land Birds of Jamaica.* Berkeley: University of California Press.
POWER, D. M. (Ed.), 1980. *The California Islands: Proceedings of a Multidisciplinary Symposium.* Santa Barbara: Museum of Natural History.
WILLIAMSON, M., 1981. *Island Populations.* Oxford: Oxford University Press.

*Biological Journal of the Linnean Society* (1986), *28:* 1–21. With 6 figures

# Mammalian community structure on islands: the importance of immigration, extinction and interactive effects

MARK V. LOMOLINO

*Biology Department, S.U.N.Y., Binghamton, New York 13901, U.S.A.*

*Accepted for publication 14 February 1986*

A general review of the patterns of species richness of insular mammals (Lomolino, 1984a) indicated that richness is determined by interactive as well as additive effects of factors affecting immigration and extinction. The present paper reports that species composition of insular mammals is also influenced by such additive and interactive effects. Therefore, insular incidence should be high for those species whose (or on those islands where) (immigration rates) are high relative to extinction rates. The model presented in this paper predicts that species have high incidence on islands if low immigration rates (poor immigrators and/or distant islands) are compensated by low extinction rates (good survivors and/or large islands), or high extinction rates are compensated for by high immigration rates. Therefore, poor immigrators may be frequent inhabitants of distant islands if their extinction rates are compensatorily low (large islands and/or low resource requirements). Conversely, extinction-prone species (large, specialist carnivores) may be frequent inhabitants of small islands if their immigration rates are compensatorily high (near islands and/or good immigrators). These 'compensatory effects' were well evidenced by the mammalian faunas of the islands in the Thousand Islands Region, New York, and Lake Michigan (U.S.A.). 'Compensatory effects' are also evidenced by mammals of other archipelagos, as well as by birds inhabiting real and habitat islands. These results are consistent with the fundamental assumption of the equilibrium theory of island biogeography, i.e. insular community structure is the result of recurrent (rather than unique) immigrations and extinctions. Accordingly, I suggest that the concept of a fixed critical minimum area for isolated populations may be meaningless unless immigrations are unimportant with respect to the fauna under study. Finally, apparently anomalous or stochastic distribution patterns of insular species may readily be explained by the deterministic model presented here which incorporates the interactive as well as additive effects of immigration and extinctions on insular community structure.

KEY WORDS:—Area – community structure – compensatory effects – equilibrium theory – extinction – immigration – island biogeography – isolation – mammals – rescue effects.

## CONTENTS

0024–4066/86/050001 + 21 $03.00/0

## INTRODUCTION

Species richness and species composition of most insular faunas should be a function of factors affecting both immigration and extinction. Unless the islands and fauna under study differ little in characteristics which affect these processes, inter-island differences in community structure should be evident and explicable within this framework (see MacArthur & Wilson, 1967).

The importance of factors affecting extinction has been documented by numerous studies providing valuable insights into the assembly of insular as well as mainland communities. It is not my purpose here to summarize these studies (see Diamond, 1975, 1984). Instead, I focus on the other side of the coin, immigration, which has received much less attention. My thesis is not that immigration is of sole importance, and I hope to avoid this pitfall. Rather, I suggest that insular community structure of at least some and perhaps many faunas results from the combined effects of factors affecting immigration as well as extinction. Furthermore, both species richness and species composition may be influenced by interactions between immigration and extinction. That is, at least for some faunas, differential immigration and extinction should not be viewed as independent determinants of insular community structure.

The purpose of this paper is (1) to assess the relative importance of isolation and vagility as determinants of mammalian community structure on islands, and (2) to test whether species richness and species composition results from the combined and sometimes interactive effects of factors affecting immigration and extinction. I first summarize the results of an earlier review on species–area and species–distance relationships of mammals (Lomolino, 1984a), and then focus on determinants of species composition.

## SPECIES RICHNESS

According to the equilibrium theory of island biogeography (MacArthur & Wilson, 1967), the species richness ($S$) of an insular fauna should result from a balance between the opposing processes of immigration and extinction. As $S$ of a new (empty) island increases, the immigration rate of new species onto the island decreases while the overall extinction rate of previously established species increases. Eventually, a dynamic equilibrium will be achieved when immigration and extinction rates are equal. The equilibrium is termed dynamic because, although $S$ remains relatively constant, species composition should change as new species replace those that go extinct.

Because immigration rates decline with isolation ($D$) while extinction rates decline with area ($A$), the equilibrium theory predicts that $S$ should be a negative function of $D$ and a positive function of $A$. Most of the earlier 'evidence' for these predictions came from studies of insular avifaunas. This led both Sauer (1969) and Gilbert (1980) to suggest that non-avian communities provide little support for the equilibrium theory (but see also MacArthur & Wilson, 1967: 9; Lassen, 1975; Simberloff, 1976; Aho, 1978). In a recent analysis of mammalian communities on 19 archipelagos, however, I concluded that

Sauer's and Gilbert's contentions were premature and are not justified (Lomolino, 1982, 1984a). $S$–$A$ and $S$–$D$ relationships of these mammalian faunas were in accord with the predictions of the equilibrium theory; that is, $S$ increased with $A$ and decreased with $D$. An apparently anomalous finding, but one consistent with that for insular avifaunas, was that $S$ was less frequently affected by isolation than by area. For the 18 non-volant faunas analysed, area was significantly correlated with $S$ for all faunas, whereas $D$ was significant for only 10 faunas. This probably results from a sampling artefact related to the nature of the $S$–$A$ and $S$–$D$ relationships. Because both relationships are essentially asymptotic functions, the greater the mean values for $A$ and $D$, the larger the variation needed to cause an appreciable (detectable) change in $S$. Because coefficients of variation for $A$ were on average more than twice those for $D$, it is not surprising that $S$ was more frequently correlated with $A$ than with $D$.

Focusing specifically on the $S$–$D$ relationship, the strength of this relationship should be affected by vagility of the fauna in question, as well as archipelago isolation. Simply stated, more vagile faunas should be less affected by isolation. Consistent with this, although 10 of 18 non-volant faunas exhibited significant $S$–$D$ relationships, $S$ and $D$ were significantly correlated for only one of four volant faunas analysed. Not surprisingly, the only volant fauna that showed a correlation inhabited the most isolated archipelago studied and thus was more likely to be affected by $D$. Therefore, high relative vagility and the sampling artefact described above should explain why mammals, and perhaps insular faunas in general, are most frequently reported to be affected by $A$ and not $D$. Such results, of course, should not be interpreted to suggest that $D$ is an unimportant determinant of community structure for these faunas. Rather, they simply imply that intra-archipelago differences in $S$ are primarily determined by area or some other factor: few ecologists would question whether the consistently depauperate nature of isolated archipelagos is ultimately a function of their consequently low immigration rates.

Finally, species richness of mammalian faunas is also affected by interactions between area and isolation (or survivorship and vagility). First, the effects of $A$ on $S$ of mammals are more pronounced (higher $z$ values) for more isolated archipelagos (Lomolino, 1984a: fig. 2) and, equivalently, for the less vagile mammals (non-volants versus bats). In addition, the effects of isolation on $S$ were more pronounced for archipelagos with smaller islands (Lomolino, 1984a: fig. 6). Again, these interactions were predicted by MacArthur & Wilson (1967: 28–29).

### SPECIES COMPOSITION

In this section I will focus primarily on the effects of isolation and differences in vagility on species composition of insular mammalian faunas. Again, this is not meant to imply that differences in area, interspecific competition, or other factors affecting survivorship are unimportant. Instead, I wish to shed more light on the importance of immigration, which has received much less attention. Granted, a number of studies have demonstrated, or at least suggested, the importance of immigration as a determinant of insular community structure (e.g. Hamilton, Barth & Rubinoff, 1964; Patrick, 1967; Grant, 1970; Vuilleumier, 1970; Diamond, 1975; Diamond, Gilpin & Mayr, 1976; Fritz,

1979). These studies, however, seem to be dwarfed in number by those which focus on insular area and factors affecting extinction of insular populations. While the controversy over the significance of $z$ values in the $S$–$A$ relationship is still raging, few studies discuss the form of the $S$–$D$ relationship, let alone values of the constants of the formula. Moreover, very little attention is given to factors affecting immigration abilities and the degree to which differences in vagility affect insular community structure (some exceptions are discussed below).

One reason for the infrequent focus on vagility and isolation may be that it is very difficult to devise an objective measure of isolation which accurately reflects likelihood of immigration. Should we use distance to the mainland, or to the nearest island with more species, or perhaps some pooled measure of inter-island distances which weighs each according to the richness (and composition) of each island in the archipelago? Moreover, straight-line distance may not be a realistic measure of isolation if currents or other factors are important components of the barrier in question (e.g. see Cameron, 1958: 120–124, fig. 8; Williamson, 1981: 74–88).

A second reason for the infrequent focus on immigration may be the sampling artefact and related effects discussed previously. Without significant $S$–$D$ relationships, there is little incentive to study immigration. Of course, this view may be flawed because, although $S$ may not change with isolation, species composition might; for example, some species may be limited to the near islands while others are common on the more distant ones.

A third and perhaps more reasonable explanation for the paucity of such studies is that direct investigations of immigration are logistically unfeasible for most insular faunas, and inferences drawn from colonization studies (i.e. the appearance of new species) are confounded because colonization is influenced by numerous factors in addition to immigration abilities (e.g. birth and death rates and niche breadths). However, studies of immigrations are feasible for some insular faunas and may provide important insights into the determinants of insular community structure.

## The winter filtering effect

Archipelagos in larger lakes or rivers which freeze during winter provide a rare opportunity to study immigration directly by tracking the movements of mammals on the snow-covered ice. Even without the use of tracking studies, however, the importance of immigration abilities may be examined indirectly by testing whether winter-active species (non-hibernators) are more frequent on islands than are seasonally inactive species.

In fact, this winter filtering effect seems to be a common phenomenon for terrestrial mammals in regions with seasonal ice cover, and has been reported for mammals on the islands of Lake Superior (Jackson, 1919), Lake Michigan (Hatt *et al.*, 1948), the Gulf of St. Lawrence (Cameron, 1958; Denman, 1965), and Basswood Lake, Minnesota (Beer, Lukens & Olson, 1954; see also Pruitt, 1951; Banfield, 1954). More recently, the winter filtering effect was also reported for the terrestrial mammals on islands off the coast of Maine (see Crowell, 1986) and in the Thousand Islands Region (Lomolino, 1983, 1986). In the latter case, I was able to directly study immigration abilities by tracking the mammals' movements across the snow-covered ice of the St. Lawrence River. In

Table 1. Summary of cross-ice movements of non-volant mammals during 33 tracking surveys along the St. Lawrence River (see Lomolino, 1983, 1986). Species are listed in order of decreasing body size (mass)

| Species | Distance travelled (m)* | | | Immigrations | Emigrations |
|---|---|---|---|---|---|
| | Max. | Mean | $\mathcal{N}$ | | |
| Odocoileus virginianus† | 2100 | 2100 | 2 | 1 | 1 |
| Canis latrans | 5315 | 765 | 88 | 59 | 55 |
| Vulpes vulpes | 2320 | 508 | 347 | 212 | 205 |
| Procyon lotor‡ | 140 | 123 | 2 | 1 | 1 |
| Mustela vison‡ | 785 | 269 | 7 | 3 | 2 |
| Ondatra zibethicus‡ | 650 | 330 | 4 | 0 | 0 |
| Mephitis mephitis | 785 | 393 | 10 | 4 | 4 |
| Sylvilagus floridanus | 950 | 378 | 10 | 3 | 2 |
| Sciurus carolinensis | 160 | 142 | 5 | 5 | 4 |
| Tamiasciurus hudsonicus | 285 | 129 | 13 | 10 | 10 |
| Condylura cristata‡ | 1068§ | 127 | 10 | 0 | 0 |
| Microtus pennsylvanicus | 595 | 224 | 12 | 1 | 0 |
| Peromyscus leucopus | 36 | 19 | 6 | 0 | 0 |
| Blarina brevicauda | 475 | 261 | 2 | 0 | 2 |

*Max. = the maximum and Mean = the average distance traveled per track; $\mathcal{N}$ = total number of tracks for this species.
†*Odocoileus virginianus* was tracked twice on the ice of the St. Lawrence River in 1979, but not during an actual tracking survey.
‡Semi-aquatic species.
§This *Condylura* found dead at end of trail ($T_{max} = -1.5°C$ and $T_{min} = -18.5°C$).

general, the larger, winter-active species were good immigrators, whereas smaller species and hibernators seldom travelled across the ice, and then only for limited distances (Table 1). Consistent with these observations, species which utilized the ice cover had significantly higher insular rankings ($P < 0.007$, Wilcoxon ranked sum test; rankings based on comparisons of frequencies of occurrence at eight mainland and 19 insular sites; see Lomolino, 1986). In addition, for similar species of small mammals such as the insectivores, the smaller species had lower insular rankings (rankings for *Sorex cinereus*, *S. fumeus*, *Blarina brevicauda* and *Condylura cristata* were 3.5, 3.5, 16 and 18, respectively; maximum rank = 23).

### Extinction–immigration interactions: compensatory effects

In this section I suggest that insular species composition is influenced not only by the combined (additive) effects of factors influencing immigration and extinction, but by interactive effects as well. One of the fundamental assumptions of the equilibrium theory is that species richness results from the effects of recurrent immigrations and extinctions. A logical corollary is that insular species composition should also be influenced by these recurrent processes (the relationship between insular incidence ($\mathcal{J}$) of a species and its immigration and extinction rates ($I$ and $E$) is $\mathcal{J} = I/(I+E)$; Diamond, 1975). For archipelagos where this applies, 'compensatory effects' should be evident, at least for some species.

By compensatory effects I refer to situations where a species should exhibit a high incidence on islands if (1) low immigration rates (poor immigrators and/or distant islands) are compensated by low extinction rates (good survivors and/or large islands), or (2) high extinction rates are compensated by high immigration rates.

Therefore, poor immigrators may be common on distant islands if their extinction rates are compensatorily low (large islands and/or low resource requirements). Conversely, extinction-prone species (large, specialist carnivores) may be common on small islands if their immigration rates are compensatorily high (near islands and/or good immigrators). According to this view, species are common on those islands where their immigration rates are high *relative to* their extinction rates. In contrast, the alternative view asserts that immigrations and extinctions are, for the most part, unique occurrences for each species, and species are common only on those islands close enough to allow immigrations and with sufficient resources to prevent extinctions. Therefore, 'compensatory effects', as I have termed them here, may be viewed as an extension of the 'rescue effect' of Brown & Kodric-Brown (1977), although the latter was applied to turnover rates and not species composition (see also Lomolino, 1984b).

These predictions may be restated by suggesting that insular occurrence of at least some species should be biased in favour of the large (versus small) distant islands, and near (versus distant) small islands. Presence–absence plots may be used to illustrate, and later test, these predictions (Fig. 1). The axes of these plots are isolation and area. The presence or absence of each species is indicated on the graph at points corresponding to area and isolation of all islands studied.

Five biologically realistic outcomes for these plots are illustrated in Fig. 1. These include a random pattern, a minimum area effect, a maximum isolation effect, a non-compensatory area–isolation effect and a compensatory effect. Minimum area effects (Fig. 1C) should be exhibited by those species whose immigration abilities are high relative to the isolation of islands considered, but whose resource requirements are such that they can only maintain populations on the largest islands. Conversely, maximum isolation effects (Fig. 1D) should be exhibited by species with low resource requirements relative to insular carrying capacities, but with limited immigration abilities relative to island isolation. Two types of patterns may be exhibited by species whose insular distributions depend upon both area and isolation (or extinction and immigration). The 'block' pattern of Fig. 1E should be exhibited by species whose insular occurrence is not influenced by compensatory effects (i.e. the alternative view of additive effects), whereas the 'diagonal' pattern of Fig. 1F is expected where compensatory effects are important.

The patterns of distributions of all species in an archipelago may be summarized in one plot. Let us consider a hypothetical and relatively simple system of three species whose insular distributions follow the dynamic (or interactive) model; i.e. compensatory effects are important (Fig. 2). Let us also assume that, for this group of ecologically similar species, larger species have greater resource requirements and greater vagility (see McNab, 1963; Jenkins, 1981; Lomolino, 1983, 1986). Note that the lines of distribution, which indicate the area–isolation coordinates at which insular incidence $= 0.5$ (i.e. $\mathcal{J} = 0.5$ and $I = E$), are expected to be curvilinear because individual species immigration rates should drop off as an approximately exponential function of isolation.

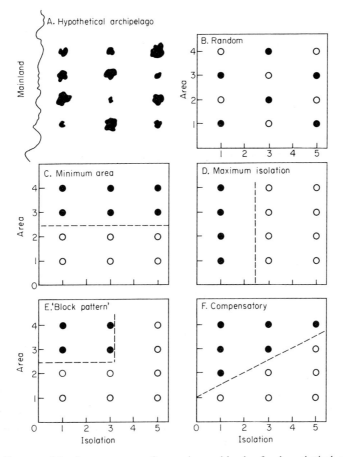

Figure 1. Patterns of insular occurrence of a species on islands of a hypothetical archipelago. Presence and absence in B–F are indicated by filled or open circles, respectively (units for area and isolation are arbitrary). The dashed lines were calculated using the discriminant analysis methods discussed in the text.

Eventually, isolation will exceed the maximum immigration abilities of a species, and this species should be absent on even the largest distant islands. Note also that as we consider larger, presumably more vagile species, the range increases over which isolation and, therefore, compensatory effects are difficult to detect ($I_A < I_B < I_C$ in Fig. 2).

This simple model suggests at least two important predictions concerning patterns of distribution. The first and most obvious is that compensatory effects should be more evident for archipelagos with a large range of area and isolation relative to resource requirements and vagility of the fauna in question. Secondly, an apparently paradoxical prediction from this model is suggested by intersection of the lines of distribution. Consider, for example, the distribution patterns of species A and B in Fig. 2. On the near islands (to the left of the intersection), species A should exhibit higher incidence on the small islands. For more isolated islands, however, the situation is reversed. Now B, the larger species, should be the more frequent inhabitant of the smaller islands. As we consider a greater range of isolation and area, this 'flip-flop' pattern should be

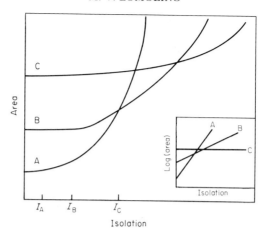

Figure 2. Lines of distribution (insular occurrence) of three species of a hypothetical community. The probability of occurrence of each species is greater than 0.5 above their respective lines of distribution. Here I assume that the larger species (C > B > A) have greater resource requirements and immigration abilities. Therefore, the intercepts of the distribution lines increase, while the slopes decrease with size ($I_A$, $I_B$ and $I_C$ approximate the lower range of immigration ability for each species). Note that the curvilinear relationships become approximately linear in the semi-log plot (see inset).

repeated in the remaining larger species. Again, the effects of area are dependent on the relative degree of isolation.

The importance of compensatory effects in structuring real insular communities may be examined using discriminant analysis. This method involved a three-step procedure. First, stepwise discriminant analysis was used to test whether area and/or isolation significantly affected insular incidence of each species considered (area was entered first, $P$-to-enter $= 0.15$, $P$-to-stay $= 0.05$). Secondly, those variables that were significant determinants of insular incidence according to the above analysis were used in a multiple discriminant analysis to calculate the slope and intercept of the lines of distribution. Thirdly, in order to distinguish between compensatory effects and the block pattern of Fig. 1F & E, I created a new variable whenever area and isolation were found to be significant variables in the stepwise discriminant analysis. This variable equalled 1 when the island coordinate was within the rectangular region of Fig. 1E, and 0 when it was outside this region. The levels of area and isolation delineating this region were derived from separate discriminant analyses for each variable ($A$ and $D$). Finally, this new variable was used in a stepwise discriminant analysis along with area and isolation to test whether the former variable best accounted for the observed pattern. [Logistic regression was not used because it requires quite large sample sizes; according to Harrell (1983: 190), the number of observations in the least frequent category should be 20 with two variables. Therefore $N$ should be $\gg 40$.] The distribution lines for the hypothetical fauna of Fig. 1, and for all real faunas to be considered herein, were drawn using the above methods. It is important to emphasize that all distribution lines in presence–absence plots were statistically, not visually, determined, and indicate significance at the $P \leqslant 0.05$ level.

These methods were used to examine the distribution patterns of the 10 species inhabiting at least two of the 19 islands I studied in the Thousand Islands

Region. Two separate sets of analyses were run using area and isolation, or log (area) and isolation as the discriminant variables. The results of these analyses were qualitatively identical in almost all cases. Therefore, for the sake of clarity, the following discussion refers to the semi-log (log (area)–isolation) analysis, which transforms the curvilinear patterns of Fig. 2 to approximate the more linear ones of Fig. 1. Isolation was measured as (1) distance to the nearest point on the mainland or large island, and (2) the distance to the mainland or nearest island with this species. For all but two species *(Microtus pennsylvanicus* and *Blarina brevicauda)*, these measures were identical, and in the case of the latter species, the results of discriminant analyses using the alternative measures of isolation were qualitatively identical.

It is important to note that relative immigration and survival abilities can be assessed independently of species distributions, based on the results of tracking studies (Table 1) and information on the body size, diet and general ecology of these species. Thus, circular arguments can be avoided when considering causative factors for observed distribution patterns.

## Mammals of the Thousand Islands Region

For the Thousand Islands fauna, not one of the 10 species examined exhibited a maximum isolation effect (Fig. 3 and Table 2). This is not surprising because the islands considered are not highly isolated and vary less than an order of magnitude in isolation, but over four orders of magnitude in area. Thus, the statistical artefact referred to earlier seems responsible for the lack of isolation (only) effects.

*Microtus* was the only species whose insular distribution was not affected by area or isolation. Again, this is not surprising because it is both a good immigrator (Table 1) and good survivor (i.e. a small, generalist herbivore).

Six of the remaining nine species exhibit minimum area effects. To a large degree, the distributions of these species with respect to area reflect their relative resource requirements. *Odocoileus* and *Vulpes*, the largest species and largest carnivore, respectively, were restricted to the two largest islands (critical minimum area, $A_c = 0.251$ km$^2$). *Procyon*, a large omnivore, inhabited the four largest islands ($A_c = 0.122$ km$^2$), whereas *Tamiasciurus*, a considerably smaller granivore-omnivore, inhabited much smaller islands ($A_c = 0.073$ km$^2$).

Considering just their resource requirements, the restrictions of *Sylvilagus* and *Tamias* to the two largest islands represent apparent anomalies. This is especially true for *Tamias* because it is a relatively small herbivore (100 g) which was quite common on the mainland but absent from six relatively large islands (0.04–0.65 km$^2$) with suitable habitat (oak and hickory forests) to support chipmunk populations. It is important to note, however, that these are relatively distant islands, five beyond 0.5 km from the nearest source community. In addition, *Tamias* is a hibernator and relatively poor immigrator, being the only species of the 10 considered here that I did not detect travelling across ice. Apparently, the only isolated islands supporting *Tamias* populations are the largest ones where the consequent low extinction rates can compensate for its poor immigration ability. The above also implies that *Tamias* may be common on small islands if they are compensatorily close to the mainland or source community. In fact, *Tamias* was captured along with *Tamiasciurus* on a small

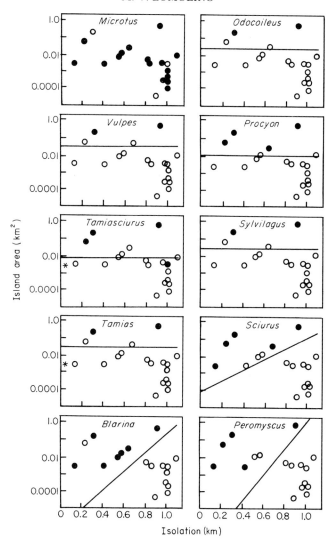

Figure 3. Insular occurrence of 10 species of non-volant mammals in the Thousand Islands Region as a function of island area and isolation. Filled and open circles indicate presence and absence, respectively. The lines indicate that insular occurrence was significantly affected by area (horizontal lines) or by area and isolation (diagonal lines; $P < 0.05$). Asterisks indicate presence of *Tamias* and *Tamiasciurus* on a small, near island which was not adequately surveyed to determine the possible presence of other species.

(0.0025 km²), but near island (0.02 km from the mainland) during these trapping surveys (data for this island were not included in this and previous community analyses because traplines were constantly disturbed so that presence or absence of other species could not reliably be determined). Similarly, Werner (1954) captured *Tamias* only on the largest and nearest of 10 islands he studied in this region (Wellesley $A = 32.13$ km², $D = 0.01$ km; Iroquois $A = 0.058$ km², $D < 0.09$). In my study, *Tamias* was absent from three relatively large, but isolated islands ($A = 0.09$, 0.07 and 0.03 km²; $D = 0.55$, 0.27 and 1.07 km, respectively). [Note that when discriminant analyses were run using the data for this island, compensatory effects were indicated for both *Tamias* and *Tamiasciurus* in the non-log, but not semi-log, model; see Table 2.]

The three remaining species clearly exhibit the type of compensatory effect depicted in Fig. 1F. That is, their insular distributions were significantly affected by both area and isolation, and the compensatory model was better than the block model in explaining the observed pattern. This group includes the two small mammals, *Peromyscus leucopus* and *Blarina brevicauda*. In contrast to *Microtus*, these small mammals are poor immigrators (Table 1; for swimming studies see also Carter & Merritt, 1981) and thus should be more limited by isolation and more likely to exhibit compensatory effects.

The differences in distribution patterns of the above small mammals is paralleled by that of the squirrels. In comparison to *Tamiasciurus*, *Sciurus* is a relatively poor immigrator, travelling much less frequently and over shorter distances across ice (Table 1). In addition, *Sciurus* is much larger than *Tamiasciurus*

Table 2. Results of discriminant analysis of species presence–absence distributions of terrestrial mammals in the Thousand Islands Region ($A$ = area in km$^2$)

| Species | Number of islands | | Model | Isolation* | | | Area* | |
|---|---|---|---|---|---|---|---|---|
| | Present | Total | | $R_c^2$ | $P_F$ | $P_\lambda$ | $P_F$ | $P_\lambda$ |
| *Blarina* | 7 | 19 | $\log A = -4.96 + 5.11D$ | 0.53 | 0.002 | 0.002 | 0.002 | 0.002 |
| | | | $A = -5.03 + 7.89D$ | 0.57 | 0.002 | 0.002 | 0.037 | 0.001 |
| | | | $(\log A = -3.87 + 4.01D$ | 0.52 | 0.082 | 0.003 | 0.003 | 0.003)† |
| *Microtus* | 16 | 19 | | | 0.890 | | 0.883 | |
| | | | | | 0.879 | | 0.890 | |
| | | | | | (0.943 | | 0.884)† | |
| *Tamiasciurus* | 4 | 19 | $\log A = -0.95 \ [A = 0.112]$ | 0.39 | 0.770 | | 0.004 | 0.004 |
| | | | $A = 1.06$ | 0.38 | 0.244 | | 0.005 | 0.005 |
| | 5§ | 20 | $\log A = -1.139 \ [A = 0.073]$ | 0.32 | 0.387 | | 0.001 | 0.001 |
| | | | $A = -1.06 + 2.91D$ | 0.44 | 0.044 | 0.007 | 0.015 | 0.015 |
| *Sciurus* | 5 | 19 | $\log A = -2.99 + 2.99D$ | 0.58 | 0.052 | 0.001 | 0.001 | 0.001 |
| | | | $A = -2.59 + 5.18D$ | 0.67 | 0.004 | 0.004 | 0.002 | 0.001 |
| *Sylvilagus* | 2 | 19 | $\log A = -0.60 \ [A = 0.251]$ | 0.77 | 0.770 | | 0.004 | 0.004 |
| | | | $A = 1.95$ | 0.44 | 0.990 | | 0.001 | 0.001 |
| *Procyon* | 4 | 19 | $\log A = -0.91 \ [A = 0.122]$ | 0.55 | 0.690 | | 0.001 | 0.001 |
| | | | $A = -0.88 + 2.96D‡$ | 0.56 | 0.030 | 0.001 | 0.003 | 0.003 |
| *Tamias* | 2 | 19 | $\log A = -0.60 \ [A = 0.251]$ | 0.77 | 0.770 | | 0.004 | 0.004 |
| | | | $A = 1.95$ | 0.44 | 0.990 | | 0.001 | 0.001 |
| | 3§ | 20 | $\log A = -0.95 \ [A = 0.112]$ | 0.27 | 0.398 | | 0.019 | 0.019 |
| | | | $A = 0.82 + 2.312D$ | 0.61 | 0.019 | 0.001 | 0.001 | 0.001 |
| *Vulpes* | 2 | 19 | $\log A = -0.60 \ [A = 0.251]$ | 0.77 | 0.770 | | 0.004 | 0.004 |
| | | | $A = 1.95$ | 0.44 | 0.990 | | 0.001 | 0.001 |
| *Odocoileus* | 2 | 19 | $\log A = -0.60 \ [A = 0.252]$ | 0.77 | 0.770 | | 0.004 | 0.004 |
| | | | $A = 1.95$ | 0.44 | 0.990 | | 0.001 | 0.001 |
| *Peromyscus* | 5 | 19 | $\log A = -6.35 + 7.09D$ | 0.59 | 0.001 | 0.001 | 0.116 | 0.001 |
| | | | $A = -4.06 + 7.00D$ | 0.75 | 0.001 | 0.001 | 0.001 | 0.001 |

*$P_\lambda$ and $P_F$ = probabilities based on Wilk's $\lambda$ and $F$ tests, respectively $R_c^2$ = average squared canonical correlation.
†Values in parentheses are results when isolation was measured as distance to nearest island with this species. This measure of isolation differed from distance to the mainland or nearest large island only for *Blarina* and *Microtus*. Antilog transformed values for area are reported in parentheses, and area and isolation were measured in km$^2$ and km, respectively. Area (or log (area)) was entered first into the stepwise discriminant analysis.
‡This apparent compensatory effect is probably spurious because it would result from *Procyon* occurring on the four largest islands.
§These results based on data including one island where *Tamias* and *Tamiasciurus* were captured, but trapping had to be terminated early due to disturbance (see text).

(0.5 versus 0.1 kg), more specialized in diet and habitat, and thus should be more affected by limited insular resources or island area. Therefore, *Sciurus* is much more likely to be affected by both area and isolation and exhibit a compensatory effect.

## Comparison with other isolated faunas

As previously indicated, the patterns of distribution of insular faunas in an archipelago may be summarized in one plot or community spectrum. In this section I present and compare four community spectra. The first is that for the Thousand Islands fauna. The second spectrum combines distribution data for the nine species occurring both on the islands in the Thousand Islands Region and those in Lake Michigan (Hatt *et al.*, 1948), and thus encompasses a much greater range of both isolation and area (Table 3; *Peromyscus leucopus* was not recorded on the islands of Lake Michigan). The remaining two spectra are constructed from information on 'relaxing' faunas of the Great Basin (Brown, 1971, 1978; Table 4) and Bass Straits (Hope, 1973; Table 5).

First, compare the spectra for the Thousand Islands with that of the combined data (Figs 4 & 5; see Appendix). As predicted by the compensatory model (Fig. 2), more species exhibit compensatory effects in the combined system which covers a much greater degree of isolation. The additional species are *Tamiasciurus* and *Sylvilagus*, so that five of the original 10 species clearly exhibit compensatory effects. For the four 'compensatory species' inhabiting both regions, the distribution lines for the larger species have higher intercepts but lower slopes (this includes *Blarina*, *Tamiasciurus*, *Sciurus* and *Sylvilagus*). Thus, the relative positions and slopes of these curves fit the model's predictions and indicate that the 'paradox of intersection' (p. 7) should be important. For example, on the near islands in the Thousand Islands Region (Fig. 4) *Blarina* should occur on much smaller islands than do *Sciurus*, whereas on the more distant islands this situation is reversed and *Sciurus* now occurs on the smaller islands, Similarly, this pattern is also evident for *Sylvilagus* versus the tree squirrels (*Sciurus* and *Tamiasciurus*) in the combined data set (Fig. 5).

Table 3. Results of presence–absence discriminant analysis for distributions of nine species of terrestrial mammals occurring in the Thousand Islands Region (Lomolino, 1983) and the islands of Lake Michigan (Hatt *et al.*, 1948)

| Species | Number of islands* | | | Isolation | | | Area | |
|---------|---------|-------|-------|-----------|-----|-----|------|-----|
|  | Present | Total | Model | $R_c^2$ | $P_F$ | $P_\lambda$ | $P_F$ | $P_\lambda$ |
| *Blarina* | 8 | 33 | $\log A = -1.68 + 1.97D$ | 0.27 | 0.025 | 0.010 | 0.041 | 0.041 |
| *Microtus* | 17 | 33 | $D = 6.79$ | 0.41 | 0.001 | 0.001 | 0.723 | |
| *Tamiasciurus* | 7 | 34 | $\log A = -1.13 + 0.11D$ | 0.33 | 0.007 | 0.002 | 0.028 | 0.028 |
| *Sciurus* | 5 | 30 | $\log A = -1.18 + 0.11D$ | 0.34 | 0.003 | 0.004 | 0.006 | 0.006 |
| *Sylvilagus* | 5 | 34 | $\log A = -0.61 + 0.07D$ | 0.39 | 0.056 | 0.001 | 0.001 | 0.001 |
| *Procyon* | 9 | 33 | $\log A = -0.349 [A = 0.447]$ | 0.56 | 0.911 | | 0.001 | 0.001 |
| *Tamias* | 8 | 34 | $\log A = -0.31 [A = 0.490]$ | 0.48 | 0.463 | | 0.001 | 0.001 |
| *Vulpes* | 10 | 34 | $\log A = -0.42 [A = 0.380]$ | 0.60 | 0.106 | | 0.001 | 0.001 |
| *Odocoileus* | 3 | 33 | $\log A = -0.05 [A = 0.891]$ | 0.31 | 0.132 | 0.004 | 0.003 | 0.003 |

*Total number of islands differs because questionable occurrences were excluded. Log (area) models only. Symbols as in Table 2.

Table 4. Results of presence–absence discriminant analysis of the distributions of 10 terrestrial mammals occurring on at least five mountaintop islands in the Great Basin*

| Species | Number of islands | | Model | $R_c^2$ | $P$ (area)† |
| | Present | Total | | | |
| --- | --- | --- | --- | --- | --- |
| *Sylvilagus nuttalli* | 12 | 19 | $\log A = 2.51 \ [A = 324]$ | 0.46 | 0.001 |
| *Sorex monticolus* | 6 | 19 | $\log A = 2.71 \ [A = 513]$ | 0.21 | 0.04 |
| *Sorex palustris* | 6 | 19 | $\log A = 2.71 \ [A = 513]$ | 0.29 | 0.017 |
| *Marmota flaviventris* | 10 | 19 | $\log A = 2.59 \ [A = 389]$ | 0.48 | 0.001 |
| *Spermophilus lateralis* | 14 | 19 | $\log A = 2.47 \ [A = 295]$ | 0.25 | 0.031 |
| *Eutamias umbrinus* | 17 | 19 | $\log A = 2.24 \ [A = 174]$ | 0.28 | 0.019 |
| *Microtus longicaudus* | 13 | 19 | $\log A = 2.49 \ [A = 309]$ | 0.33 | 0.010 |
| *Ochotona princeps* | 5 | 19 | $\log A = 2.75 \ [A = 562]$ | 0.27 | 0.023 |
| *Eutamias dorsalis* | 13 | 19 | | | 0.110 |
| *Neotoma cinerea* | 17 | 19 | | | > 0.50 |

*For this data set, $P$(isolation) $> 0.15$ for all species. Symbols as in Table 2.
†$P_F$(area) $= P_\lambda$ (area) in all cases. Area in km².

As these spectra also indicate, the larger, more vagile species are limited by area alone, with *Odocoileus*, the largest species studied, limited to the largest islands. As before, the distribution pattern of *Tamias* appears anomalous, but may be explained by the type of compensatory effect discussed earlier (i.e. a small, but poor immigrator being limited to the largest islands because of low extinction).

Finally, *Microtus* exhibits a maximum isolation effect in the combined system (Fig. 5). Quite surprisingly and perhaps fortuitously, the critical isolation (6.79 km) agrees almost perfectly with the maximum immigration ability I calculated for *Microtus* during preliminary treadmill experiments at winter temperatures ($\bar{x} = 6.77$ km, s.d. $= 0.59$, $N = 3$, ambient temperature $= +7.3°C$; Lomolino, 1983: 110). Unfortunately, only one of the 34 islands in this combined system lies between 1.1 and 6.4 km (none between 2.4 and 6.4 km). Therefore, it is impossible to tell at present whether *Microtus* was affected by isolation alone or by compensatory effects within this range of isolation.

In summary, the distributions of mammals in these temperate archipelagos are in good agreement with the compensatory model. It may now be instructive

Table 5. Results of presence–absence discriminant analysis of the distributions of five species of terrestrial mammals occurring on at least three islands in Bass Straits (after Hope, 1973)*

| Species | Present | Total | Model | $R_c^2$ | $P$ (area)† |
| --- | --- | --- | --- | --- | --- |
| *Macropus rufogriseus* | 4 | 26 | $\log A = 1.98 \ [A = 95.5]$ | 0.77 | < 0.001 |
| *Thylogale billardieri* | 9 | 26 | $\log A = 1.98 \ [A = 95.5]$ | 0.51 | < 0.001 |
| *Potorous tridactylus* | 3 | 26 | $\log A = 2.15 \ [A = 141.3]$ | 0.67 | < 0.001 |
| *Trichosurus vulpecula* | 5 | 26 | $\log A = 1.68 \ [A = 47.9]$ | 0.47 | < 0.001 |
| *Pseudocheirus peregrinus* | 4 | 26 | $\log A = 1.98 \ [A = 95.5]$ | 0.77 | < 0.001 |

*Excludes introductions. $P$(isolation) $> 0.15$ for all species. Symbols as in Table 2.
†$P_F$ (area) $= P_\lambda$ (area) in all cases. Area in km².

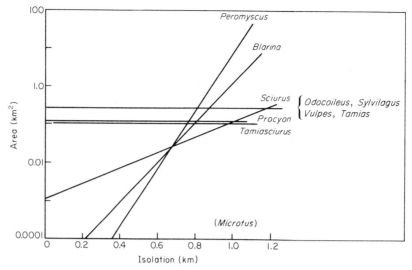

Figure 4. A community spectrum summarizing the patterns of insular occurrence of non-volant mammals in the Thousand Islands Region. Note that only *Microtus* exhibited a random pattern of insular occurrence with respect to island area and isolation (see Fig. 1B).

to focus on the two systems where isolation effects should be negligible, the relaxation faunas of Bass Straits and the Great Basin (Hope, 1973; Brown, 1978). Because these faunas are thought to be undergoing relaxation (without recolonization), their species should only exhibit minimum area effects. If compensatory or isolation effects are observed, then either the methods employed or the designation of these faunas as 'relaxation' ones would be

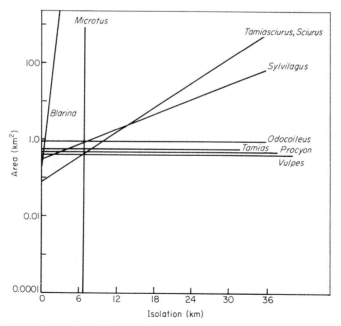

Figure 5. A community spectrum for non-volant mammals of the island of Lake Michigan and the Thousand Islands Region, combined.

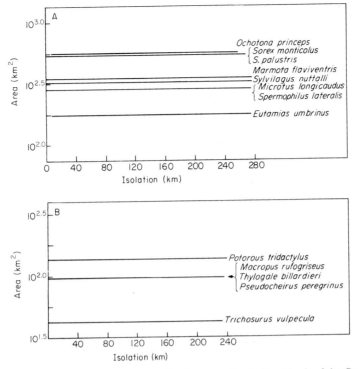

Figure 6. Community spectra for two relaxation faunas on landbridge islands of the Great Basin (A) and Bass Straits (B). Because these mammalian faunas are primarily affected by extinctions without contemporary immigrations, their species should only exhibit minimum area effects (see Fig. 1C).

suspect. Fortunately, only minimum area effects were exhibited (Fig. 6, Tables 4 & 5, Appendix). All five of the species occurring on three or more islands in Bass Strait, and eight of the 10 species occurring on at least five islands in the Great Basin exhibited minimum area effects. In the latter archipelago, *Eutamias dorsalis* and *Neotoma cinerea* exhibited the random pattern of Fig. 1B; i.e. their insular occurrence was not significantly affected by area or isolation of the islands considered.

Table 6. Characteristics of the islands and faunas of the four archipelagos considered in this study

| Archipelago | Critical area (km²) | | | Body mass (kg) | | | Isolation (km)† | | |
|---|---|---|---|---|---|---|---|---|---|
| | $\bar{x}$ | (s.d.) | $N^*$ | $\bar{x}$ | (s.d.) | Range | $\bar{x}$ | (s.d.) | Range |
| Thousand Islands | 0.22 | (0.08) | 6 | 13.09 | (34.28) | 0.02–110 | 0.77 | (0.30) | 0.17–1.04 |
| Combined Temperate (Thousand Islands + Lake Michigan) | 0.55 | (0.23) | 4 | 14.54 | (36.03) | 0.02–110 | 6.62 | (9.40) | 0.1–35.4 |
| Bass Straits | 95.1 | (33.0) | 5 | 5.52 | (4.93) | 0.9–12.4 | 64.5 | (43.2) | 28–225 |
| Great Basin | 377.3 | (124.5) | 8 | 0.46 | (0.93) | 0.007–3 | 67.2 | (73.4) | 6.4–278 |

*$N$ = number of species exhibiting a minimum area effect.

†Isolation = distance to nearest large island or source community.

A closer examination of the results of discriminant analyses of these relaxation faunas reveals a striking difference between critical minimum areas $(A_c)$ of these species and those of the temperate archipelagos. For the species exhibiting minimum area effects, the 'relaxation faunas' of the Great Basin and Bass Straits require island areas between two and three orders of magnitude greater than those of the less isolated, temperate archipelagos (Table 6). This is despite the fact that the latter faunas include much larger species, in general, and the largest species studied, *Odocoileus*. These results are not that surprising, however, when one considers the differences in isolation and consequent immigration rates of these four faunas (Table 6). Mammals of the Thousand Islands Region and Lake Michigan may persist on very small islands in large part by virtue of their high immigration rates (i.e. recurrent immigrations prevent extinction or rapidly re-establish the populations). In contrast, the much more isolated relaxation faunas are limited to only those islands where they can persist (without recurrent immigrations and/or recolonization) for perhaps thousands of years. Again, a compensatory effect is evident, although this time operating at the archipelago rather than island level. That is, although individual species of these faunas do not exhibit the type of compensatory effect depicted in Fig. 1F, they (as a group) are restricted to the very large islands where their consequently low extinction rates can compensate for their generally low immigration rates.

## DISCUSSION AND CONCLUSIONS

The obvious implication from these distribution patterns is that, in archipelagos where community structure results from recurrent immigrations and extinctions, the effects of these selective forces on insular occurrence may be inseparable. That is, common or frequently encountered insular species are those whose immigration rates are high relative to their extinction rates. Moreover, species are common only on those islands near and/or large enough to fulfill the above condition (i.e. a high relative immigration rate). To support these species, distant islands need to be large and smaller islands must be less isolated. Therefore, species composition of communities on more distant islands may be biased in favour of the better survivors (as well as better immigrators), while those on the smaller islands may be biased in favour of the better immigrators (as well as good survivors). Equivalently, good immigrators may be common on small (as well as distant) islands.

The insular distributions of *Microtus* and *Peromyscus* species on archipelagos may be a case in point. Numerous authors have noted that *Microtus* frequently inhabits much smaller islands than does *Peromyscus* (primarily *P. maniculatus* and *P. leucopus*). This is despite the fact that the habitat on many and perhaps most of these islands is more favourable to *Peromyscus* (see Crowell, 1973, 1983; Redfield, 1976; Melhop & Lynch, 1978; Carter & Merritt, 1981). Rather than offering the common interpretation of higher resource requirements for *Peromyscus* species, I submit that the differences in distributions of these small mammals with respect to island area may be better explained by compensatory effects. Even if populations of these species have comparable extinction rates on small islands, *Microtus* may be more common because of its greater vagility (Table 1; for comparison of swimming abilities see Carter & Merritt, 1981). Especially pertinent is the observation of Crowell (1973: 54) that colonization rates for *M. pennsylvanicus* on islands off the coast of Maine were substantially higher than those of *P. leucopus* (0.043 and 0.028/year), whereas extinction rates for introduced populations were nearly equal (0.057 and 0.065/year). Similarly, Pokki (1981) has shown that *Microtus agrestis* is quite common on small islands in the Tvarminne Archipelago, Finland, by virtue of its rapid recolonization rate which balances ('compensates' for) its frequent extinctions (84 colonizations and 81 extinctions recorded on 71 islands over six years).

The sciurids exhibit a pattern similar to that of the above small mammals. In the Thousand Islands Region, *Tamias* was restricted to the two largest islands, whereas the substantially larger and more vagile tree squirrels inhabited islands approximately one-tenth the size of the smallest ones with *Tamias* (Fig. 3, note semi-log scale).

Compensatory effects have also been reported for rodents on islands off the coast of Maine, U.S.A., and shrews on islands in Finland (Crowell, 1986; Hanski, 1986). Therefore, this may be a general phenomenon affecting distributions of many insular mammals. Compensatory (or rescue) effects may also be important in determining distributions of insular birds. Fritz (1979) reported that for spruce grouse (*Canachites canadensis*) in habitat islands of the Adirondack Region of New York, U.S.A., immigrations and extinctions were frequent, and the only small islands where spruce grouse were common residents were the less isolated ones. Similarly, J. Diamond (pers. comm.) reports that nine New Hebridean bird species are restricted to islands large enough to support at least thousands of territories, probably because of the low immigration rates of these species (Diamond & Marshall, 1977).

These findings strongly suggest that the concept of a fixed critical minimum area for isolated mammalian populations may be meaningless unless immigrations are unimportant to the dynamics of the system under study. Although not the focus of this paper, this has obvious implications with respect to designing nature reserves and the preservation of endangered species. More isolated populations of the same species require larger areas (actually, larger populations) to avoid extinction. Similarly, less vagile species need to be maintained at higher numbers.

The above patterns, including the paradoxical pattern predicted by the compensatory model (Fig. 2), have important implications with respect to the structuring of insular communities. Observed 'patterns' of insular occurrence may often appear anomalous or stochastic if resource requirements and immigration abilities are viewed as important, but independent (non-interactive), factors. Indeed, those who adopt this more tranditional view may conclude that communities such as the mammalian faunas of the Thousand Islands and Lake Michigan are random assemblages of species (with respect to area and isolation), or that some other factor such as competition is 'the' important structuring force. As I have attempted to show here, however, such apparently anomalous distributions are actually predicted by a deterministic model which incorporates the interactive as well as additive effects of immigration and extinction on insular community structure.

## ACKNOWLEDGEMENTS

I thank James Brown, Jared Diamond, Lawrence Heaney, William McShea, Bruce Patterson and Thomas Schoener for their insights and their comments on earlier versions of this manuscript.

## REFERENCES

AHO, H. J., 1978. Freshwater snail populations and the equilibrium theory of island biogeography. *Annales Zoologici Fennici, 15:* 146–154.

BANFIELD, A. W. F., 1954. The role of ice in the distribution of mammals. *Journal of Mammalogy, 35:* 104–107.

BEER, J. R., LUKENS, P. R. & OLSON, D., 1954. Small mammal populations on islands of Basswood Lake, Minnesota. *Ecology, 35:* 437–445.

BROWN, J. H., 1971. Mammals on mountaintops: nonequilibrium insular biogeography. *American Naturalist, 105:* 467–478.

BROWN, J. H., 1978. The theory of biogeography and the distribution of boreal birds and mammals. *Great Basin Naturalist Memoirs, 2:* 209–228.

BROWN, J. H. & KODRIC-BROWN, A., 1977. Turnover rates in insular biogeography: effect of immigration on extinction. *Ecology, 58:* 445–449.

CAMERON, A. W., 1958. Mammals of the islands in the Gulf of St. Lawrence. *National Museum of Canada Bulletin, 154:* 1–164.

CARTER, J. L. & MERRIT, J. F., 1981. Evaluation of swimming ability as a means of island invasion by small mammals in coastal Virginia. *Annals Carnegie Museum of Natural History, 50:* 31–46.

CROWELL, K. L., 1973. Experimental zoogeography: introduction of mice to small islands. *American Naturalist, 107:* 535–558.

CROWELL, K. L., 1983. Islands—insights or artifacts?: Population dynamics and habitat utilization in insular rodents. *Oikos, 41:* 442–454.

CROWELL, K. L., 1986. A comparison of relict versus equilibrium models for insular mammals of the Gulf of Maine. *Biological Journal of the Linnean Society, 28:* 37–64.

DENMAN, N. S., 1965. Colonization of the islands of the Gulf of St. Lawrence by mammals. *Ecology, 46:* 340–341.

DIAMOND, J. M., 1975. Assembly of species communities. In M. L. Cody & J. M. Diamond (Eds), *Ecology and Evolution of Communities:* 342–444. Cambridge: Harvard University Press.

DIAMOND, J. M., 1984. "Normal" extinctions of isolated populations. In M. Nitecki (Ed.), *Extinctions:* 191–246. Chicago: University of Chicago Press.

DIAMOND, J. M., GILPIN, M. E. & MAYR, E., 1976. Species distance relation for birds of the Solomon Archipelago, and the paradox of great speciators. *Proceedings of the National Academy of Sciences of the U.S.A., 73:* 2160–2164.

DIAMOND, J. M. & MARSHALL, A. G., 1977. Distribution ecology of New Hebridean birds: a species kaleidoscope. *Journal of Animal Ecology, 46:* 703–727.

FRITZ, R. S., 1979. Consequences of insular population structure: distribution and extinction of spruce grouse populations. *Oecologia, 42:* 57–65.

GILBERT, F. S., 1980. The equilibrium theory of island biogeography: fact or fiction? *Journal of Biogeography, 7:* 209–235.

GRANT, P. R., 1970. Colonization of islands by ecologically dissimilar species of mammals. *Canadian Journal of Zoology, 48:* 545–553.

HAMILTON, R. H., BARTH, R. R. & RUBINOFF, I., 1964. The environmental control of insular variation in bird species abundance. *Proceedings of the National Academy of Sciences of the U.S.A., 53:* 132–140.

HANSKI, I., 1986. Population dynamics of shrews on small islands accord with the equilibrium model. *Biological Journal of the Linnean Society, 28:* 23–36.

HARRELL, F. E., 1983. The LOGIST procedures. *SAS Supplemental Library users guide:* 181–202. Cary, NC: SAS Institute Inc.

HATT, R. T., VAN TYNE, J., STUART, L. C. & POPE, C. H., 1948. Island life in Lake Michigan. *Cranbrook Institute of Science, Bulletin, 27:* 1–175.

HOPE, J. H., 1973. Mammals of Bass Strait Islands. *Proceedings of the Royal Society of Victoria, 85:* 163–195.

JACKSON, H. H. T., 1919. An apparent effect of winter inactivity on the distribution of mammals. *Journal of Mammalogy, 1:* 58–64.

JENKINS, S. H., 1981. Common patterns in home range–body size relationships in birds and mammals. *American Naturalist, 118:* 126–128.

LASSEN, H. H., 1975. The diversity of freshwater snails in view of the equilibrium theory of island biogeography. *Oecologia, 19:* 1–8.

LOMOLINO, M. V., 1982. Species–area and species–distance relationships of terrestrial mammals in the Thousand Island Region. *Oecologia, 54:* 72–75.

LOMOLINO, M. V., 1983. *Island biogeography, immigrant selection, and mammalian body size on islands.* Unpublished Ph.D. dissertation, State University of New York, Binghamton.

LOMOLINO, M. V., 1984a. Mammalian island biogeography: effects of area, isolation and vagility. *Oecologia, 61:* 376–382.

LOMOLINO, M. V., 1984b. Immigrant selection, predation and the distributions of *Microtus pennsylvanicus* and *Blarina brevicauda* on islands. *American Naturalist, 123:* 468–483.

LOMOLINO, M. V., 1986. Immigration abilities and insular community structure of mammals in temperate archipelagoes. *Ohio Journal of Science*, in press.

MACARTHUR, R. H. & WILSON, E. O., 1967. The theory of island biogeography. *Monographs in Population Biology, Princeton University Press, 1.*

McNAB, B. K., 1963. Bioenergetics and determination of home range size. *American Naturalist, 97:* 133–140.

MELHOP, P. & LYNCH, J. F., 1978. Population characteristics of *Peromyscus leucopus* introduced to islands inhabited by *Microtus pennsylvanicus. Oikos, 31:* 17–26.

PATRICK, R., 1967. The effect of invasion rate, species pool, and sizes of area on the structure of the diatom community. *Proceedings of the National Academy of Sciences of the U.S.A., 58:* 1135–1142.

POKKI, J., 1981. Distribution, demography and dispersal of the field vole, *Microtus agrestis* (L), in the Tvarminne Archipelago, Finland. *Acta Zoologici Fennici, 164:* 1–48.

PRUITT, Jr, W. O., 1951. Mammals of the Chase Osborn Reserve, Sugar Island, Michigan. *Journal of Mammology, 32:* 470–473.

REDFIELD, J. A., 1976. Distribution, abundance, size, and genetic variation of *Peromyscus maniculatus* on the Gulf Islands of British Columbia. *Canadian Journal of Zoology, 54:* 463–474.

SAUER, J. D., 1969. Oceanic islands and biogeographic theory. *Geography Reviews, 59:* 582–593.

SIMBERLOFF, D. S., 1976. Experimental zoogeography of islands: Effects of island size. *Ecology, 57:* 629–648.

VUILLEUMIER, F., 1970. Insular biogeography in continental regions. I. The Northern Andes of South America. *American Naturalists, 104:* 373–388.

WERNER Jr, W. E., 1954. *The distribution and ecology of amphibians, reptiles, and mammals of the Thousand Island Region, New York.* Unpublished Ph.D. dissertation, Cornell University, Ithaca.

WILLIAMSON, M. H., 1981. *Island Populations.* New York: Oxford University Press.

M. V. LOMOLINO

APPENDIX

Table A1. Species occurrence of terrestrial mammals in the Thousand Islands Region during 1978 and 1979*

| Island number | 1 | 2 | 3 | 4 | 5 | 6 | 7 | 8 | 9 | 10 | 11 | 12 | 13 | 14 | 15 | 16 | 17 | 18 | 19 | 20 |
|---|---|---|---|---|---|---|---|---|---|---|---|---|---|---|---|---|---|---|---|---|
| Area (km²) | 5.9085 | 1.7527 | 0.6536 | 0.2481 | 0.0312 | 0.0878 | 0.1162 | 0.0316 | 0.0328 | 0.0915 | 0.0437 | 0.0352 | 0.0295 | 0.0028 | 0.113 | 0.0016 | 0.0008 | 0.0028 | 0.0004 | 0.0250 |
| Isolation (km)† | 0.93 | 0.31 | 0.24 | 0.65 | 0.17 | 0.55 | 0.58 | 0.41 | 0.86 | 1.11 | 0.83 | 9.97 | 1.03 | 0.98 | 1.01 | 1.03 | 1.04 | 1.03 | 0.90 | 0.02 |
| *Blarina brevicauda* | P | P | A | P | P | P | P | P | A | A | A | A | A | A | A | A | A | A | A | A |
| *Microtus pennsylvanicus* | P | A | P | P | P | P | P | P | P | P | P | P | A | P | P | P | P | P | A | A |
| *Peromyscus leucopus*‡ | P | P | P | A | P | A | A | P | A | A | A | A | A | A | A | A | A | A | A | A |
| *Tamias striatus* | P | P | A | A | A | A | A | A | A | A | A | A | A | A | A | A | A | A | A | P |
| *Tamiasciurus hudsonicus* | P | P | P | A | P | A | A | A | A | A | A | A | A | A | A | A | A | A | A | P |
| *Sciurus carolinensis* | P | P | P | P | P | A | A | A | A | A | A | A | A | A | A | A | A | A | A | A |
| *Procyon lotor* | P | P | A | P | A | A | A | A | A | A | A | A | A | A | A | A | A | A | A | A |
| *Vulpes vulpes* | P | P | A | A | A | A | A | A | A | A | A | A | A | A | A | A | A | A | A | A |
| *Odocoileus virginianus* | P | P | A | A | A | A | A | A | A | A | A | A | A | A | A | A | A | A | A | A |
| *Sylvilagus floridanus* | P | P | A | A | A | A | A | A | A | A | A | A | A | A | A | A | A | A | A | A |
| Isolation–M§ | 0.93 | 0.31 | 0.24 | 0.65 | 0.17 | 0.55 | 0.08 | 0.41 | 0.86 | 1.07 | 0.83 | 0.97 | 1.03 | 0.10 | 0.12 | 0.12 | 0.12 | 1.03 | 0.26 | — |
| Isolation–B§ | 0.93 | 0.31 | 0.24 | 0.65 | 0.17 | 0.55 | 0.08 | 0.08 | 0.46 | 0.80 | 0.83 | 0.97 | 1.03 | 0.98 | 1.01 | 1.03 | 1.04 | 1.03 | 0.90 | — |

*P = presence, A = absence.

†Isolation = distance to mainland or nearest large island.

‡This includes two colonizations in 1979, subsequent to initial trapping in 1978.

§Isolation–M and isolation–B = isolation measured as distance to nearest island with either *Microtus* or *Blarina*, respectively.

Table A2. Species occurrence of terrestrial mammals on islands in Lake Michigan (Hatt et al., 1948): includes the nine species which also occurred in the Thousand Islands Region*

| Island number | 1 | 2 | 3 | 4 | 5 | 6 | 7 | 8 | 9 | 10 | 11 | 12 | 13 | 14 |
|---|---|---|---|---|---|---|---|---|---|---|---|---|---|---|
| Area (km²) | 151.4 | 52.9 | 20.4 | 13.7 | 3.6 | 1.1 | 0.52 | 0.47 | 0.31 | 0.065 | 0.013 | 0.010 | 0.041 | 0.98 |
| Isolation (km)† | 24.1 | 11.3 | 11.3 | 28.2 | 35.4 | 19.3 | 6.4 | 11.3 | 8.0 | 19.3 | 17.7 | 8.9 | 0.1 | 2.4 |
| Blarina brevicauda | A | A | A | A | A | A | A | A | A | A | A | A | A | P |
| Microtus pennsylvanicus | A | A | A | A | A | A | A | A | A | A | A | A | A | P |
| Tamias striatus | P | P | P | P | P | A | A | A | A | A | A | A | A | A |
| Tamiasciurus hudsonicus | A | P | P | A | A | A | A | A | A | A | A | A | A | A |
| Sciurus carolinensis | i‡ | i | i | A | A | A | A | A | A | A | A | A | A | A |
| Procyon lotor | P | P | P | P | P | P | P | A | P | A | A | A | A | A |
| Vulpes vulpes | P | P | P | P | P | P | P | A | A | A | A | A | A | A |
| Odocoileus virginianus | P | i | A | A | A | A | A | A | A | A | A | A | A | A |
| Sylvilagus floridanus | P | A | P | A | A | A | A | A | A | A | A | A | A | A |

*P = presence, A = absence.

†Isolation = distance to the mainland or nearest larger island with this species.

‡ "i" indicates that this species was introduced and therefore this entry was not included in the analysis.

*Biological Journal of the Linnean Society* (1986), *28:* 23–36. With 5 figures

# Population dynamics of shrews on small islands accord with the equilibrium model

ILKKA HANSKI

*Department of Zoology, University of Helsinki, P. Rautatiekatu 13, SF-00100 Helsinki, Finland*

*Accepted for publication 14 February 1986*

Three of the six species of shrew in Finland, *Sorex araneus, S. caecutiens,* and *S. minutus,* are common on the mainland and widespread on islands in lakes. The islands range from 0.01 to 500 ha in area, and from 10 to 3000 m in isolation (distance from the mainland). The species–area relationship, the lack of importance of habitat diversity, the increasing frequency of unoccupied small islands with isolation, and direct observations of small populations, all suggest that populations on small islands have a high extinction rate. Demographic stochasticity is the main cause of extinctions in the superior competitor, *S. araneus,* which occurs consistently on islands greater than 2 ha. The small species, *S. caecutiens* and *S. minutus,* are more sensitive to environmental stochasticity than is *S. araneus,* and are inferior to it in interspecific competition; these factors probably contribute to the absence of the small species from many islands tens of hectares in area. Frequent colonization of islands less than 500 m from the mainland is indicated by large numbers of shrews trapped from tiny islets where breeding is not possible, by increasing epigenetic divergence of island populations with isolation, and by observations of dispersal to and colonization of islands. Dispersal ability decreases with decreasing individual size, which may partly explain the absence of the small shrews from many relatively large islands. The shrew populations persist in a dynamic equilibrium on the islands. Epigenetic morphological variation is a useful tool in ecological studies of island populations.

KEY WORDS:—*Sorex* – island biogeography – extinction – demographic stochasticity – environmental stochasticity – competition – colonization – epigenetic variation.

## CONTENTS

## INTRODUCTION: PATTERNS

MacArthur & Wilson's (1967) equilibrium theory of island biogeography was founded on patterns of occurrence of land and freshwater birds on oceanic islands, because such data were readily available (MacArthur & Wilson, 1963). More recent studies have shown that the equilibrium theory does not explain well the occurrence of birds on oceanic islands (Abbott, 1980), and claim that

23

24                                          I. HANSKI

the theory remains largely untested and may be untestable, even, for example, for birds on oceanic islands (Gilbert, 1980). In the 1970s the equilibrium theory was applied to a diverse set of systems, ranging from insects on individual plants (Kuris, Blaustein & Alio, 1980) to the design of nature reserves (Diamond & May, 1981). Nonetheless, as with other ecological theories published so far, the domain of useful application of the equilibrium theory is smaller than the range that examples in the literature might suggest.

In spite of the criticism it has received, MacArthur & Wilson's (1967) theory remains crucially important for spatial and temporal scales that permit direct observations and experiments on the processes of colonization and extinction. Small mammals colonizing small, near-shore islands belong to this category (Crowell, 1973; Lomolino, 1982; Adler & Wilson, 1985), although certain patterns can be found that are surprising in the framework of the equilibrium theory. I shall give an example in the final section of this paper.

A widely held misconception about shrews (*Sorex*) is that they make extremely poor colonizers because of their high metabolic rate (Vogel, 1980), small energy reserves (Hanski, 1985), and hence short starvation time (Crowcroft, 1957). In reality, shrews can be found on quite isolated islands in northern Europe (2–4 km; Hanski, unpubl. obs.), where they have had to disperse by themselves, possibly in winter when the islands are connected to the mainland by ice. The familiar species–area relationship holds true for shrews on islands in lakes in Finland (Fig. 1). The results in Fig. 1 have been corrected for sample size, as it is impractical to conduct an exhaustive survey of shrews on islands greater than

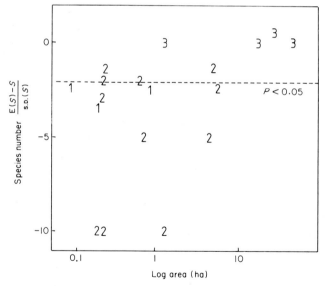

Figure 1. Species–area relationship for the three common species of shrew in E Finland (Lake Koitere). As it is impossible to ascertain the absence of shrews on large islands, the *y*-axis values are calculated as standardized deviations from the expected number of species E(*S*) for the observed sample size (rarefaction; see Simberloff, 1979; the reference sample is the pooled mainland sample of 178 individuals of the three common shrew species). The observed number of species is given by the figure representing the datum point. Six island communities do not show significant (< 2 s.d.) reduction in species number while 10 communities do. The latter tend to come from smaller islands than the former (*t* = −2.57, *P* < 0.03, df = 8).

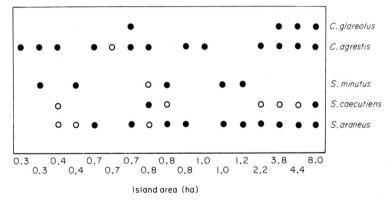

Figure 2. Local populations (●) and captures of probable immigrants (○) on 17 islands in Lake Sysmä in E Finland in July 1982 (for details see Hanski & Kuitunen, 1986). The two species of vole present in the region are also included. Islands increase in size from left to right. The common shrew, *Sorex araneus*, and the bank vole, *Clethrionomys glareolus*, occurred non-randomly, on islands greater than a species-specific 'critical' size, *c.* 0.7 and 3 ha, respectively (one-tailed Mann–Whitney *U* test, $P < 0.01$ and $P < 0.025$, respectively; cf. Schoener & Schoener, 1983).

10 ha. Some species occur on practically every island greater than a critical size (e.g. *S. araneus* in Fig. 2), suggesting a minimum viable population size; other species occur more erratically (e.g. *S. caecutiens* in Fig. 2), suggesting that factors other than island area can be important in determining the presence of some species.

The species–area relationship is predicted by, but does not prove, the equilibrium theory (Connor & McCoy, 1979). The observation about minimum island size (Fig. 2) has several possible explanations. Can any patterns be found that would discriminate between the alternative hypotheses, such as the equilibrium theory, habitat diversity, colonization of the islands before they became isolated following the last glaciation, etc.?

Figure 3 shows the occurrence of *Sorex araneus* on 68 islands in two lakes in E Finland. The islands range from 0.1 to 428 ha in area and from 30 to 2800 m in isolation (distance from the mainland). *Sorex araneus* was present on every island greater than 1.6 ha ($N = 27$), regardless of isolation, and it was absent on every island smaller than 0.63 ha ($N = 21$). This leaves 20 islands in the range from 0.63 to 1.6 ha, of which 10 were occupied. Of these 20 islands, the less isolated ones tended to be occupied (one-tailed Mann–Whitney *U* test, $0.05 < P < 0.1$), indicating a compensatory effect between island area and isolation, as described and discussed by Lomolino (1986). This result strongly suggests that the patterns in Figs 1 & 2 have a dynamic explanation.

The rest of this paper is devoted to two topics. First, colonization and extinction are discussed in some detail in two following sections. It will be shown that, for the system of shrews on islands in the lakes, the colonization and extinction processes accord well with the assumptions of the equilibrium theory. Secondly, this conclusion can be strengthened by an analysis of epigenetic morphological variation in the island populations. Such variation, previously studied in much more isolated island populations (e.g. Berry, Jakobson & Peters, 1978), yields useful results in ecological as well as microevolutionary studies.

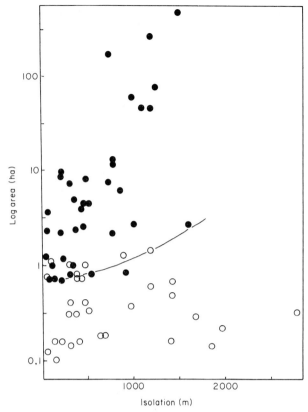

Figure 3. Presence/absence of *Sorex araneus* on 68 islands in two lakes in E Finland as a function of island size and isolation (Lakes Sysmä and Koitere). The species was present on islands represented by a dot and absent on islands represented by an open circle (a single individual was caught from seven of the latter islands, but these individuals are believed to represent immigrants rather than breeding populations). The line is a tentative limit between occupied and unoccupied islands; see text for a statistical test.

## DISPERSAL TO ISLANDS

The physiological ability of shrews to disperse to islands can be studied experimentally. For instance, Skarén (1980) has found that juvenile *S. minutus* (weight *c.* 3 g) and *S. araneus* (*c.* 6 g) swim at rates of 600 and 850 m/h, respectively. In principle, if one knew the energetic cost of swimming, which is not known sufficiently accurately, one could calculate the maximum distance a shrew could swim (cf. Hanski, 1984). Skarén (1980) observed his young shrews to swim up to 500 m, although not always in a straight line. An old *S. araneus* (*c.* 10 g) is able to swim for at least 1 h and cover 1000 m (Hanski, unpubl. obs.). Because the starvation time (Hanski, 1985) and swimming rate (Skarén, 1980) of shrews increase with body weight, we can safely conclude that, from the physiological viewpoint, big shrews make better colonizers than small ones.

Predation risk is high for swimming shrews. In one of 10 experiments we conducted, a shrew was caught by a fish (probably *Esox*) near the shore. Teplov (1943) reported the surprisingly large number of 270 *S. araneus* found in the stomachs of 2486 trout in Siberia. Gulls also have been observed to prey upon swimming shrews (Skarén, 1980).

In winter the lakes are frozen. Some anecdotal observations (Pedersen, 1972; A. Kaikusalo, pers. comm.) suggest that shrews may disperse across the ice to islands at least 500 m from the mainland. As the cost of running must be lower than the cost of swimming, I suspect that experiments will reveal much longer distances. Perhaps the likeliest season for successful long-distance dispersal is late spring, when shrews are large (mature) and very active (mating), when the ambient temperatures are high, and the lakes are covered by breaking, black ice. Shrews may mistakenly wander onto the ice from the remaining patches of snow on the shores. Ice may break up in wind and shrews can be carried relatively fast over long distances. Plenty of arthropods occur on the ice at this time of the year, prolonging the time a shrew can spend on the ice. And lastly, a pregnant female may be carried to an island, or she may run across the ice by herself, increasing the likelihood of a successful island colonization (below).

The physiological ability of species to disperse to islands is one thing; what animals do in reality is another matter. This is dramatically demonstrated by some temperate (Palmgren, 1927) and tropical birds (Diamond, 1973) that are 'psychologically' unable to disperse over insignificant expanses of water. Here is an instance where experiments cannot resolve the matter, and we must instead turn to observational data.

Tiny islets, less than 100 m² in area, provide no opportunities for shrews to overwinter and breed, and are thus convenient natural traps for dispersers. It can be safely assumed that any shrews caught from such islets have dispersed there from the mainland or large islands in spring or in summer. Lake Sysmä in E Finland has 25 islets, most of which are situated 100–300 m from the mainland (see the map in Hanski & Kuitunen, 1986). So far we have analysed the results for 3 years, and these data prove conclusively that summer dispersal is commonplace (Table 1). Interspecific differences of the kind predicted from physiological considerations (size) are apparent: in contrast to the consistent abundance of *Sorex araneus*, *Sorex minutus* is relatively less common on the islets than on the mainland. The middle-sized species, *S. caecutiens*, was significantly ($P < 0.05$) less numerous than *S. araneus* on the islets in 1985, but there was no significant difference in the two other years.

Table 1. Trapping results of three species of shrew on 25 small islets in three summers (Lake Sysmä E Finland). These numbers are compared with the pooled samples from the mainland ($\chi^2$; trapping effort has not been constant)

| Year | S. araneus | S. caecutiens | S. minutus | $\chi^2$ | P |
|---|---|---|---|---|---|
| 1982 | | | | | |
| Islets | 6 | 5 | — | | |
| Mainland | 110 | 31 | 19 | 4.94 | 0.08 |
| 1983 | | | | | |
| Islets | 17 | 5 | 1 | | |
| Mainland | 30 | 10 | 16 | 5.71 | 0.06 |
| 1985 | | | | | |
| Islets | 24 | 2 | — | | |
| Mainland | 104 | 37 | 23 | 8.84 | 0.01 |
| Pooled sample (%)* | | | | | |
| Islets | 78 | 20 | 2 | | |
| Mainland | 64 | 21 | 15 | | |

*The last two rows give the species composition (%) in the pooled islet and mainland samples.

Table 2. The numbers of shrews trapped from the island Veitsisaari in 1982–1985 (island area 3.8 ha, distance from the mainland 450 m). The species composition on the mainland is shown in the lower part of the table. *Sorex minutus* colonized the island in 1984

| Species | 1982 | 1983 | 1984 | 1985 |
|---|---|---|---|---|
| Veitsisaari ($N$) | | | | |
| S. araneus | 76 | 27 | 11 | 14 |
| S. caecutiens | 1 | 1 | — | — |
| S. minutus | — | — | 5 | 9 |
| Mainland (%) | | | | |
| S. araneus | 69 | 54 | 62 | 57 |
| S. caecutiens | 19 | 18 | 9 | 20 |
| S. minutus | 12 | 28 | 29 | 23 |

Having addressed the questions about shrews' ability to disperse to islands, and whether they do so in practice, we need to ask about the consequences of such dispersal: how frequently do dispersers breed on islands? At the present time this question can be answered only qualitatively. Two lines of evidence can be used here, direct observations and the epigenetic divergence of island populations.

Table 2 gives an example of colonization. The island in question is 3.8 ha in area, and was first trapped in 1982, when only *S. araneus* was present but had an extremely dense population, most probably > 50 individuals/ha (one juvenile *S. caecutiens*, probably an immigrant, was also caught; Table 2). *Sorex minutus* was found on the island in 1984, and again in 1985 in good numbers (Table 2), strongly suggesting that colonization had taken place in 1984. A noteworthy point is that *S. minutus* was relatively abundant on the mainland in 1983–1984 (Table 2), increasing the probability of colonization because of increased numbers of potential dispersers. We have an interesting observation bearing on this suggestion. A nearby smaller island (0.8 ha, 140 m from the mainland) had been emptied by very intensive trapping in 1983. The island proved to be empty in spring 1984, excepting a pregnant *S. minutus* female, caught at the end of May. It is almost certain that it had moved to the island after mating, in spring 1984. The alternative explanations of this trapping result are extremely unlikely.

These findings are in agreement with the observation that the most widely distributed small mammal species on islands tend to be those which reach the highest population densities on the mainland (Adler & Wilson, 1985). The colonization events are likely to be correlated with changes in mainland population sizes.

We have had little success so far in experimentally introducing *S. caecutiens* and *S. minutus* to small islands (*c.* 1 ha). Four attempts have been made in late summer by introducing 10–15 juveniles to an island. The above example raises the possibility that some (many?) colonizations may be accomplished by pregnant females.

The second kind of evidence for frequent colonization of islands comes from studies of epigenetic morphological variation in island and mainland populations (Hanski & Kuitunen, 1986). We have studied mostly cranial foramina. From the results one can calculate the mean epigenetic divergence of

Table 3. Regression analyses of the mean epigenetic divergence of 17 *S. araneus* island populations from eight nearby mainland populations. Note that island isolation and area do not explain much of the divergence when analysed separately, but a multiple regression model explains more than half of the variation in the epigenetic divergence

| Independent variable | Simple regressions | | | | Multiple regression | | | |
|---|---|---|---|---|---|---|---|---|
| | *t* | $R^2$ | *F* | *P* | *t* | $R^2$ | *F* | *P* |
| Isolation | 0.72 | 0.03 | 0.51 | N.S. | 3.61 | 0.61 | 11.05 | 0.005 |
| Area (log) | −2.24 | 0.25 | 5.02 | 0.05 | −4.57 | | | |

island populations from the conspecific mainland populations (Hanski & Kuitunen, 1986). In a data set for 17 island populations of *S. araneus*, island area and isolation explained only little or none of the variation in simple linear models of divergence, but a multiple regression model employing both area and isolation as independent variables explained 61% of the variation in the epigenetic divergence (Table 3). There are no reasons to believe that the divergence is due to mechanisms other than genetic drift. The area effect thus stems from larger islands having larger effective population sizes and hence slower drift, while the isolation effect suggests that more gene flow (dispersers that breed) reaches nearer than farther islands. These dispersers have not established new populations, but as the dispersal process itself is the same for individuals that penetrate existing populations and establish new ones, these data conclusively show that farther islands are colonized less frequently than nearer ones. Incidentally, dispersal to existing populations may contribute to the result in Fig. 3 (the rescue effect of Brown & Kodric-Brown, 1977).

Assuming that the cause of divergence is genetic drift, we would expect populations of small species, because the individuals are poor dispersers, to diverge more quickly than populations of large species on a given set of islands. In particular, Table 1 showed the inferior dispersal ability of the smallest species, *S. minutus*, which consequently should diverge more quickly than the other species. This is tested in Fig. 4, with data for six same-island populations of *S. araneus* and *S. minutus*. The islands range from 2 to 45 ha in area and from 80 to 1620 m in isolation (distance from the mainland). They had equal average densities of the two species (total catches: *S. araneus* 78 and *S. minutus* 70). The divergences of the two species on the islands show a good correlation, but *S. minutus* populations have diverged twice as much as the same-island *S. araneus* populations from the respective conspecific mainland populations.

In conclusion, there is no doubt whatever that shrews frequently disperse to and breed on islands situated less than around 1000 m from the mainland or other occupied islands. Dispersal to near islands is more frequent than to far islands for obvious reasons. Small species (here especially *S. minutus*) are worse dispersers than large ones (here especially *S. araneus*), hence a given island is more isolated for small than for large species. And lastly, some colonizations may be accomplished by pregnant females in late spring.

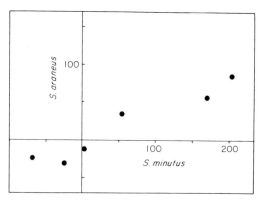

Figure 4. Correlation of the mean epigenetic divergence (from conspecific mainland populations) in six same-island populations of *S. araneus* and *S. minutus* (Lake Koitere, E Finland, in 1983). $r = 0.959$, $P < 0.01$.

## EXTINCTIONS

An island population may go extinct for two reasons. The environment may deteriorate to the extent that deaths (plus possible emigration) exceed births (plus possible immigration). For instance, the island may be colonized by a superior competitor, which may decrease the birth rate or increase the death rate of the resident species. Secondly, stochasticity may lead to extinctions even if the average growth rate of a small population is positive. A further useful distinction can be made between environmental and demographic stochasticity (May, 1973). The former is exemplified by weather affecting breeding; the latter stems from discrete birth and death events.

Demographic stochasticity is always important in small populations, whether the population is small because of small island area or because of competition with other species. Two small islands were emptied by very intensive trapping in May–June 1983, before the first litters had been weaned. Four and eight shrews were caught from the islands (Table 4). In both cases every female was breeding, but clearly, when dealing with such small numbers, the probability of only one sex surviving the winter, or of all individuals dying, is relatively large.

Table 4. Two small islands were emptied by very intensive trapping in May–June 1983 (*c*. 200 pitfalls for 6 weeks on each island; Hanski & Kuitunen, 1986). The individuals detailed in the table are likely to represent the total populations at the time of trapping

| | |
|---|---|
| Island Kekosaari (0.8 ha, isolation 0.32 km) | |
| *S. araneus* | 1 adult male |
| | 1 pregnant female |
| *S. caecutiens* | 2 pregnant females |
| Island Mustasaari (0.7 ha, isolation 0.14 km) | |
| *S. araneus* | 3 adult males |
| | 2 pregnant females |
| | 3 lactating females |

Note that the sizes of these two islands, 0.7 and 0.8 ha, fall within the range 0.63–1.6 ha, where presence or absence of *S. araneus* was uncertain in Fig. 3. Taking 5 shrews/ha as an estimate of the minimum size of a population in spring (Table 4), the probability of extinction due to only one sex surviving the winter is 0.25 for an island of 0.63 ha, but much lower, 0.008, for an island of 1.6 ha. These admittedly crude calculations suggest that demographic stochasticity sets the lower size limit of islands occupied by *S. araneus* (Figs 2 & 3). If environmental stochasticity were overridingly important, we would expect the species to be absent from some islands in the range from 1.6 to (say) 5 ha, which was not observed (Fig. 3). Some form of environmental stochasticity may, however, contribute to the determination of minimum population size in spring.

Small populations are expected to diverge quickly, but because their extinction probability is high, they do not have much time to diverge. In any case, whether due to the initial founder effect or rapid genetic drift, small populations are expected to have reduced genetic variation, which should lead to reduced epigenetic variation. This has been observed: small-island populations of *S. araneus* have more fixed epigenetic traits than large-island or mainland populations (Table 5).

Let us now turn to the small species, which are absent from many relatively large islands (Fig. 1); e.g. in the data set shown in Fig. 2, *S. caecutiens* and *S. minutus* have only one population on the four largest islands (2.2–8.0 ha). There are no obvious habitat differences between the islands in Fig. 2 that could explain this result (Hanski & Kuitunen, 1986).

Isolation could, in principle, contribute to the observed pattern, as the smaller shrews are worse dispersers than *S. araneus* (Table 1), and as island area and isolation tend to be positively correlated ($r = 0.60$, $P < 0.025$, for the islands in Table 3). However, in the example in Fig. 2 at least, isolation is almost certainly not the explanation, for the following reasons: (a) isolation of

Table 5. The number of constant epigenetic traits in a random sample of eight individuals from 13 populations of *S. araneus*. Means and 95% confidence intervals (C.I.) were calculated with Monte Carlo simulation (for the traits see Hanski & Kuitunen, 1986). Note that all five small-island populations have more traits fixed than any of the five mainland populations ($P = 0.004$)

| Population | | Island size (ha) | Sample size | Mean | 95% C.I. |
|---|---|---|---|---|---|
| Mainland | $M_1$ | | 34 | 3.48 | 2–6 |
| | $M_2$ | | 17 | 2.44 | 1–4 |
| | $M_3$ | | 10 | 1.82 | 1–3 |
| | $M_4$ | | 29 | 3.09 | 1–6 |
| | $M_5$ | | 22 | 3.37 | 2–6 |
| Large island | $L_1$ | 3.8 | 76 | 2.98 | 1–5 |
| | $L_2$ | 8.0 | 25 | 5.36 | 3–8 |
| | $L_3$ | 4.4 | 37 | 4.21 | 2–6 |
| Small island | $S_1$ | 2.2 | 8 | 9.00 | |
| | $S_3$ | 0.8 | 11 | 3.56 | 1–6 |
| | $S_5$ | 0.7 | 11 | 5.05 | 4–7 |
| | $S_8$ | 1.0 | 10 | 5.28 | 5–6 |
| | $S_{14}$ | 0.7 | 11 | 5.58 | 4–8 |

the three large islands where *S. caecutiens* and *S. minutus* were absent is not greater (average 380 m) than isolation of the seven islands with one of these species present (average 370 m); (b) the bank vole *Clethrionomys glareolus*, a relatively poor colonizer (see Crowell, 1973, for the close relative *C. gapperi*), was nonetheless present only on the largest islands and one small one (Fig. 2); (c) single individuals of *S. caecutiens*, believed to be immigrants, were caught from the large islands in 1982 (Fig. 2); and (d) in later years (1983–1985), both *S. caecutiens* and *S. minutus* have been resident or present as immigrants on some of the large islands (Hanski, unpubl. obs.).

Assuming that demographic stochasticity affects all the species in roughly the same way, which seems probable, island area cannot explain the absence of the small shrews from the islands, unless the average densities of the small shrews tend to be substantially lower than the density of *S. araneus*. This at first seems improbable, because a given amount of food resources should support larger, not smaller, populations of small species. Variance in food availability works, however, to the opposite direction, as the small shrews are more vulnerable than the large species to 'energy crises', temporary food shortages (Hanski, 1985). It is difficult to evaluate which effect—mean or variance—is more important, but extinction due to environmental stochasticity remains a possible explanation of the absence of the small shrews from many relatively large islands (2–10 ha).

An alternative or complementary explanation to environmental stochasticity is interspecific competition. Interference competition between closely related shrews has been reported to occur in nature (Hawes, 1977), and our laboratory studies have shown that the largest species, *Sorex araneus*, is superior in interference competition to the small species (Saarikko & Hanski, unpubl. obs.). The importance of resource competition is indicated by a positive relationship between the densities of shrews and their prey populations (Judin, 1962; Butterfield, Coulson & Wanless, 1981). Unfortunately, convincing evidence for competition is difficult to extract from observational data on island occupancy (e.g Grant & Abbott, 1980)—experiments are much to be preferred, and are now in progress.

In summary of the results on extinction, the large *S. araneus* appears to have a relatively low extinction rate except on the smallest islands, less than 2 ha in area, where demographic stochasticity becomes an important factor. The absence of the small species from many islands in the range 2–10 ha is partly explicable by their lower colonization rate (previous section), but the small species also seem to have a higher extinction rate than *S. araneus*. Two possible explanations are environmental stochasticity and interspecific competition. A critical experiment to discriminate between these two hypotheses would consist of introducing *S. minutus* to empty, isolated 2 ha islands, and following the extinction rate of such populations in the absence of interspecific competition.

## CONCLUSIONS

The assumptions of the equilibrium theory of MacArthur & Wilson (1967) about the colonization and extinction processes are satisfied for the system of shrews on small islands, and I conclude that the patterns in Figs 1–3 are due to a dynamic equilibrium between colonization and extinction. There are altogether six species of shrew in the mainland species pool, but three species are not found

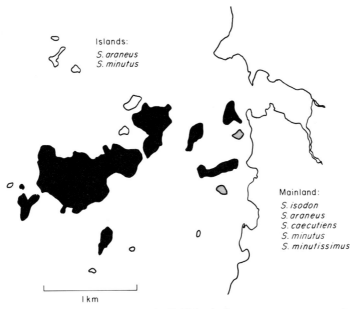

Figure 5. An archipelago in Lake Koitere in E Finland. *Sorex araneus* was present alone on the lightly shaded islands, while *S. minutus* co-occurred on the heavily shaded islands in 1983. *Sorex caecutiens* was common on the mainland, with two other rare species, but it was absent from the islands. Colonization is likely to take place from island to island, along the island chain, and the occurrences of the species on the islands cannot be considered independent from each other. Hence the pattern is not as unexpected as might first appear.

on the islands, apparently because two of them are rare (*Sorex isodon* and *S. minutissimus*) while the third one is a habitat specialist (*Neomys fodiens*; Hanski & Kuitunen, 1986). The small number of species on the islands makes the community approach superfluous—it is more instructive to study individual species, and to elucidate the idiosyncrasies in their occurrence on the islands.

Because of their relatively limited dispersal powers, small mammals are likely to colonize an archipelago, such as shown in Fig. 5, mostly from island to island rather than from mainland to island. This can create patterns that are surprising in the light of the equilibrium model. In the example in Fig. 5, *S. araneus* and *S. minutus* were present on many islands in 1983, but *S. caecutiens* was absent in the whole archipelago, though this species is the second commonest one on the mainland (after *S. araneus*). Dispersal to these islands undoubtedly takes place mostly along the island chain. *Sorex caecutiens* has probably been present on the islands, but has gone extinct, perhaps because of competition (*S. caecutiens* is intermediate in size between *S. araneus* and *S. minutus*) or simply during some severe environmental perturbation. For some reason it has failed to (re)colonize the nearest islands, and is hence missing from many islands. One consequence of island-to-island dispersal is that construction of realistic null models to test whether species are distributed independently on islands (*à la* Connor & Simberloff, 1979) is very difficult if not impossible for mammals, and was not attempted in this study.

The largest species, *Sorex araneus,* is superior in competition to the two small species, *S. caecutiens* and *S. minutus,* and probably little affected by their presence. Demographic stochasticity seems to be the main factor limiting the occurrence of *S. araneus* on the islands. The results suggest that 'normal' environmental stochasticity, excluding exceptional 'catastrophes', is not very important—large-island (> 2 ha) populations have small extinction probabilities. This conclusion rests on the assumption that dispersal does not 'rescue' such populations at a high rate. Further long-term data to settle this question are required from islands 1.6–5 ha in area and isolated by more than 500 m from the mainland.

In contrast, the occurrence of the small species on the islands appears to be affected by environmental stochasticity or interspecific competition, or both. Small size makes small species vulnerable to both. The presence of two of the five *S. minutus* populations in Fig. 2 on the smallest islands (0.3–0.4 ha) occupied by any species of shrew supports the competition hypothesis, but without knowing the stability of these populations this result remains inconclusive.

I conclude by indicating three areas where further research is needed. First, epigenetic morphological variation has emerged as a useful tool in the course of this study (details and references in Hanski & Kuitunen, 1986). In particular, the isolation effect on mean epigenetic divergence of island populations proves conclusively that the likelihood of successful colonization decreases with increasing isolation. The analysis of epigenetic variation in ecological (as opposed to microevolutionary) island studies deserves more attention than it has received so far. It can contribute substantially to the understanding of populations' stability.

Secondly, dispersal studies focusing on individuals and their decisions to move or not to move (reviewed in Greenwood, 1980; Dobson, 1982) are relevant for island biogeography, and form a bridge between behavioural and population ecology. We have found that while young *S. araneus* males are more numerous than young females in trap catches on the mainland, the reverse is true on many islands (Hanski & Kuitunen, 1986). Who is dispersing, and when and why, are important questions, to which island biogeographic studies, for example a detailed analysis of the individuals in Table 1, may contribute partial answers.

Thirdly, the size of the species has many predictable (and testable) effects on its occurrence on islands. In a nutshell, small size means smaller individual food requirements, greater potential density, and hence a smaller role for demographic stochasticity on a given set of islands. On the other hand, small individual size makes the population vulnerable to both environmental stochasticity and interspecific competition, and may lower dispersal rate to islands. On the basis of these considerations, large species should occur consistently on most islands greater than a minimum size set by demographic stochasticity, while small species may be expected to occur in a more erratic distribution. Naturally, these conclusions should not be applied to taxa with markedly different biological characteristics from shrews. In particular, the extraordinarily high metabolic rate of shrews, and hence the great importance of individual size in their biology, make them a somewhat special case.

### ACKNOWLEDGEMENTS

This work would have been impossible to carry out without the help of the following students in the field and in the laboratory: M. Hanski, J. Heikkilä, R.

Heinonen, A. Huotarinen, J. Kuitunen, J.-L. Tast and T. Tast. J. Aho is thanked for the facilities at the Mekrijärvi Research Station (University of Joensuu). Y. Haila, L. Heaney, O. Järvinen and B. Patterson sent constructive comments to the manuscript. The study was supported by the Academy of Finland.

## REFERENCES

ABBOTT, I., 1980. Theories dealing with the ecology of landbirds on islands. *Advances in Ecological Research, 11:* 329–371.

ADLER, G. H. & WILSON, M. L., 1985. Small mammals on Massachusetts islands: the case of probability functions in clarifying biogeographic relationships. *Oecologia (Berlin), 66:* 178–186.

BERRY, R. J., JAKOBSON, M. E. & PETERS, J., 1978. The house mice of the Faroe Islands: a study in microdifferentiation. *Journal of Zoology, London, 185:* 73–92.

BROWN, J. H. & KODRIC-BROWN, A., 1977. Turnover rates in insular biogeography: effect of immigration on extinction. *Ecology, 58:* 445–449.

BUTTERFIELD, J., COULSON, J. C. & WANLESS, G., 1981. Studies on the distribution, food, breeding biology and relative abundance of the pygmy and common shrews (*Sorex minutus* and *S. araneus*) in upland areas of northern England. *Journal of Zoology, London, 195:* 169–180.

CONNOR, E. F. & McCOY, E. D., 1979. The statistics and biology of the species-area relationship. *American Naturalist, 113:* 791–833.

CONNOR, E. F. & SIMBERLOFF, D., 1979. The assembly of species communities: chance or competition? *Ecology, 60:* 1132–1140.

CROWELL, K. L., 1973. Experimental zoogeography: introduction of mice to small islands. *American Naturalist, 107:* 535–558.

CROWCROFT, P., 1957. *The Life of the Shrew.* London: Reinhardt.

DIAMOND, J. M., 1973. Distributional ecology of New Guinea birds. *Science, 179:* 759–769.

DIAMOND, J. M. & MAY, R. M., 1981. Island biogeography and the design of natural reserves. In R. M. May (Ed.), *Theoretical Ecology:* 163–186. Oxford: Blackwell Scientific Publications.

DOBSON, F. S., 1982. Competition for mates and predominant juvenile male dispersal in mammals. *Animal Behaviour, 30:* 1183–1192.

GILBERT, F. S., 1980. The equilibrium theory of island biogeography: fact or fiction? *Journal of Biogeography, 7:* 209–235.

GRANT, P. R. & ABBOTT, I., 1980. Interspecific competition, island biogeography and null hypotheses. *Evolution, 34:* 332–341.

GREENWOOD, P. J., 1980. Mating systems, philopatry and dispersal in birds and mammals. *Animal Behaviour, 28:* 1140–1162.

HANSKI, I., 1984. Food consumption, assimilation and metabolic rate in six species of shrew (*Sorex* and *Neomys*). *Annales Zoologici Fennici, 21:* 157–165.

HANSKI, I., 1985. What does a shrew do in an energy crisis? In R. M. Sibly & R. H. Smith (Eds), *Behavioural Ecology:* 247–252. Oxford: Blackwell Scientific Publications.

HANSKI, I. & KUITUNEN, J., 1986. Shrews on small islands: epigenetic variation elucidates population stability. *Holarctic Ecology,* in press.

HAWES, M. L., 1977. Home range, territoriality and ecological separation in sympatric shrews *Sorex vagrans* and *Sorex obscurus. Journal of Mammalogy, 58:* 354–367.

JUDIN, B. S., 1962. [Ecology of shrews (genus *Sorex*) of West Siberia.]In A. I. Cherepanov (Ed.), [*The Problems of Ecology, Zoogeography and Systematics of Animals.*] Novosibirsk. [In Russian.]

KURIS, A. M., BLAUSTEIN, A. R. & ALIO, J. J., 1980. Hosts as islands. *American Naturalist, 116:* 570–586.

LOMOLINO, M. V., 1982. Species–area and species–distance relationships of terrestrial mammals in the Thousand Island region. *Oecologia (Berlin), 54:* 72–75.

LOMOLINO, M. V., 1986. Mammalian community structure on islands: importance of immigration, extinction and interactive effects. *Biological Journal of the Linnean Society, 28:* 1–21.

MACARTHUR, R. H. & WILSON, E. O., 1963. An equilibrium theory of insular zoogeography. *Evolution, 17:* 373–387.

MACARTHUR, R. H. & WILSON, E. O., 1967. *The Theory of Island Biogeography.* Princeton: Princeton University Press.

MAY, R. M., 1973. *Complexity and Stability in Model Ecosystems.* Princeton: Princeton University Press.

PALMGREN, P., 1927. Die Haubenmeise (*Parus cristatus* L.) auf Åland. *Acta Societatis pro Fauna et Flora Fennica, 56:* 1–13.

PEDERSEN, J. A., 1972. Activity of a common shrew *Sorex araneus* on the snow. *Fauna (Oslo), 25:* 121.

SCHOENER, T. W. & SCHOENER, A., 1983. Distribution of vertebrates on some very small islands. I. Occurrence sequences of individual species. *Journal of Animal Ecology, 52:* 209–235.

SIMBERLOFF, D., 1979. Rarefaction as a distribution-free method of expressing and estimating diversity. In J. F. Grassle, G. P. Patil, W. Smith & C. Taillie (Eds), *Ecological Diversity in Theory and Practice:* 159–176. Maryland: International Cooperating Publishing House.

SKARÉN, U., 1980. Vesi *Sorex*-päästäisten leviämisesteenä. *Savon Luonto, 12:* 44–47.

TEPLOV, V. P., 1943. The significance of the common shrew (*Sorex araneus* L.) and some other vertebrates in the nutrition of *Thymallus thymallus* L. *Zoologicheskiĭ Zhurnal, 22:* 366–368. [In Russian, English summary.]

VOGEL, P., 1980. Metabolic levels and biological strategies of shrews. In K. Schmidt-Nielsen, L. Bolis & C. R. Taylor (Eds), *Comparative Physiology: Primitive Mammals:* 170–180. Cambridge: Cambridge University Press.

*Biological Journal of the Linnean Society* (1986), *28*: 37–64. With 3 figures

# A comparison of relict versus equilibrium models for insular mammals of the Gulf of Maine

KENNETH L. CROWELL

*Department of Biology, St. Lawrence University, Canton, New York 13617, U.S.A.*

*Accepted for publication 14 February 1986*

For the mammalian faunas of 24 landbridge islands in the Gulf of Maine (0.003–279 km² in size), area accounts for 86% of variance in species richness. The slope, $z$, of the species–area curve is 0.247. For the seven largest islands ($> 10$ km²), the non-equilibrium hypothesis of relaxation following saturation in the post-Pleistocene is suggested by (1) elevated slope of the species–area curve (0.353), (2) correlation of species richness with island age ($r = -0.81$) and water depth to mainland ($r = -0.70$), (3) highly non-random nested subsets of species ranked by island area, and (4) discontinuity with the extremely depauperate faunas of oceanic islands of the eastern North Atlantic. The alternative hypothesis of a dynamic equilibrium determined by recurrent immigration and extinction is supported by (1) documented turnover in 16 species, (2) correlation of species–area residuals with distance ($r = -0.90$), (3) distribution dependent upon vagility with reduction or absence of hibernators and other poor dispersers, (4) low levels of endemism, and (5) congruence of community structure with that of mainland fauna for both trophic level and body size.

I conclude that while some insular populations may be relictual, the faunal composition of most of these islands is dependent on recurrent colonization, much of which takes place over ice bridges. However, true equilibrium is perturbed by climatic shifts, range expansions, and human disturbance.

KEY WORDS:—Biogeography – equilibrium – Gulf of Maine – island – landbridge – mammals – relaxation – relict – turnover.

## CONTENTS

0024–4066/86/050037 + 28 $03.00/0          

## INTRODUCTION

In the first three chapters of their classic monograph, MacArthur & Wilson (1967) cited only one study involving mammals. They suggested that on remote islands some taxa may not have reached equilibrium, while MacArthur (1972: 100–101) proposed that mammalian faunas on large landbridge islands of recent origin may not yet have relaxed to equilibrium. MacArthur and Wilson called for future studies on "groups that are both species-rich and more sensitive to geographic barriers in order fully to test and to extend the basic equilibrium model" (MacArthur & Wilson, 1967: 25). Since then, considerable attention has been focused on the extent to which taxa with low vagility fail to conform to the equilibrium model. These studies have involved birds (Abbott & Grant, 1976) and lizards (Wilcox, 1978) as well as mammals (Brown, 1971; Patterson, 1984; Heaney, 1984). On the other hand, Lomolino (1982, 1984a) contended that mammalian faunas are often in equilibrium, but that this may be obscured by the effects of low vagility. Lomolino (1983, 1984b), Dueser & Brown (1980) and Alder & Wilson (1985) all found evidence for equilibrium in insular mammals on coastal or riparian islands.

The equilibrium model rests on two assumptions: that the rate of extinction decreases monotonically with area and that the rate of immigration decreases with isolation. Several predictions follow: (1) the number of species will increase directly with area; (2) species richness will decrease with distance; (3) the number of species will fluctuate about an equilibrium level; (4) there will be turnover, with extinction balanced by colonization; (5) successful colonization will be non-random, and will be determined by the dispersal abilities and demographic characteristics of the source species.

While many insular faunas conform to the first prediction, a positive species–area relationship is not a sufficient condition for equilibrium, because in non-equilibrial faunas it results from area-dependent extinction or relaxation. The other predictions are difficult to test, and only turnover can provide direct evidence for equilibrium (but see Abbott, 1983). In this paper, I analyse the terrestrial mammalian fauna of coastal landbridge islands in order to discriminate between relict and equilibrium hypotheses, examining each of the above predictions in turn. Although the faunas of these islands may well have had access to landbridges, I shall argue that most species seem to be in equilibrium, with recurrent extinction and immigration.

## METHODS

### Description of study area

This paper is based on the distributions of non-volant terrestrial mammals on 26 islands in the Gulf of Maine. The Gulf of Maine, located in the western North Atlantic, is enclosed by Nova Scotia, Brown's Bank, George's Bank and Cape Cod. I have focused on 24 coastal islands of the State of Maine (Fig. 1). All were connected to the mainland by landbridges for a considerable time

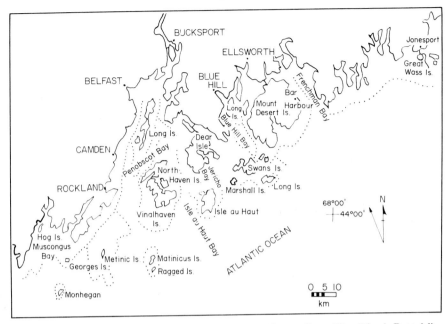

Figure 1. Section of Coast of State of Maine, Muscongus Bay to Great Wass Island. Dotted line represents sea level at 8000 BP (−40 m) (redrawn from Crowell, 1973: fig. 3).

following glacial recession, which occurred about 13 500 BP (Stuiver & Borns, 1975). Comparisons are made with two more isolated islands, Grand Manan Island and Monhegan Island. Because they are separated from the mainland by depths of 60 m or more, which was the maximum depression in sea level following deglaciation of this region, they could not have been connected to the mainland by landbridges.

Bedrock of the region is igneous, primarily granitic. Because of the maritime climate and influence of the Labrador Current, dominant vegetation is a combination of boreal and spruce–northern hardwood associations (Crowell, 1983). Red oak (*Quercus rubrum*) is found on less exposed well-drained sites, and there is evidence that hardwoods were more prevalent in pre-colonial times (Conkling, 1981).

### Faunal distributions

Records of occurrence were compiled by a variety of methods, including field work, personal communications and published works. Field studies included direct sightings, observation of signs, and use of Victor and Museum Special snap traps and Sherman live traps. My students and I conducted these studies between 1962 and 1985 (Crowell, 1973, 1983).

Most of the 17 small coastal islands (Table 1) are located in Penobscot and Jericho Bays (Crowell, 1973; Fig. 1) and were visited by us, as were five of seven larger islands, Deer Isle, Vinal Haven Island, Swans Island, Isle au Haut, and Great Wass Island (Appendix, Table A1). Other sources of distributional information were as follows: Mt Desert Island, Coman (1981), Manville (1942, 1960); Swans Island, N. Bailey (pers. comm.); Isle au Haut, Manville (1964), R. S.

Table 1. Zoogeographic variables for 17 islands of mid-coastal Maine: area; least distance to mainland, Deer Isle or Mt Desert Island ($D_M$); distance to nearest larger islands ($D_I$); and resident non-volant mammals. Decimals denote frequency of occurrence for labile species. ?, unconfirmed; E, extirpated

| Island | Area (km²) | $D_M$ (km) | $D_I$ (km) | Number of species | *S. cinereus* | *Tamiasciurus* | *P. maniculatus* | *Microtus* | *Clethrionomys* | *Lepus* | *M. vison* | *Lutra* | *Odocoileus* |
|---|---|---|---|---|---|---|---|---|---|---|---|---|---|
| Dave's | 0.003 | 3.22 | 0.22 | 1.1 | 0.1 | | | + | | | | | |
| Ram | 0.005 | 5.50 | 0.69 | 1.5 | | | | + | | | 0.5 | | |
| Fort | 0.008 | 2.00 | 2.00 | 2·0 | | | | + | | | + | | |
| Rock | 0.008 | 2.00 | 0.67 | 2.0 | 0.5 | | | | | | | | |
| Potato | 0.013 | 2.37 | 0.28 | 1.3 | 0.3 | | | + | | | 0.5 | | |
| Second | 0.013 | 1.30 | 0.78 | 1.5 | | | | + | | | 0.5 | | |
| Scraggy | 0.023 | 3.90 | 1.91 | 3.0 | | | | + | | | + | | |
| Mark | 0.026 | 2.22 | 1.48 | 2.1 | 0.1 | | | + | + | | + | | |
| Farrell | 0.065 | 2.78 | 1.33 | 1.0 | | | | + | | | | | |
| Camp | 0.088 | 1.13 | 1.13 | 2.5 | + | | | + | | | 0.5 | | |
| Merchant | 0.285 | 4.50 | 1.44 | 4.5 | + | + | | + | | | 0.5 | | + |
| Crotch | 0.518 | 0.325 | 0.325 | 3.5 | + | + | | + | | | 0.5 | | ? |
| Hardwood | 0.830 | 1.20 | 1.20 | 3.0 | | | | + | | | + | | + |
| Eagle | 1.052 | 2.82 | 2.82 | 3.0 | | | | + | | | + | | + |
| Kimball | 1.114 | 7.69 | 0.09 | 6.0 | + | + | ? | + | | + | + | ? | + |
| Hog* | 1.243 | 0.10 | 0.10 | 10.0 | + | + | | + | + | + | + | | + |
| Matinicus | 3.108 | 22.00 | 12.40 | 4.0 | + | | + | + | | | E? | ? | |

*See Appendix, Table A1 for other species.

Palmer and W. Stevens (pers. comm.); Matinicus Island, R. S. Palmer (pers. comm.); Monhegan Island, G. Clough (pers. comm.); Hog Island, T. French and J. Mackiewicz (pers. comm.), D. Morse (1966); Hardwood Island, P. Blanchard (pers. comm.); and Grand Manan Island, A. MacKay (pers. comm.), Ingersoll & Gorham (1979). Distributions of mainland species (Appendix, Table A1) are from Fefer & Schettig (1980). Generic names used hereafter are given in Appendix, Table A1.

Because historical records are not uniformly available for all islands, several species which have been regionally extirpated since the 17th century are not considered. The pine marten (*Martes americana*) occurs only rarely and locally in coastal Maine, but remains from Indian shell heaps indicate its presence in Maine as little as 820 years ago (Snow, 1970). Remains of the extinct sea mink (*Mustela macrodon*), extirpated during the last century, are also common in faunal remains of archaeological sites (Manville, 1942, 1966). It has apparently been replaced by the common mink (*Mustela v. vison*) of which it may have been a subspecies (Manville, 1966). Other species extirpated by the end of the 19th century include the timber wolf (*Canis lupus*), eastern cougar (*Felis concolor*), Canada lynx (*Lynx canadensis*) and woodland caribou (*Rangifer tarandus*; Coman, 1981;

Manville, 1942; Moorehead, 1922; Norton, 1930). *Alces* was also extirpated during the past century, but it has since returned and has been recorded from Mt Desert Island, Swans Island, Hog Island and Deer Isle. In the past it certainly occurred on Mt Desert Island, and fossil evidence indicates a wider distribution on the larger islands (Bourque, 1971, 1975); but because records are not available for all islands, *Alces* is omitted from the species–area analysis. *Castor* was extirpated by the late 18th century and even *Odocoileus* was eliminated from much of the region in the late 19th and early 20th centuries. Both species are now common. *Peromyscus leucopus* (Aquadro, Kilpatrick & Crowell, 1980), *Canis latrans*, and *Sylvilagus* (Norton, 1930) have only recently expanded their ranges to include mid-coastal Maine. Excluding the extirpated species listed above, the source pool for mid-coastal Maine is approximately 33 species of non-volant mammals, though some species are limited to only eastern or western portions of the region (Appendix, Table A1).

For all islands, every effort has been made to distinguish between resident breeding species and transients. The period 1885–1920 was used as a base period for determining native species for the large islands (Appendix, Table A1), thus excluding species presumed to have colonized via highway bridges since 1925 (Appendix, Table A2). Although absent during this period, *Castor* and *Ursus* are logically included among the native fauna of Mt Desert Island. Certainly these species were formerly present (Manville, 1942), and they have since returned (Coman, 1981). Eleven mainland species have been recorded only from Mt Desert Island (Appendix, Table A1). Not only is it the largest and least isolated of the group, but it has also received the most intensive study (Manville, 1942, 1960; Coman, 1981). Therefore, it is possible that some of these 11 species, chiefly small mammals, occur on other large islands.

It would seem unlikely that the small islands can support relict populations. Franklin (1980) proposed an effective population size of 500 for long-term persistence. Allowing for habitat patchiness, bottlenecks, and factors determining $N_e$, even cricetids should require an area exceeding $4 \text{ km}^2$. For purposes of analysis and discussion, I therefore divided the 24 coastal islands into two subsets: 17 smaller islands with area $3 \text{ km}^2$ or less and seven large islands whose area exceeds $5 \text{ km}^2$.

Several geographic variables are used for analysis of determinants of species richness, including area ($A$), distance to the mainland ($D_M$) and distance to the nearest larger island ($D_I$) (Tables 1 and 2). Areas for islands larger than Hog Island were obtained from the State of Maine Bureau of Taxation and Forestry. Areas for the other small islands were obtained by personal survey or calculated from United States Coast and Geodedic Survey Nautical Charts and U.S. Geological Survey 15′ Series Quadrangle maps as were elevations, distances and depths. For the larger islands, two environmental indices are included: elevation as an index of habitat diversity and human population density as an index of disturbance. In three cases the distance to nearest island ($D_I$) is to smaller islands because they clearly serve as stepping stones from the mainland to a large island. These stepping stones are Thompson Island (Mt Desert Island), Little Deer Isle (Deer Isle), and Beal's Island (Great Wass Island). For the 17 small islands, distance to Mt Desert Island or Deer Isle was used for the $D_M$ variable when it was less than the distance to the actual mainland.

Two estimates of elapsed time since post-Pleistocene submergence of

Table 2. Zoological variables for seven large islands of the Gulf of Maine: area, least distance to the mainland $(D_M)$, least distance to nearest larger island $(D_I)$, greatest water depth to mainland, maximum topographic elevation, human population density and number of native non-volant mammal species

| | Variable | | | | | | |
|---|---|---|---|---|---|---|---|
| Island | Area $(km^2)$ | $D_M$ (km) | $D_I$ (km) | Depth (m) | Age (1000 years) | Elevation (m) | Population $(/km^2)$ | Mammal species |
| Mt Desert | 279.20 | 0.5 | 0.16 | 0.1 | 1.0 | 466.0 | 16.8 | 29 |
| Deer Isle | 71.85 | 1.6 | 0.80 | 18.0 | 6.8 | 55.0 | 39.0 | 17 |
| Vinal Haven | 51.90 | 10.0 | 8.00 | 35.0 | 8.5 | 45.5 | 24.5 | 11 |
| Swans | 27.97 | 6.0 | 5.83 | 30.0 | 8.0 | 71.5 | 18.6 | 9 |
| Isle au Haut | 26.68 | 18.0 | 5.74 | 27.0 | 7.7 | 54.3 | 2.2 | 10 |
| Long | 24.35 | 2.5 | 2.50 | 19.0 | 6.9 | 58.5 | 24.6 | 10 |
| Great Wass | 10.88 | 2.6 | 0.37 | 6.0 | 4.0 | 30.5 | 1.8 | 11 |

landbridges are used, depth and age. Water depth is a function of eustatic rise in sea level which followed the maximum post-glacial depression of 60 m at 10 000 BP (Stuiver & Borns, 1975). But in the western North Atlantic relative sea level is also influenced by isostatic subsidence, which has occurred at a decreasing rate (Borns, pers. comm.; Aquadro, 1978). Therefore, rates of change in sea level were used to estimate time of submergence or island age (Table 2). However, depths today may differ from those in the past. Tides probably originated in the Gulf of Maine 4000–6000 BP when sea levels rose over Brown's Bank (Grant, 1970). Not only did effective depth change at this time, but tidal scouring may have since altered the depth of many channels, causing elapsed time to be overestimated.

## Statistical methods

The Mann–Whitney $U$ test was performed on an Apple II-plus using Dynacomp Inc., Basic Statistical Subroutines. All other statistical analysis (product–moment correlation, stepwise multiple regression, and Fisher exact test) were performed with the MUSIC StatPak on an IBM 4341 at St. Lawrence University.

## RESULTS

### Determinants of species richness

Here I test the first two predictions of the equilibrium theory using data for island area, isolation, and species richness given in Tables 1 and 2. I use correlation and stepwise multiple regression analyses to test the first two predictions of the equilibrium theory, that species richness varies directly with area and isolation. Correlations for all 24 coastal islands and for the seven large islands which exceed 5 km² in area appear in Tables 3 and 4, respectively. The results of stepwise regression analyses are given in Table 5. Both transformed and untransformed values for area and species richness were used. However, for the purposes of comparison, emphasis is placed on the power function and its

Table 3. Correlation matrix for zoogeographic variables of 24 coastal islands. Correlations below the diagonal employ natural logarithms of area and species

| | Log area | Distance to mainland | Distance to island | Species |
|---|---|---|---|---|
| Area | — | −0.078 | −0.027 | 0.889*** |
| $D_M$ | 0.275 | — | 0.854*** | −0.005 |
| $D_I$ | 0.424* | 0.854*** | — | 0.046 |
| Log species | 0.926*** | 0.164 | 0.22 | — |

*$P < 0.05$; ***$P < 0.001$.

slope, $z$. This is done out of convention and does not necessarily imply greater biological significance for this model (Abbott, 1983; Connor & McCoy, 1979; but see Lawlor, 1986).

### The species–area relationship

For the 24 coastal islands the power function provides the best fit and $S = 4.84A^{0.25}$ (Fig. 2). Clearly the coefficient $z$ is very close to the value of 0.263 predicted by Preston (1962).

For the 17 smaller islands, the best simple regression model is for log species–area ($r = 0.93$, $P < 0.001$). For the power function, $S = 4.26A^{0.21}$. The slope, $z = 0.215$, does not differ significantly from the expected value, 0.263, or from the $z$ values for the sets of seven and 24 islands. The low slope in part results from the fact that even the smallest islands have one or two species (*Microtus* and *Mustela* or occasionally *Sorex*), thus elevating the lower end of the curve, while the meagre fauna of Matinicus Island holds down the higher end of the curve. In addition, clustering of islands may raise immigration rates and thus lower $z$ values (MacArthur & Wilson, 1967: 31).

For the seven larger islands the semi-log and untransformed species–area models again yield stronger correlations than the log-transformed model, and in the power function $z = 0.353$ (Table 5). This slope does not differ from 0.263 ($t = 1.04$). It lies at the upper limit of the range of $z = 0.20–0.35$ generally reported for islands in equilibrium (MacArthur & Wilson, 1967), but it also falls within the range of $z$ values for non-equilibrial terrestrial mammals on landbridge islands as reviewed by Lawlor (1986).

Table 4. Correlation matrix for zoogeographic variables of seven large coastal islands of Maine. Correlations below the diagonal employ the natural logarithms of area and species

| | Log area | $D_M$ | $D_I$ | Depth | Age | Elevation | Species |
|---|---|---|---|---|---|---|---|
| Area | — | −0.387 | −0.419 | −0.597 | −0.769* | 0.977*** | 0.971*** |
| $D_M$ | −0.273 | — | 0.755* | 0.657 | 0.055 | −0.366 | −0.484 |
| $D_I$ | −0.151 | 0.755* | — | 0.922** | 0.779* | −0.418 | −0.581 |
| Depth | −0.298 | −0.657 | 0.922** | — | 0.769* | −0.632 | −0.699 |
| Age | −0.687 | 0.575 | 0.779* | 0.951*** | — | −0.810* | −0.814* |
| Elevation | −0.831* | −0.366 | 0.418 | −0.632 | −0.810* | — | 0.923** |
| Log species | 0.876** | −0.504 | −0.613 | −0.694 | −0.785* | 0.861* | — |

*$P < 0.05$, **$P < 0.01$, ***$P < 0.001$.

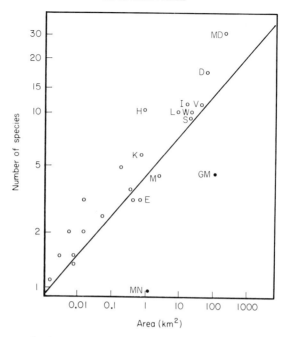

Figure 2. Species–area plot for 24 coastal islands, log $S = 1.58 + 0.247$ log $A$ ($r = 0.93$, $P < 0.001$). D, Deer Isle; E, Eagle Island; H, Hog Island; I, Isle au Haut; K, Kimball Island; L, Long Island; M, Matinicus Island; MD, Mt Desert Island; S, Swans Island; V. Vinal Haven Island; W. Great Wass Island. Other islands are listed in order of area in Table 1. Two oceanic islands (MN, Monhegan Island; and GM, Great Manan Island) (●), are not included in the regression.

In contrast to these coastal islands, the remote oceanic islands, Grand Manan and Monhegan, are markedly depauperate. Grand Manan, which lies 10 km off the New Brunswick coast and is 155.4 km², has only four native species, *Microtus*, *Peromyscus*, *Lutra* and *Tamiasciurus* (A. Mackay, pers. comm.; Ingersoll & Gorham, 1979). Monhegan Island, which is only 1.7 km² and is isolated by 27.4 km, has no known native mammals (G. Clough, pers. comm.). When these two islands of the Gulf of Maine are combined with three oceanic islands of the nearby Gulf of St. Lawrence, Newfoundland, Anticosti and the Magdalene Islands (Cameron, 1958), $z = 0.18$ ($r = 0.90$, $P = 0.05$). This low slope does not differ significantly from that of the seven landbridge islands ($t = 1.74$,

Table 5. Results of stepwise multiple regression of log species richness on geographic variables. Coefficients, levels of significance and contributions to the coefficient of determination are upon entry of the respective variables

| Island set | Variable | Coefficient | $P$ | Contribution to $R^2$ |
|---|---|---|---|---|
| 24 | Log area | 0.247 | <0.0001 | 0.86 |
|  | $D_1$ | −0.056 | 0.044 | 0.03 |
| 17 Small | Log area | 0.215 | <0.0005 | 0.59 |
|  | $D_1$ | −0.051 | <0.001 | 0.04 |
| 7 Large | Log area | 0.353 | <0.01 | 0.77 |
|  | Depth | −0.016 | <0.005 | 0.21 |
|  | Elevation | −0.001 | 0.125 | 0.02 |

$P > 0.10$), but it accords well with the findings of Lawlor (1986) for oceanic islands.

The species–area relation obtained for the seven large landbridge islands predicts a species richness of 28 for an island the area of Grand Manan. Clearly, extreme isolation has caused a discontinuity between the faunas of these two oceanic islands and those of the coastal islands. Is this due to isolation *per se*, or is it an effect of their different histories and were the coastal islands colonized via landbridges?

*Isolation effects*

I used stepwise multiple regression to identify additional determinants of species richness. For all 24 islands and for the 17 smaller islands, distance to the nearest larger island $(D_I)$ contributes significantly to the models and is second to area in its contribution to the coefficient of determination, $R^2$ (Table 5). Additional variables of $D_I^2$ and $D_M^2$ yielded no significant curvilinear effects and are omitted from Tables 3 and 4. For the 24 islands the best multivariate model is $S = (5.47A^{0.266})$ $(e^{-0.056D_I})$ $(r = 0.94, P < 0.0001)$. For the 17 smaller islands, $S = (5.10A^{0.244})$ $(e^{-0.051D_I})$ $(r = 0.9, P < 0.001)$.

For the seven large landbridge islands, the best multivariate regression incorporated elevation as well as $D_I$:

$$S = 10.72 + 0.112A - 0.496D_I - 0.029 \text{ Elevation}$$

$(r = 0.99, \ P < 0.0001)$; and the best model for transformed variables is $S = (5.71A^{0.296})$ $(e^{-0.0162 \text{ Depth}})$ $(r = 0.9; P < 0.001)$.

For all sets of islands, inter-island distance, $D_I$, correlates more strongly with species richness than does distance to mainland, $D_M$; and with one exception $D_I$ is entered after area in each multiple regression model. Because this holds despite Mt Desert Island and Deer Isle being treated as source areas, colonization would appear to take place via stepping stones. MacArthur & Wilson (1967: 125–128) predicted that species richness should be a normal function of isolation $(e^{-D^2})$ for such animals as mammals which either disperse actively (by swimming or crossing ice) or depend on waif dispersal or rafting, but I find agreement with the exponential function $(e^{-D})$, which describes passive dispersal. This is, however, consistent with Lomolino's (1984a) demonstration that for non-volant mammals the normal and exponential models provide equally good fits.

Has inclusion of aquatic mustelids and rodents (*M. vison*, *Lutra*, *Castor* and *Ondatra*) in the insular faunas distorted species–area and isolation effects? Exclusion of these species from estimates of species richness has little effect on the analyses for all 24 coastal islands, the only difference being a slightly stronger distance effect. But because the fauna of each of the seven large islands includes three or four of the aquatic species, these comprise a smaller proportion of the larger faunas. Therefore, when only terrestrial species are considered, $z$ is increased to 0.442, suggesting non-equilibrium. However, in the multivariate model $D_I$ is entered after area: $S = (0.600A)$ $(e^{-0.074D_I})$, $(r = 0.99)$; whereas, were those relict faunas, one would expect depth or age to pre-empt distance.

In order to distinguish between the landbridge relict and equilibrium hypotheses, it is essential to differentiate between the effects of isolation in time *vis-à-vis* distance effect. For the seven large islands, $D_I$ is entered into the

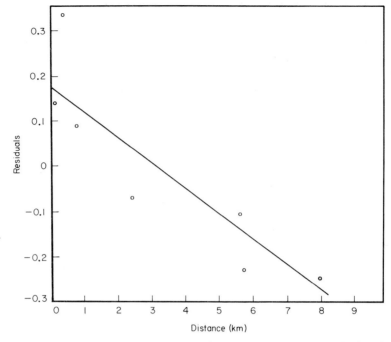

Figure 3. Distance effect for seven large islands of Maine: species–area residuals plotted against distance to nearest larger island or stepping stone. $\Upsilon = 0.191 - 0.057\ D_{\mathrm{I}}(r = 0.90, P < 0.005)$.

untransformed multivariate models after area. For these islands, depth and distance are strongly correlated and small changes in estimates of species richness cause distance to the nearest larger island $(D_{\mathrm{I}})$ to be substituted for depth in the transformed model. I therefore forced $D_{\mathrm{I}}$ into the regression analysis by removing depth from the eligible variables. The resulting equation is $S = (4.80 A^{0.316})\ (\mathrm{e}^{-0.06 D_{\mathrm{I}}})\ (r = 0.98,\ P < 0.002)$, and the level of significance is nearly that of the area–depth model. Regression of log species–log area residuals against either depth or distance yields highly significant negative slopes. For $D_{\mathrm{I}}$, $r = 0.90$, $P < 0.01$ (Fig. 3).

Time since isolation is a better estimate of island age than is depth, and the correlations of species and log species with age are significant (Table 4). However, it was possible to force age into the regression analysis only after eliminating other measures of isolation for the seven islands; age therefore provides a weaker model than do depth or distance, which are almost interchangeable. Moreover, $D_{\mathrm{I}}$ is entered into the untransformed model. Thus the data are consistent with both the relict and equilibrium hypotheses, but they favour the latter.

Clearly, the 24 coastal islands conform to the first two predictions of the MacArthur–Wilson theory: species richness increases with island area and decreases with spatial and temporal isolation. For all models, area is the principal correlate with species richness, accounting for 60–94% of variance in species richness for the sets of 17 small, seven large and all 24 islands. In no case does $z$ differ significantly from the expected 0.263. Isolation is the second most significant variable, accounting for as much as 20% of the variance in species on the seven large islands.

## Turnover

While species–area and species–distance effects are consistent with equilibrium, turnover with complementary immigration and extinction is a necessary condition. In this study information on turnover comes from three sources: direct observation on small islands, historical accounts for larger islands and faunal remains in archaeological sites. These are considered in sequence. In Crowell (1973) I discussed turnover in native populations of *Microtus pennsylvanicus* and introduced *Peromyscus* and *Clethrionomys*. On the smallest islands, *Microtus* is the only native rodent and turnover consisted of its periodic extinction and recolonization. Rates of extinction ($E$) and immigration ($I$) on eight islands (only three of which showed turnover) were 0.047 and 0.053/year respectively (Crowell, 1973: table 6). Thus the absolute rate ($T_{abs}$), defined as $\frac{1}{2}(I+E)$, was 0.05/year. In the same group of islands, four extinctions occurred among six introduced populations of *Peromyscus*, two remaining extant currently after 23 years. For these six populations, $I = 0$ and $T_{abs} = 0.025$/year. In both *Microtus* and *Peromyscus* the occurrence of extinctions was correlated with area of suitable habitat, mean population size ($K$) (Crowell, 1973), and with the coefficient of variation of population size, in accord with Karr (1982) and Diamond (1984). Turnover was also observed in *Sorex cinereus* on four of the same group of islands. During a total of 34 island-years, five colonizations and six extinctions were observed. The average rate of turnover, 0.16, is extraordinarily high, suggesting that some of the populations of this species on the smallest islands may be transitory.

Instances of turnover on the larger islands, which are listed in Appendix 2, were difficult to assess for several reasons. Whereas I censused the smaller islands every year, frequently turnover for the large islands could be dated to within only 5–10 years. Insofar as possible, records of transients or 'pseudoturnover' (Lynch & Johnson, 1974) were omitted. However, persons interviewed may not make the critical distinction between low populations and extinction. This may be especially true for hunters and trappers who think in terms of exploitable population levels, although many are astute observers with an intimate knowledge of their islands. Because of the interaction of human impact with environmental factors, a sharp distinction between natural extinctions and those caused by man cannot be made. Finally, natural colonizations and introductions (made both by the State and surreptitiously by individuals) are often confounded. Again, this is particularly true for game species and fur bearers such as *Odocoileus*, *Lepus* and *Castor*, which suffer frequent extinctions and also colonize naturally. Similarly, Manville (1942) attributed the presence of *Castor*, *Sciurus* and *Erethizon* on Mt Desert Island to introductions of small numbers in the first quarter of the century; but supplementary natural immigration must be suspected. *Lepus*, extirpated from Matinicus 50 years ago, was reintroduced *c.* 1978 (A. Bunker, pers. comm.).

Rates of turnover for eight of the larger islands are summarized in Table 6. In accord with the equilibrium model, there are almost equal numbers of immigrations and extinctions on each of the respective islands and for the group as a whole. For the period 1885–1985, mean rates of relative turnover for the eight islands, defined as percentage turnover per species per year (Schoener, 1983), were 0.16 extinctions and 0.152 immigrations per species per year. Hence

Table 6. Turnover on coastal islands of Maine, *c.* 1885–1985 (see Table A2). Introductions and presumed colonizations via highway bridges are excluded

| Island | Mean species | Extinctions | Immigrations |
|---|---|---|---|
| Mt Desert | 31 | 3–5 | 3–5 |
| Deer Isle | 18.5 | 3–5 | 3–5 |
| Vinal Haven | 11 | 2–3 | 2 |
| Swans | 9 | 0–1 | 0 |
| Isle au Haut | 10 | 2 | 1 |
| Long | 10 | 1–2 | 1 |
| Great Wass | 10 | 2 | 1 |
| Hog | 12 | 2–4* | 3–6* |
| Mean | 13.9 | 2.31 | 2.12 |

*Includes single breeding record for red fox and raccoon.

mean relative turnover was 0.159/year, and the range was from 0.028 on Swans Island to 0.312 on Hog Island. The mean rate of absolute turnover was 0.022/year. These values (apparently the first reported for insular mammals; but see Smith, 1980) are at the lower end of the range of values reported for birds and one order of magnitude less than those for lizards (Schoener, 1983).

Certainly turnover does not occur uniformly among the respective species on the eight islands in Table 6. Of the 17 most frequent species (Table 7), nine experienced a total of 27 turnover events (Table 6), while no turnover was observed in the remaining eight species. In the past, extinctions occurred most

Table 7. Occurrence of native species on seven large coastal islands ranked by area. ×, present; E, extirpated, ?, uncertain status

| Species | Mt Desert | Deer Isle | Vinal Haven | Swans | Isle au Haut | Long | Great Wass |
|---|---|---|---|---|---|---|---|
| *Microtus pennsylvanicus* | X | X | X | X | X | X | X |
| *Lepus americanus* | X | X | X | X | X | X | X |
| *Tamiasciurus hudsonicus* | X | X | X | X | X | X | X |
| *Mustela vison* | X | X | X | X | X | X | X |
| *Odocoileus virginianus* | X | X | X | X | X | X | X |
| *Sorex cinereus* | X | X | X | X | X | | X |
| *Peromyscus maniculatus* | X | X | X | X | X | X | |
| *Ondatra zibethicus* | X | X | X | ? | X | E? | X |
| *Vulpes vulpes* | X | X | E | | E | X | E |
| *Castor canadensis* | X | X | X | E? | | X | X |
| *Lutra canadensis* | X | X | X | | X | ? | ? |
| *Ursus americanus* | X? | X | | ? | | | |
| *Mustela erminea* | X | X | | | | | X |
| *Condylura cristata* | X | X | | | | ? | |
| *Clethrionomys gapperi* | X | X | | | | | |
| *Blarina brevicauda* | X | | | | | X | |
| *Lynx rufus* | X? | X | | | | | |
| *Martes pennanti* | E | E | | | | | ? |

*Eleven additional species occur only on Mt Desert Island (see Appendix 2).

frequently among carnivores and ungulates, which include the larger and less abundant species. Extinctions are frequent among the aquatic rodents (*Castor* and *Ondatra*), which are not only fur-bearers but occupy patchy habitats and may therefore be highly subject to population fluctuations. Most observed extinctions may be directly or indirectly attributed to man; but only 40% of immigrations constituted recolonizations by these same species. When only that turnover during the past 50 years which is not directly attributable to human disturbance is considered, $I = 0.02$, $E = 0.008$ and $T_{abs} = 0.0138$/year.

MacArthur & Wilson (1967) predicted that immigration should decrease with distance, while extinction should vary inversely with area if species richness is equal. Because species richness varies directly with area, absolute extinction will increase with area while relative extinction will decrease with area. As a consequence of the first two predictions, it is also predicted that absolute turnover will vary directly with distance, and both $T_{abs}$ and $T_{rel}$ will vary inversely with area (Williamson, 1978). Moreover, effects of distance and area on both immigration and extinction may be confounded. Area (island diameter) may affect the likelihood of immigration (MacArthur & Wilson, 1967: 127), while distance may directly affect the extinction rate (Brown & Kodric-Brown, 1977). I tested these predictions for the data in Table 6, using correlation and regression analysis.

Aside from the direct correlation of absolute extinction rate with species richness ($r = 0.740$, $P < 0.05$), no results showed significant agreement with the above predictions. Agreement with the predictions which was not significant included direct variation of extinction rate with area ($r = 0.548$), inverse correlation of relative extinction with log area ($r = -0.485$), inverse correlation of relative turnover with area ($r = -0.623$), and an inverse relationship between immigration rate and both log distance to island ($r = -0.543$) and $D_I$ ($r = -0.490$). The following findings were contrary to prediction: absolute extinction rate varied significantly and inversely with both $D_I$ ($r = -0.750$, $P < 0.01$) and log $D_I$ ($r = -0.740$, $P < 0.05$); relative extinction also varied inversely with log $D_I$ ($r = -0.607$); absolute turnover varied directly with area ($r = 0.418$), and there were significant inverse correlations between absolute turnover and both log $D_I$ ($r = -0.726$, $P < 0.05$) and $D_I$ ($r = -0.672$). Thus, my findings agree weakly with the predictions of MacArthur & Wilson (1967) for the effects of area on rates of extinction and turnover and the effect of distance on immigration, but both extinctions and turnover decreased with isolation.

Finally, faunal remains from archaeological sites provide evidence for the past presence and subsequent extinction of many species not currently found on the outer islands. Bourque (1971) reported *Alces*, *Ursus* and *Procyon* from a site on Deer Isle dated at 800–1000 BP. From the Turner Farm Site on North Haven, which is the oldest such site to be excavated (Bourque and Speiss, pers. comm.), species found in levels as old as 4500 BP include *Alces*, *Ursus*, *Martes pennanti*, *Mephitis*, *Lynx* and *Erethizon*. The period of 3500–4700 BP was hypsithermal and hardwood forests reached maximum diversity then (Bradstreet & Davis, 1975). Some of these mammal species may have undergone extinction as a result of the ensuing climatic deterioration. Hence most islands, including Matinicus and Monhegan, may have had appreciably larger faunas than at present. Faunal analysis of archaeological sites may thus provide the most accurate

profile of the indigenous fauna of this region. If this is so, species–area curves
based on recent records are far too low in intercept, if not in slope.


### Community structure

Analysis of the species comprising insular communities should provide further
insights into the processes of colonization and extinction which have shaped
them.

#### Nested subsets

From examination of Table 1 and Appendix Table A1 it is apparent that the
occurrence of species on the respective islands is far from random. *Microtus*
inhabits even the smallest of islands; *Mustela vison* is found on most islands, as is
*Sorex cinereus* if isolation is not too great. *Tamiasciurus* and *Odocoileus* occur on
islands larger than 25 ha, while *Lepus* occupies only those islands larger than
110 ha.

A similar pattern of non-random distribution with respect to area is also
evident among the seven larger islands. While Mt Desert Island supports most
mainland species, only a limited subset of the source fauna is found on the other
islands. In Table 7 these species are arranged in rank order of frequency of
occurrence. Their occurrence frequencies with regard to island area are highly
predictable, as revealed by the thorough analysis by Patterson & Atmar (1986).
Because of the small sample size, conventional statistical analysis is of limited
utility; nevertheless, the Mann–Whitney $U$ test does reveal several significant
patterns of occurrence. *Lynx rufus* and *Clethrionomys* occur on only the two closest
and largest islands ($P = 0.047$), *Mustela erminea* and *Martes pennanti* occur on the
three closest islands ($P = 0.028$), and *Lutra* and *Ondatra* are native to four of the
five largest islands ($P = 0.057$).

The occurrences of *Mustela erminea* on Great Wass and *Blarina* on Long Island
are explained by lack of isolation. The absence of *Peromyscus* from Great Wass
Island is highly anomalous, as is the absence of *Vulpes* from Swans Island. The
apparent absences of *Sorex* from Long Island and *Lutra* from Swans Island may
well be erroneous. With these exceptions, every species found on a given island is
found on all larger islands, and there is little substitution of possible vicariants.
The similarity in the composition of these independent faunas strongly indicates

Table 8. Comparison of trophic structure of mainland and insular communities
of mammals

| Island | Number of species | | | |
|---|---|---|---|---|
| | Insectivores | Herbivores | Carnivores | Total |
| Coastal Maine | 7 | 16 | 10 | 33 |
| Mt Desert | 6 | 13 | 10 | 29 |
| Deer Isle | 2 | 8 | 7 | 17 |
| Vinal Haven | 1 | 7 | 3 | 11 |
| Swans | 1 | 7 | 1 | 9 |
| Isle au Haut | 1 | 6 | 3 | 10 |
| Long | 1 | 7 | 2–3 | 10–11 |
| Great Wass | 1 | 6 | 3–5 | 10–12 |

deterministic processes. Patterson & Atmar (1986) attribute such patterns to non-random persistence and extinction in relictual faunas.

*Retention rules*

Because of constraints imposed on population maintenance and stability by energetics and resource availability, the following rules governing the persistence of mammalian species on landbridge islands may be predicted (Brown, 1971, 1978): herbivores will be better represented than carnivores, small body size will be favoured over large, and habitat and foraging generalists will prevail over specialists. These expectations are tested for the sum total of species occurring on the larger islands, Mt Desert Island excepted. First, are there differences in the representation of trophic levels between the six islands and mainland? A $3 \times 2$ $\chi^2$ test showed no significant differences between islands and mainland in the apportionment of species among the three trophic levels ($\chi^2 = 2.5$, $P < 0.2$), although the representation of insectivores on the islands is only one-half that of the mainland ($\chi^2 = 3.24$, $P < 0.1$). Inspection of Table 8 shows that six of the eight species which occur on at least six of the large islands are herbivores; but contrary to prediction, the proportion of carnivores is not reduced on the islands, except for Swans Island.

I was able to demonstrate no significant differences in the distribution of body sizes between mainland and island communities. *Sorex cinereus* is found on most islands rather than the larger *Blarina*; and *Mustela erminea* occurs on Deer Isle, and probably Great Wass Island, instead of the larger *M. frenata*; but the number of species in the 11–100 g body weight class was 40% fewer on the six large islands, Mt Desert Island excepted. This paucity of small rodents and insectivores does not conform to the prediction that small body size favours retention or persistence (Brown, 1971; Patterson, 1984). Rather, it accords with Lomolino's contention (Lomolino, 1983, 1984b) that large body size is a critical factor for dispersal.

With regard to niche breadth, density compensation and niche shifts appear to facilitate the success of some species on small islands (Crowell, 1983). For example, deer and bear forage in the intertidal zone (Conkling, 1981), as does *Sorex* (T. Herman, pers. comm.). For the set of larger islands, inclusion of elevation in two multiple regression models for species richness indicates that increased environmental heterogeneity allows the establishment of habitat specialists.

Finally, habitat and foraging requirements, sometimes abetted by constraints imposed by body size and vagility, appear to preclude substitution of confamilial species. *Sorex cinereus* is found on most islands instead of *Blarina*, which prefers less boreal habitats. *Tamiasciurus*, which prefers conifer seeds, is never replaced by *Sciurus*, a resident of deciduous woodlands. The opportunistic *Microtus* replaces the more specialized *Clethrionomys* on all but the least isolated islands (Crowell, 1973; Crowell & Pimm, 1976). Aside from aquatic mustelids, *Vulpes* is the most widely distributed carnivore.

*Missing species*

As striking as the non-random occurrence of species is the uniform absence of certain species from islands, other than Mt Desert Island. *Sorex fumeus, Marmota, Sciurus,* and *Erethizon* were absent from the original fauna of Mt Desert Island, but all except *Sorex* are now established. These four species are uniformly missing from all other islands studied. In addition, the other large islands lack three insectivores (*Parascalops*, *Sorex palustris* and *Microsorex*), *Glaucomys* and all hibernators but *Ursus* (*Zapus*, *Napeozapus*, *Tamias*, *Mephitis*, *Procyon* and *Marmota*). Can the absence of these species from large landbridge islands be accounted for by their being prone to extinction? Because *Castor* and *Ondatra* depend on freshwater wetlands, their populations on islands appear to be unstable due to limited carrying capacity. Scarcity of mast may exclude some granivores from outlying islands. Attempts to experimentally introduce *Napeozapus* were unsuccessful. Although I successfully introduced *Tamiasciurus*, *Tamias* and *Glaucomys* to small islands (Crowell, 1983), these sciurid populations did not persist. Hence bottlenecks caused by fluctuation of cone and mast crops could cause the extinction of granivores on isolated islands.

To the extent that they are relatively *K*-selected, hibernators may have difficulty in founding populations as well as being extinction prone. They are often monoestrous and have smaller litters (Kirkland & Kirkland, 1979; Adler, Reich & Tamarin, 1984). Chapman (pers. comm.) suggests that on islands, limited habitat heterogeneity would limit not only the quantity and quality of food resources, but also the availability of denning sites. Thus absence of hibernators and granivores from islands may be explained by their vulnerability to extinction.

### DISCUSSION

#### *Area and distance*

Equilibrium may be expected on landbridge islands too small to maintain relict faunas and on oceanic islands of sufficient proximity to source areas to be not limited by colonization. Non-equilibrial faunas are found on oceanic islands too remote to have reached equilibrium (MacArthur, 1972) and on large landbridge islands which may reach a steady state as both immigration and extinction approach zero (Wilcox, 1978; Heaney, 1984). The ecologically balanced faunas of the coastal islands in the Gulf of Maine contrast with the colonization-limited faunas of oceanic islands of the western North Atlantic. Did they originate from colonization via post-Pleistocene landbridges or by subsequent immigration? And are they now primarily relictual or equilibrial?

Elevated $z$ values and lack of distance effect are often associated with non-equilibrial faunas on isolated islands. Brown (1971) and Patterson (1980) both reported species–area slopes of 0.43 for non-volant mammals of two mountain systems of the American West. Brown (1971, 1978) found no effect due to isolation. Heaney (1984) likewise reported no significant distance effect for mammals on islands of SE Asia, but he found a moderately low $z$ value of 0.235. One of the highest $z$ values for mammals is 0.509 reported by Dueser & Brown (1980) for rodents on very small coastal islands of Virginia; they concluded that these islands are in equilibrium and attribute the high $z$ value to low immigration and high extinction rates. By contrast, for coastal islands of Massachusetts, Adler & Wilson (1985) report a $z$ value of 0.06, apparently the result of high species richness on semi-isolated islets.

For coastal islands of Maine, I found that area and isolation together account for 80–97% of the variance in species richness. Frequent turnover on 17 islands smaller than 3 km² indicates that their faunas are in equilibrium. For seven islands larger than 10 km², the slope of the species–area curve is 0.353.

Depth or distance account for over 85% of residual variance, and because area and isolation covary, the $z$ value of the species–area relationship is reduced when the effect of isolation is removed. Depth is usually used to estimate island age (Wilcox, 1978; Heaney, 1984), and correlation of age with species richness is indicative of non-equilibrium. However, for the landbridge islands of the Gulf of Maine, distance rather than temporal isolation appears to be the primary factor. Depth and distance are strongly correlated and distance to the nearest island $(D_1)$ can be substituted for depth with little sacrifice of statistical significance. Moreover, because of isostatic changes in this region, island age is a non-linear function of depth, and the correlation of age with species–area residuals is weaker than that of depth or distance.

Thus, in contrast to landbridge faunas which are apparently relaxing towards equilibrium (Brown, 1971; Heaney, 1984; Patterson, 1984), the faunas of the Maine islands showed a significant distance effect, implying continuing immigration. The distances there are one to two orders of magnitude smaller than for the montane islands of Brown (1971) and Patterson (1984) and, for islands of equal area, species richness is correspondingly higher; but the distances reported by Heaney (1984) for the closer islands of the Sunda Shelf (12–20 km) approximate those of the more remote Maine islands.

Distance effect for the smaller landbridge islands of Maine is apparent in the contrast between the fauna of Hog Island with those of more remote islands. Hog Island has 10 native species while Eagle, Kimball, and Matinicus Islands support three, six and four species, respectively. Because Hog Island may be too small to have a relict fauna, its rich fauna can be accounted for by its lack of isolation.

Another effect of isolation is revealed in the comparison between the faunas of Grand Manan, an oceanic island, and those of smaller, but almost equally distant, landbridge islands such as Vinal Haven. Certainly the depauperate fauna of Grand Manan must be due in part to its history. However, it is separated from the mainland by an open channel, while Vinal Haven lies in a bay with land on three sides. Hence the absence of such vagile species as *Vulpes* from Grand Manan may be due to its position rather than its history.

Species occurrence frequencies reveal a pattern of nested subsets when islands are ranked in order of either area or degree of isolation. Patterson & Atmar (1986) attribute nested subsets among montane faunas to the occurrence of ordered and predictable extinctions in relict faunas following saturation. However, both the uniform absence of species of low vagility from the faunas of large islands and the predictable occurrence patterns of species on islands far too small to support relict populations suggest that dispersal ability may be limiting. Therefore, on islands within the dispersive range of the taxon under consideration, differences in colonizing ability may complement differential extinction as a cause of nested subsets.

Because of its relation to trophic level and body size (Harestad & Bunnell, 1979; Peters & Raelson, 1984), home range size should allow an estimate of the minimum population size which an island of given area can support. According to Harestad & Bunnell (1979), an island 100 ha in area might support a minimum of 24 *Lepus*, 58 *Tamiasciurus* and 182 *Peromyscus*, yet 73 ha Bradbury Island, which is less than one-half the size home range they cite for *Odocoileus*, supports a population of 10–15 deer but no *Peromyscus*. While this density of deer is more than twice that representative of mainland levels, it can hardly be a viable population level. However, *Odocoileus* easily swims between islands, and its population on Bradbury Island is probably maintained by constant immigration. On the other hand, because of lower vagility, *Peromyscus* may be unable to colonize at all. Therefore, if there is a minimum critical area of population size, there is also a maximum critical distance over which each species can effectively disperse. Vagility thus complements carrying capacity as a determinant of population maintenance (cf. Lomolino, 1986).

*Peromyscus* occurs only on islands larger than Matinicus (3.1 km$^2$), however isolated, but it is absent from intervening smaller islands. I earlier concluded (Crowell, 1973) that the species was in equilibrium, although there was no evidence for turnover (cf. Gilbert, 1980). Aquadro (1978) studied genetic variability in populations of *Peromyscus* on six of these landbridge islands in order to assess their degree of isolation in time and space. He found no more morphological or genetic differentiation than exists among mainland populations. Using multiple regression analysis, he attributed variability in mean heterozygosity to distance, area and island age, in that order. From this Aquadro (1978) inferred limited but sustained gene flow since the time of land-bridge submergence. In contrast to Aquadro's findings, differentiated subspecies of *Peromyscus maniculatus* occur on the more isolated oceanic islands of Grand Manan, Anticosti, and the Magdalen Islands (Cameron, 1958). Thus, lack of endemism is consistent with an equilibrium hypothesis for the Maine landbridge islands. While other factors may be involved, it would appear that gene flow takes place to large outlying landbridge islands, but the rate of immigration is too low to sustain populations on smaller islands.

## Vagility and colonization

Differences in colonizing ability may make a strong contribution to the success of some species and total absence of others on these islands. Colonization, or immigration as used by MacArthur & Wilson (1967), consists of two phases. These are dispersal (immigration in the limited sense) and the subsequent establishment of a population.

Species present on oceanic islands must cross water barriers (MacArthur, 1972; Diamond, 1972). Ten species found on the oceanic islands of the Gulf of St. Lawrence (Cameron, 1958) also inhabit coastal Maine. These species, which are among the 13 most frequent species on the Maine islands (Table 7), include *Tamiasciurus, Peromyscus, Lepus, Mustela erminea, Lutra* and *Ursus*.

*Sorex cinereus, Mustela vison* and *Odocoileus* are absent from the oceanic islands but occur on many coastal Maine islands. By comparing the species present on landbridge islands with those also found on islands perhaps too small to support relictual populations, other species which may disperse across water can be identified. Six species (*Sorex cinereus, Tamiasciurus, Microtus, Lepus, Mustela vison* and *Odocoileus*) which occur on most of the large landbridge islands (Table 7), are also found on several small islands and may well be in equilibrium. But because certain species, for example *Sorex cinereus*, can cross water barriers of

1–2 km, it does not follow that their populations on larger and more isolated islands are necessarily equilibrial.

Five species occur only on the two or three islands closest to the mainland. Fossil evidence indicates that *Martes* and *Lynx rufus* were more widely distributed in the past (Bourque and Speiss, pers. comm.), but *Condylura*, *Blarina* and *Clethrionomys* evidently have low vagility. In an analysis of the distribution of small mammals on coastal islands of Massachusetts, Adler & Wilson (1985) found that the distribution of *Blarina* and *Clethrionomys* depends on nearness to source areas. *Blarina* and *Clethrionomys* do occur on Hog Island, as do *Tamias* and *Glaucomys*. Because Hog Island may be too small to maintain a relict fauna, these species must be able to cross limited water barriers. Thus, I have recently found *Clethrionomys* on Scraggy Island (Table 1), and Thurber & Herman (1984) report it on small coastal islands on Nova Scotia.

Possible modes of dispersal across water barriers include rafting, swimming and crossing ice. Both observation and evidence from recurrent turnover (Appendix, Table A2) indicate that the aquatic mustelids, *Mustela* and *Lutra*, colonize islands as distant as 12 km by swimming. The aquatic rodents, *Ondatra* and *Castor*, suffer frequent extinction, and where isolation exceeds 5 km they appear to have difficulty in colonizing islands such as Swans and Isle au Haut. *Odocoileus* and *Alces* (Manville, 1960) are frequently observed swimming between islands, and *Ursus* must also; witness the number of "Bear Islands"! Schemnitz (1975) reported an *Odocoileus* swimming from Isle au Haut to Vinal Haven Island, a distance of at least 10.8 km. Small mammals may swim distances of less than 1 km (Crowell, 1973), and non-hibernating rodents may cross ice (Beer, Lukens & Olson, 1954; Lomolino, 1984b). In Maine, local residents describe crossing of ice by *Vulpes*. Lomolino (1983) has tracked 13 species of mammals on ice in the St. Lawrence River, and has recorded distances as great as 1 km for insectivores and small rodents. However, much of the travel occurred in the spring, when animals are more active, whereas in coastal Maine, sea ice now occurs during mid-winter and only at intervals of a decade or so (Crowell, 1973). Absence of hibernators from most Maine Islands implies that crossing ice is a common mode of dispersal.

The fact that some species have colonized islands only after the building of highway bridges indicates that water constitutes an effective barrier to their dispersal. In addition to the recent arrival of *Erethizon*, *Procyon* and *Mephitis* on Great Wass Island and/or Deer Isle (see Appendix, Table A2), *Sciurus* has recently colonized Little Deer Isle. I would suggest that *Marmota*, *Procyon* and *Mephitis*, and possible *Erethizon* and *Sciurus*, may have reached Mt Desert Island by bridge during the past 150 years.

Several groups of low vagility may be identified among species absent from all but the least isolated of islands. The body form of some species (*Condylura*, *Erethizon*, *Marmota* and *Mephitis*) suggests that they may be poor swimmers. *Procyon*, ubiquitous on Virginia barrier islands (Dueser, pers. comm.), may be repelled by the cold water (*c*. 10°C) of the Gulf of Maine. Sciurids may be unlikely to venture into water (Denman, 1965); Lomolino (1983) found that *Tamiasciurus* travelled on ice more frequently than *Sciurus*. Finally, some species (e.g. *Blarina* and *Sorex fumeus*) may be relatively rare in source areas or littoral habitats, but this is subject to regional variation. Where *Blarina* is abundant in the source area, it occurs frequently on islands (Lomolino, 1984b; Adler &

Wilson, 1985). Several of the source species which occur only on Mt Desert Island are rare on the mainland, for example *Synaptomys*, *Sorex palustris* and other insectivores.

Therefore, both direct and indirect evidence indicates that most mammals occurring on coastal landbridge islands are able to cross salt water barriers 0.5–1.5 km wide, and thus their populations need not be regarded as relictual. Common species native to one or more of the large islands for which I have no evidence of dispersal across water include *Condylura*, *Marmota* and *Mephitis*, while *Blarina*, *Clethrionomys* and *Tamias* cross only short distances.

## Landbridges and missing species

Several species are absent from all islands but Mt Desert and/or Hog Island. These include three true hibernators (*Zapus*, *Napeozapus* and *Marmota*), three partial hibernators (*Tamias*, *Procyon* and *Mephitis*), three scansorial species (*Erethizon*, *Glaucomys* and *Sciurus*), three soricids and *Synaptomys*. What is the most parsimonious explanation for the absence of these species from most large coastal islands?

If these are landbridge islands with relictual populations, then either the missing species were not present at the time of the landbridges, or they have since become extinct. If, instead, the faunas are in equilibrium, then the missing species either have exceedingly low immigration rates or are highly subject to extinction.

Heaney (1984) has presented fossil evidence for the prior presence of now-extinct mammals on the landbridge islands of the Sunda Shelf, and similar evidence exists for mammals inhabiting the mountain ranges of western North America (Patterson, 1984; Brown, 1986). Nonetheless, it would seem that because of a peninsula effect resulting from progressive loss of area and habitat diversity and increase in isolation, many landbridge islands may never have had a full complement of source species, causing rates of extinction to be overestimated.

Because *Erethizon*, *Marmota*, *Procyon* and *Mephitis* are absent from Cape Breton and Prince Edward Island, two large landbridge islands in the Gulf of St. Lawrence, Cameron (1958) concluded that these species had not immigrated to Nova Scotia before the landbridges were submerged. Most of the species missing from the Maine islands inhabit deciduous or mixed forest and associated seres. Such habitats (birch–oak–pine) may have appeared as early as 9700 BP, although diverse hardwood forests were not present until some time later (Bradstreet & Davis, 1975). Lacking palaeontological data on the dispersal of these mammal species after glaciation, we must assume that they were present before the submergence of landbridges.

This supposition appears to be supported by remains from Amerindian middens. If this material represents resident individuals rather than transported carcasses, then we must explain the recent disappearance of many mammals from the outer islands. Their extinction may have been due to vegetational change. However, Conkling (pers. comm.) points out that we should not underestimate the intensity of exploitation by early colonists, who may have extirpated a broad segment of the original fauna by both direct exploitation and drastic habitat alteration. Certainly *Alces*, *Erethizon* and many carnivores might easily have been extirpated in colonial times. However, if landbridges allowed these larger species to colonize the islands, what of the several small insectivores and rodents which are present only on large and/or near islands like Mt Desert Island, Deer Isle and Hog Island? Certainly they would not have been extirpated by man, but must have undergone extinction on islands smaller than Mt Desert Island. Perhaps even that island is not large enough to support relictual populations; but because of its proximity to the mainland, these species may be maintained by rescue effect (Brown & Kodric-Brown, 1977). Absence of these species from outlying islands can then best be explained by the inability to colonize all but the closest islands.

By comparing insular bird faunas off New Guinea, Diamond (1972) elegantly separated relict species from those colonizing across water. Using logistic regression to analyse the distribution of small mammals on coastal islands, Adler & Wilson (1985) identified some species (*Sorex, Blarina* and *Tamias*) as being restricted by distance while others (*Scalopus* and, to a lesser extent, *Zapus*) were limited by area. Because of the confounding covariation between area and distance in the Maine islands, I am not able to make this distinction, and have been forced to conclude that Mt Desert Island, the only island on which the hibernators occur, is close enough to the mainland to receive continuous immigration. Nevertheless, because of the history of these islands, the correlation between species richness and island age, and the existence of nested subsets, I am hesitant to abandon the non-equilibrium model. Patterson (pers. comm.) suggests that we recognize a continuum from isolated landbridge islands having non-equilibrial faunas to those of intermediate isolation with both relict species and those in equilibrium to islands so near, and/or small, that all species are in equilibrium.

### Equilibrium or sequential change?

Would that it were possible to construct the history of these faunas from their origins as long as 10 000 years ago. Clearly their composition has not remained constant, but has apparently responded to changes in vegetation influenced by climatic shifts (cf. Sanger, 1975). Certainly, major changes were inflicted by European settlement beginning in the 17th century and extirpations continued into the first half of this century. Since then, reversion of agricultural lands to forest and decreased exploitation of wild populations appear to have allowed recolonization by many previously extirpated species (cf. Stanton, 1963), resulting in a partial reconstitution of the original fauna.

Can this be viewed as a return to prior equilibrium? Three levels of turnover may be perceived: first, the one just alluded to, recolonization of extirpated species, including *Castor, Lynx rufus, Martes pennanti, Odocoileus* and *Alces*; secondly, short-term turnover on small islands of highly vagile species such as *Microtus, Sorex, Tamiasciurus* and *Ondatra*; and thirdly, invasion by opportunistic species associated with secondary forests and disturbed habitats. Such species (*Procyon, Mephitis, Sciurus* and *Canis*) have been introduced or have colonized with the aid of bridges.

Turnover, *sensu* MacArthur & Wilson (1967), would seem to imply not only a numerical balance between immigration and extinction, but replacement among species of like trophic level, habitat or guild (cf. Abbott & Grant, 1976;

Abbott, 1983). However, my third level of turnover is marked by the arrival of a new set of species. While this recent wave of colonizations may fortuitously compensate for earlier extinctions, it comprises a new set of species; and species richness on several of the least isolated islands has actually increased 10–15% above levels prevailing during the past century. Hence, community structure tracks environmental change, whether due to climatic shifts or the influence of man, and like Heaney (1986), I find sequential episodes of disequilibrium in which the essentially uniform process of equilibrium is redirected by events in time.

In order better to resolve questions in mammalian biogeography, further work is indicated on several fronts. More precise information on the dating of landbridges and the history of faunal distributions would enhance our understanding of the relative importance of the effects of isolation in time as opposed to space. Such evidence may be obtained from geological and palaeoecological studies and from the investigation of genetic and morphologic variability. Studies of evolutionary divergence clarifying conditions leading to endemism can elucidate the extent and degree of isolation. Better documentation of the importance of different modes of dispersal is needed. We need to understand better the roles of minimum population size and bottlenecks in the process of extinction and thus to define the minimum area necessary for maintenance of isolated populations for which immigration approaches zero. Finally, because rates of immigration and extinction may depend upon the local climate and ecological matrix as well as on differences between taxa, more precise application of the theory of island biogeography to conservation will depend upon autecological studies *in situ*.

CONCLUSIONS

The 24 coastal islands of this study meet the major predictions of the MacArthur–Wilson equilibrium theory: mammalian species richness varies both directly with area and inversely with distance, and there is continuing turnover while numbers of species remain relatively constant. Not surprisingly, populations on the smaller islands are dependent upon continued immigration. Although landbridges to the seven larger islands were submerged as early as 8500 BP, in contrast with the faunas of oceanic islands there is no clear evidence of endemism. Landbridge islands support more species, but not different species, from those found on oceanic islands in the same region. Although they exhibit nested subsets, these communities do not show the loss of extinction-prone elements such as carnivores which is expected on non-equilibrial islands. Rather, they differ from mainland communities in having fewer insectivores, small rodents and hibernators. The absence of these elements is attributed to their poor dispersive abilities due to small body size and inactivity in winter. Thus immigrant selection among species may play a strong role in determining community structure.

Turnover on these islands has been documented in at least 15 species representing 10 families of terrestrial mammals. Rates were lower than reported for other vertebrates (Schoener, 1983). Most turnover occurred in a limited set of species and these were not always unimportant to the community (cf. Schoener, 1983); indeed, *Microtus* is the dominant species on the smaller islands.

Extinctions were more frequent in species with fluctuating population levels such as *Microtus*, *Vulpes* and *Ondatra*.

Certainly species richness fluctuates as communities respond to environmental changes, but I would suggest that the essential feature of equilibrium is continued immigration and extinction. Whether or not numbers of species remain constant may be trivial, but there is a fundamental difference between isolated non-equilibrial faunas and those subject to continuing colonization. The role of landbridges in the initial colonization of these coastal islands remains unclear, but a significant distance effect in conjunction with confirmed turnover indicates that these are not isolated faunas undergoing relaxation. To the extent that they are dependent upon continued immigration, the mammalian populations on these islands must be regarded as being in equilibrium.

In constructing their theory, MacArthur & Wilson (1967) clearly opted for the elegance of generality. As excellent naturalists, I doubt that they were as naive as their critics imply (Sauer, 1969; Gilbert, 1980). Certainly, we must interpret particular faunas in terms of regional history, the local environment and the biological characteristics of its species. The focus must not be restricted to numbers of species, but should be directed towards the processes of colonization and extinction which determine them. But operating under the *ceteris paribus* assumption, does not the equilibrium theory serve as a null hypothesis against which we assess the real world? Paraphrasing Picasso, MacArthur once observed "a theory is a lie which makes you see the truth" (unpubl. ms.). If the equilibrium theory has forced us to pose new questions and to seek new evidence in order to better understand mammalian communities, its purpose has been fulfilled.

## ACKNOWLEDGEMENTS

The study was supported by Grant GB-18323 from the National Science Foundation and a Faculty Research Grant from St. Lawrence University. J. Chapman, D. and T. Crowell, T. Howe and R. Abbott conducted faunal surveys. B. Bourque, G. Clough, T. French and R. Palmer permitted use of unpublished observations; N. Bailey, Mrs E. Beal, R. Davis, L. Eaton, H. Hatch, J. Kepes, C. Richards and J. Stevens provided information. M. Lomolino, G. Morlock and L. Plourde assisted with analysis of data. T. Budd drew the graphs, H. Vreeland prepared the bibliography and R. Taylor typed the manuscript. Editorial comments by L. R. Heaney and B. D. Patterson provided invaluable fine-tuning.

## REFERENCES

ABBOTT, I. 1983. The meaning of $z$ in species–area regressions and the study of species turnover in island biogeography. *Oikos, 41:* 385–390.

ABBOTT, I. & GRANT, P. R., 1976. Non-equilibrial bird faunas on islands. *American Naturalist, 110:* 507–528.

ADLER, G. H., REICH, L. M. & TAMARIN, R. H., 1984. Demography of the meadow jumping mouse (*Zapus hudsonicus*) in eastern Massachusetts. *American Midland Naturalist, 112:* 387–391.

ADLER, G. H. & WILSON, M. L., 1985. Small mammals on Massachusetts islands: the use of probability functions in clarifying biogeographic relationships. *Oecologia, 66:* 178–186.

AQUADRO, C. F., KILPATRIC, C. W. & CROWELL, K. L., 1980. Colonization of suitable habitat by *Peromyscus leucopus* in coastal Maine. *Journal of Mammalogy, 61:* 727–730.

AQUADRO, C. F., 1978. *Evolutionary genetics of insular* Peromyscus: *electrophoretic, morphological and chromosomal variation.* Unpublished M.Sc. thesis, University of Vermont.

BEER, J. R., LUKENS, P. R. & OLSON, D., 1954. Small mammal populations on islands of Basswood Lake, Minnesota. *Ecology, 35:* 437–445.

BOURQUE, B. J., 1971. *Prehistory of the central Maine coast.* Unpublished Ph.D. thesis, Harvard University.

BOURQUE, B. J., 1975. Comments on the Late Archaic populations of central Maine: The view from the Turner Farm. *Arctic Arthropology, 12:* 35–45.

BRADSTREET, T. D. & DAVIS, R. B., 1975. Mid-postglacial environments in New England with emphasis on Maine. *Arctic Anthropology, 12:* 7–22.

BROWN, J. H., 1971. Mammals on mountaintops: nonequilibrium insular biogeography. *American Naturalist, 105:* 467–478.

BROWN, J. H., 1978. The theory of biogeography and the distribution of boreal birds and mammals. *Great Basin Naturalist Memoirs, 2:* 209–228.

BROWN, J. H., 1986. Two decades of interaction between the MacArthur–Wilson model and the complexities of mammalian distributions. *Biological Journal of the Linnean Society, 28:* 231–251.

BROWN, J. H. & KODRIC-BROWN, A., 1977. Turnover rates in insular biogeography: effect of immigration on extinction. *Ecology, 58:* 445–449.

CAMERON, A. W., 1958. Mammals of the islands in the Gulf of St. Lawrence. *National Museum of Canada Bulletin, 154:* 1–165.

CONKLING, P. W., 1981. *Islands in Time.* Camden: Down East Books.

COMAN, D. R., 1981. *The Native Mammals, Reptiles and Amphibians of Mount Desert Island, Maine.* Bar Harbor: Darkman Press.

CONNOR, E. F. & McCOY, E. D., 1979. The statistics and biology of the species-area relationship. *American Naturalist, 113:* 791–833.

CROWELL, K. L., 1973. Experimental zoogeography: introduction of mice onto small islands. *American Naturalist, 107:* 535–558.

CROWELL, K. L., 1983. Islands—insight or artifact?: Population dynamics and habitat utilization in insular rodents. *Oikos, 41:* 492–454.

CROWELL, K. L. & PIMM, S. L., 1976. Competition and niche shifts of mice introduced onto small islands. *Oikos, 27:* 251–258.

DENMAN, N. S., 1965. Colonization of the islands of the Gulf of St. Lawrence by mammals. *Ecology, 46:* 340–341.

DIAMOND, J. M., 1972. Biogeographic kinetics: estimation of relaxation times for avifaunas of southwest Pacific islands. *Proceedings of the National Academy of Sciences of the U.S.A., 69:* 3199–3203.

DIAMOND, J. M. 1984. "Normal" extinctions in isolated populations. In M. Nitecki (Ed.), *Extinctions:* 191–246. Chicago: University of Chicago Press.

DUESER, R. D. & BROWN, W. C., 1980. Ecological correlates of insular rodent diversity. *Ecology, 61:* 50–56.

FEFER, I. & SCHETTIG, P. A., 1980. *An ecological characterization of coastal Maine.* U.S. Fish and Wildlife Service, Vol. 3, 11 FWS/OBS-80/29. Newton Center, MA: U.S. Dept. of Interior.

FRANKLIN, I. R., 1980. Evolutionary change in small populations. In M. E. Soule & B. A. Wilcox (Eds), *Conservation Biology:* 135–150. Sunderland, MA: Sinauer Associates, Inc.

GILBERT, F. S., 1980. The equilibrium theory of island biogeography: fact or fiction? *Journal of Biogeography, 7:* 209–235.

GRANT, D. R., 1970. Recent coastal submergence of the Maritime Provinces, Canada. *Canadian Journal of Life Sciences, 7:* 676–689.

HARESTAD, A. S. & BUNNELL, F. L., 1979. Home range and body weight—a re-evaluation. *Ecology, 60:* 389–402.

HEANEY, L. R., 1984. Mammalian species richness on islands of the Sunda Shelf, Southeast Asia. *Oecologia, 61:* 11–17.

HEANEY, L. R., 1986. Biogeography of mammals in SE Asia: estimates of rates of colonization, extinction and speciation. *Biological Journal of the Linnean Society, 28:* 127–165.

INGERSOLL, L. K. & GORHAM, S. W., 1979. A history of the mammals of Grand Manan. *Journal New Brunswick Museum, 1979:* 108–124.

KARR, J. R., 1982. Population variability and extinction in the avifauna of a tropical land bridge islands. *Ecology, 63:* 1975–1978.

KIRKLAND Jr, G. D., & KIRKLAND, C. J., 1979. Are small mammal hibernators *K*-selected? *Journal of Mammalogy, 60:* 164–168.

LAWLOR, T. E., 1986. Comparative biogeography of mammals on islands. *Biological Journal of the Linnean Society, 28:* 99–125.

LOMOLINO, M. V., 1982. Species–area and species–distance relationships of terrestrial mammals in the Thousand Island Region. *Oecologia, 54:* 72–75.

LOMOLINO, M. V., 1983. *Island biogeography, immigrant selection and mammalian body size on islands.* Unpublished Ph.D. thesis, SUNY, Binghamton.

LOMOLINO, M. V., 1984a. Mammalian island biogeography: effects of area, isolation and vagility. *Oecologia, 61:* 376–382.

LOMOLINO, M. V., 1984b. Immigrant selection, predatory exclusion and the distributions of *Microtus pennsylvanicus* and *Blarina brevicauda* on islands. *American Naturalist, 123:* 468–483.

LOMOLINO, M. V., 1986. Mammalian community structure on islands: the importance of immigration, extinction and interactive effects. *Biological Journal of the Linnean Society, 28:* 1–21.

LYNCH, J. F. & JOHNSON, N. K., 1974. Turnover and equilibria in insular avifaunas with special reference to the California Channel Islands. *Condor, 76:* 370–384.

MACARTHUR, R. H., 1972. *Geographical Ecology, Patterns in the Distribution of Species.* New York: Harper and Row.

MACARTHUR, R. H. & WILSON, E. O., 1967. *The Theory of Island Biogeography.* Monographs in Population Biology, 1. Princeton, NJ: Princeton University Press.

MANVILLE, R. H., 1942. Notes on the mammals of Mt. Desert Island, Maine. *Journal of Mammalogy, 23:* 391–398.

MANVILLE, R. H., 1960. Recent changes in the mammal fauna of Mt. Desert Island, Maine. *Journal of Mammalogy, 41:* 15–416.

MANVILLE, R. H., 1964. The vertebrate fauna of Isle au Haut, Maine. *American Midland Naturalist, 72:* 396–407.

MANVILLE, R. H., 1966. The extinct sea mink, with taxonomic notes. *Proceedings of the United States National Museum, 122:* 1–12.

MOOREHEAD, W. K., 1922. *A Report on the Archaeology of Maine.* Andover, MA: Andover Press.

MORSE, D. H., 1966. Hog Island and its breeding vertebrate fauna. *Man and Nature, 22:* 127–133.

NORTON, A. H., 1930. The mammals of Portland, Maine, and vicinity. *Proceedings of the Portland Society of Natural History, 4:* 1–195.

PATTERSON, B. D., 1980. Montane mammalian biogeography in New Mexico. *Southwestern Naturalist, 25:* 33–40.

PATTERSON, B. D., 1984. Mammalian extinction and biogeography in the southern Rocky Mountains. In M. Nitecki (Ed.), *Extinctions:* 247–293. Chicago: University of Chicago Press.

PATTERSON, B. D. & ATMAR, W., 1986. Nested subsets and the structure of insular mammalian faunas and archipelagos. *Biological Journal of the Linnean Society, 28:* 65–82.

PETERS, R. H. & RAELSON, J. V., 1984. Relations between individual size and mammalian population density. *American Naturalist, 124:* 489–517.

PRESTON, F. W., 1962. The canonical distribution of commonness and rarity, Parts I and II. *Ecology, 43:* 185–215, 410–432.

SANGER, D., 1975. Culture change as an adaptive process in the Maine-Maritimes region. *Arctic Anthropology, 12:* 60–75.

SAUER, J. D., 1969. Oceanic islands and biogeographic theory. *Geographic Review, 54:* 582–593.

SCHEMNITZ, S. D., 1975. Marine island–mainland movements of white-tail deer. *Journal of Mammalogy, 56:* 535–537.

SCHOENER, T. W., 1983. Rate of species turnover decreases from lower to higher organisms: a review of the data. *Oikos, 41:* 372–377.

SMITH, A. T., 1980. Temporal changes in insular populations of the pika (*Ochotona princeps*). *Ecology, 61:* 8–13.

SNOW, P. R., 1970. A Middle Woodland site in the coast of Maine. *Bulletin of the Maine Archaeological Society, 10:* Nos. 1 & 2.

STANTON, D. C., 1963. *A history of the white-tailed deer in Maine.* Game Division Bulletin, 8. Augusta, Maine: Dept. of Inland Fisheries and Game.

STUIVER, M. & BORNS, H. W., Jr, 1975. Late Quaternary marine invasion in Maine; its chronology and associated coastal movement. *Geological Society of America Bulletin, 86:* 99–104.

THURBER, G. D. & HERMAN, T. B., 1984. Distribution of small mammals on nine small coastal islands in southwestern Nova Scotia. *Canadian Field Naturalist, 98:* 245–247.

WILCOX, B. A., 1978. Supersaturated island faunas: a species–age relationship for lizards on post-Pleistocene landbridge islands. *Science, 199:* 996–998.

WILLIAMSON, C. B., 1978. A comment on equilibrium turnover rates for islands. *American Naturalist, 112:* 241–243.

WILLIAMSON, M., 1983. The land-bird community of Skokholm: ordination and turnover. *Oikos, 41:* 378–384.

APPENDIX

Table A1. Distribution of non-volant mammals on the mainland and on coastal islands of the State of Maine. MDI, Mt Desert Island; DI, Deer Isle; VH, Vinal Haven; SI, Swans Island; IH, Isle au Haut; LI, Long Island; GW, Great Wass Island

| Species | Island | | | | | | | | |
|---|---|---|---|---|---|---|---|---|---|
| | Maine | MDI | DI | VH | SI | IH | LI | GW | Hog |
| *Sorex cinereus,* masked shrew | + | + | + | + | + | + | | + | + |
| *Sorex palustris,* water shrew | + | + | | | | | | | |
| *Sorex fumeus,* smokey shrew | + | | | | | | | | |
| *Microsorex hoyi,* pygmy shrew | + | + | | | | | | | |
| *Blarina brevicauda,* short-tailed shrew | + | + | | | | ? | + | | + |
| *Parascalops breweri,* hairy-tailed mole | + | + | | | | | | | |
| *Condylura cristata,* star-nosed mole | + | + | + | | | ? | ? | | |
| *Sciurus carolinensis,* grey squirrel | + | I | | | | | | | |
| *Tamias striatus,* eastern chipmunk | + | + | | | | | | | |
| *Tamiasciurus hudsonicus,* red squirrel | + | + | + | + | + | + | + | + | + |
| *Glaucomys sabrinus,* northern flying squirrel | + | + | | | | | | | + |
| *Marmota monax,* woodchuck | + | C | | | | | I | | |
| *Castor canadensis,* beaver | + | + | + | + | E? | I? | C | + | |
| *Synatomys cooperi,* southern bog lemming | + | + | | | | | | | |
| *Peromyscus maniculatus,* deer mouse | + | + | + | + | + | + | + | | |
| *Peromyscus leucopus,* white-footed mouse | C | C | | | | | | | ? |
| *Clethrionomys gapperi,* red-backed vole | + | + | + | | | | | | + |
| *Microtus pennsylvanicus,* meadow vole | + | + | + | + | + | + | + | + | + |
| *Ondatra zibethicus,* muskrat | + | + | + | + | ? | + | E? | + | T |
| *Zapus hudsonius,* meadow jumping mouse | + | + | | | | | | | |
| *Napeozapus insignis,* woodland jumping mouse | + | + | | | | | | | |

| Species | Island | | | | | | | | |
|---|---|---|---|---|---|---|---|---|---|
| | Maine | MDI | DI | VH | SI | IH | LI | GW | Hog |
| *Erethizon dorsatum,* porcupine | + | I | C | | | | | | C |
| *Lepus americanus,* snowshoe hare | + | + | + | + | + | + | + | + | + |
| *Sylvilagus transitionalis,* New England cottontail | † | | | | | | | | C? |
| *Vulpes vulpes,* red fox | + | + | + | E | | E | + | E | ? |
| *Urocyon cinereoargenteus,* grey fox | † | | | | | | | | |
| *Canis latrans,* eastern coyote | C | C? | C? | | | | | | |
| *Mustela erminea,* short-tailed weasel | + | + | + | | | ? | | + | ? |
| *Mustela frenata,* long-tailed weasel | + | + | | | | | | | |
| *Mustela vison,* mink | + | + | + | + | + | + | + | + | + |
| *Mephitis mephitis,* striped skunk | + | + | C | | | | | C | |
| *Martes pennanti,* fisher | ‡ | E | E | | | | | E? | |
| *Lutra canadensis,* river otter | + | + | + | + | | + | ? | E? | |
| *Ursus americanus,* black bear | § | + | + | | T | | | | |
| *Procyon lotor,* raccoon | + | + | C | I | I | I | | C | ? |
| *Felis rufus,* bobcat | § | +? | + | | | | | | |
| *Alces alces,* moose | + | T | T | | T | | | T | T |
| *Odocoileus virginianus,* white-tailed deer | + | + | + | + | + | + | + | C | + |
| Totals (excluding moose)* | | | | | | | | | |
| Native species prior to 1920* | 34 | 29 | 17 | 11 | 9±1 | 10 | 10±1 | 9–11 | 10 |
| Extirpated (E) | 0 | 1 | 1 | 1 | 1 | 1 | 1–2 | 2? | 0 |
| Colonized since 1930 (C) | 2 | 2–3 | 3–4 | 0 | 0 | 0 | 1 | 3 | 2 |
| Introduced (I) | 0 | 2 | 0 | 1 | 1 | 1–2 | 1 | 0 | 0 |
| Resident (1985)* | 36 | 32 | 19 | 11 | 9±1 | 10+ | 11±1 | 12 | 12±1 |

*Adjusted for unverified records and uncertain status (?).

†Not east of Rockland.

‡Rare east of Ellsworth.

§Rare west of Rockland.

+, extant native species; E, extirpated; C, colonized since 1930; I, introduced; T, transient, ?, unverified or uncertain status.

## Table A2. Components of turnover for several islands of mid-coastal Maine

*Mt. Desert Island* (Coman, 1981; Manville, 1942, 1960; Aquadro *et al.*, 1980)
 Extinctions
  *Castor canadensis, c.* 1800
  *Martes pennanti, c.* 1925
  *Ursus americanus, c.* 1890
  *Felis rufus, c.* 1925
 Colonizations
  *Marmota monax, c.* 1930*
  *Peromyscus leucopus, c.* 1975
  *Ursus americanus, c.* 1977
  *Canis latrans*(?), *c.* 1980*
  *Felis rufus, c.* 1944
 Introductions
  *Sciurus carolinensis**
  *Castor canadensis*
  *Erethizon dorsatum, c.* 1915*
*Deer Isle*
 Extinctions
  *Vulpes vulpes, c.* 1916–1920
  *Martes pennanti, c.* 1940
  *Ursus americanus*(?), before 1920
  *Procyon lotor, c.* 1940
  *Odocoileus virginianus* (?), before 1920
 Colonizations
  *Vulpes vulpes, c.* 1930
  *Canis latrans,* 1983 (possibly via bridge)
  *Ursus americanus*(?), *c.* 1960
  *Felis rufus, c.* 1980
  *Odocoileus virginianus*(?), *c.* 1925
 Colonizations via bridge (built 1939)
  *Sciurus carolinensis,* 1983, Little Deer Isle only
  *Erethizon dorsatum,* 1940–1960
  *Mephitis mephitis,* 1940–1960
  *Procyon lotor,* 1940–1960
*Vinal Haven Island*
 Extinctions
  *Castor canadensis, c.* 1972
  *Ondatra zibethicus, c.* 1973
  *Vulpes vulpes, c.* 1900
 Colonizations
  *Castor canadensis, c.* 1981–1982 (introduced?)
  *Ondatra zibethicus, c.* 1975

*Isle au Haut*
 Extinctions
  *Ondatra zibethicus*(?), *c.* 1975
  *Castor canadensis, c.* 1981–1982 (introduced?)
 Colonizations
  *Ondatra zibethicus, c.* 1980
 Introductions
  *Castor canadensis, c.* 1981 (not established)
  *Procyon lotor, c.* 1979–80
*Swans Island*
 Extinctions
  *Castor canadensis*(?)
 Introductions
  *Castor canadensis*(?)
  *Procyon lotor, c.* 1970
*Long Island (Isleboro)*
 Extinctions
  *Ondatra zibethicus*(?)
  *Lutra canadensis*(?)
 Colonizations
  *Castor canadensis, c.* 1970
 Introductions
  *Marmota monax,* before 1970
*Great Wass Island*
 Extinctions
  *Martes pennanti c.* 1916
  *Lutra canadensis c.* 1915
  *Odocoileus virginianus*(?), *c.* 1890
 Colonizations
  *Odocoileus virginianus* 1942
 Colonizations via Bridge (*c.* 1960)
  *Procyon lotor*
  *Mephitis mephitis*
*Hog Island*
 Extinctions
  *Peromyscus leucopus*(?), *c.* 1960
  *Lepus americanus, c.* 1910
  *Vulpes vulpes, c* 1964
  *Procyon lotor, c.* 1976
 Colonizations
  *Peromyscus leucopus*(?), *c.* 1980
  *Erethizon dorsatum, c.* 1984
  *Lepus americanus, c.* 1979
  *Sylvilagus transitionalis, c.* 1930
  *Vulpes vulpes,* 1962–1963 (single breeding female)
  *Procyon lotor,* 1975 (single breeding female)

*Possibly colonization via bridge (built 1837, replaced 1950).

*Biological Journal of the Linnean Society* (1986), *28:* 65–82. With 4 figures

# Nested subsets and the structure of insular mammalian faunas and archipelagos

BRUCE D. PATTERSON

*Division of Mammals, Field Museum of Natural History, Chicago, Illinois 60605, U.S.A.*

AND

WIRT ATMAR

*AICS Research Inc., P.O. Box 4691, University Park, New Mexico 88003, U.S.A.*

*Accepted for publication 14 February 1986*

The nested subset hypothesis was formulated to describe and explain patterns in the community structure of insular mammal faunas which are in the state of 'relaxation'. The hypothesis states that the species comprising a depauperate fauna should constitute a proper subset of those in richer faunas, and that an archipelago of such faunas arranged by species richness should present a nested series. The non-randomness of this pattern is evaluated for montane mammals in the American Southwest using Monte Carlo simulations under two sets of conditions. First, we constructed model archipelagos with the observed distribution of species richnesses, drawing individual species at random (without replacement) from the species pool (RANDOM0). Secondly, we constructed model archipelagos having the observed distribution of species richnesses, but weighted the selection of species by their actual frequencies of occurrence (RANDOM1). The degree of nestedness in the model archipelagos was then used to assess the non-randomness of the observed structure. Actual Southwestern mammal faunas have a far more nested structure than model archipelagos produced by either RANDOM0 or RANDOM1, and there is virtually zero probability that observed structure is represented in the distribution of scores from either simulation run. Similar analyses were conducted on other archipelagos to determine the generality of this relationship and to identify variables putatively responsible for its production. Mammal faunas of large islands off the coast of Maine, U.S.A., studied by Crowell (1986) also comprise nested subsets, as do those inhabiting islands off the coast of Baja California, Mexico, studied by Lawlor (1983). Significantly, when the Baja archipelago is divided into landbridge islands (which are presumed to be relaxing to lower species level) and oceanic islands (where species number is limited by successful overwater dispersal), only the former show significant nestedness under the more stringent conditions of RANDOM1. These results and theoretical considerations suggest that selective extinction of species may be chiefly responsible for the nestedness in natural archipelagos. Our conclusions have obvious implications for the design of natural preserves (e.g. SLOSS): several small fragments of a single biota can be expected to support nested subsets of the species originally present or that would likely be retained in a single large preserve. Even more sobering are arguments raised which suggest that the faunas of preserves established in different habitats within the same biome might be expected to converge in composition via selective extinction.

KEY WORDS:—Extinction – nested subsets – biogeography – archipelago – faunas – simulation – montane mammals – American Southwest.

0024–4066/86/050065 + 18 $03.00/0

CONTENTS

INTRODUCTION

Patterns of distribution of small mammal species inhabiting forested habitats in the southern Rocky Mountains, U.S.A. (Fig. 1), have recently been analysed by Patterson (1984). In concert with palynological and palaeontological evidence, the distributional data suggested that extinctions have chiefly determined the absence of various species on isolated mountain ranges. The historical process producing this pattern can be described as follows. During glacial intervals of the Pleistocene, cooler, effectively more mesic climates throughout the Southwest enabled species now restricted to mountaintop habitats to expand their ranges to lower altitudes and latitudes. In this way, most or all of the species characteristic of boreal and boreocordilleran habitats came to inhabit various marginal, isolated mountain ranges throughout this arid region. However, with the retreat of continental glaciers and the return of warmer, drier climates, boreal habitats and taxa retreated to higher altitudes and latitudes, leaving southern populations stranded on isolated mountaintops. The fates of these disjunct populations were apparently determined by local extinction probabilities.

Several lines of evidence suggested the strong, selective nature of these extinctions (Patterson, 1984). First, the dependence of species richness on area (slope of the log species : log area regression, $z = 0.36$) shows the strong, positive relationship characteristic of 'non-equilibrium' biotas (e.g. Brown, 1971); island systems in colonization–extinction equilibrium typically show lower $z$ values (MacArthur & Wilson, 1967). However, $z$ values are complexly dependent on numerous factors and are therefore difficult to interpret (Connor & McCoy, 1979; Abbott, 1983). Nevertheless, Lawlor (1986) clearly demonstrates that these parameters contain useful biological information by successful qualitative prediction of species–area relationships using various mammal species and archipelagos.

In addition, quantitative contrast of species–area relationships in adjacent 'mainland' and island areas is instructive (Brown, 1971). This approach allows only the degree of intersample isolation (i.e. colonization rates) to vary significantly, controlling for the host of other factors that affect $z$ values. Species–area regressions for 'mainland' and island situations in the Southwest are presented in Fig. 2. Different slopes (0.07 versus 0.36) obtained for the same region and species in situations allowing both colonization and extinction versus only extinction (respectively) underscore the impact of post-glacial extinctions on species richness of isolated faunas.

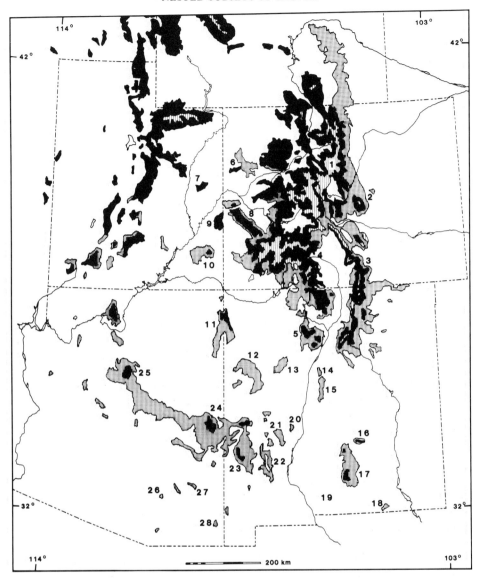

Figure 1. Distribution of montane habitats in the southern Rocky Mountains, after Küchler (1964). Numbers correspond to mountain ranges under study (see also Patterson, 1984): 1, Rocky Mountains 'mainland'; 2, Pikes Peak; 3, Sangre de Cristo; 4, San Juan; 5, Jemez; 6, Rabbit Hills; 7, Tavaputs Plateau; 8, Uncompaghre Plateau; 9, LaSal; 10, Abajo; 11, Chuska; 12, Zuni; 13, Mt Taylor; 14, Sandia; 15, Manzano; 16, Capitan; 17, Sacramento; 18, Guadalupe; 19, Organ; 20, Magdalena; 21, San Mateo; 22, Black Range; 23, Mogollon; 24, White; 25, San Francisco; 26, Santa Catalina; 27, Pinaleño; 28, Chiricahua. ▨, Xeric forests; ■, mesic forests; ▥, alpine meadow.

These extinctions were evidently highly selective. Each of 26 montane mammal species occurs on 'significantly larger mountain ranges than those where each is absent (Patterson, 1984). This is apparently a consequence of species-specific extinction rates being inversely proportional to montane area (and total population size). Additionally, within two subsets of montane species,

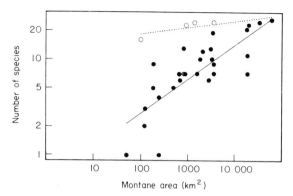

Figure 2. Regression of species richness of montane mammals versus area of montane habitats (in km²) using log-transformed variables. Filled circles indicate 28 mountain ranges analysed in this study. The least-squares regression (continuous line) is given by the equation: $\log S = -0.267 + 0.357 \log A$ ($r = 0.802$; $P < 0.01$). Open circles denote four distinct areas within the Rocky Mountains 'mainland' (range 1): U.S. National Forest portions of both Larimer and Boulder counties, Rocky Mountain National Park, and a 5.6 km radius surrounding Grand Lake, Grand Co. These points are connected (dotted line) to the remainder of range 1 by a line having the equation: $\log S = 1.125 + 0.070 \log A$ ($r = 0.815$, $P < 0.1$). Although smaller sampling areas do contain fewer species, the highly significant difference between the slopes of these lines (0.07 versus 0.36) can be attributed to extinction (without possible recolonization) on isolated mountain ranges.

carnivores and xeric forest herbivores, the number of mountain ranges on which a species occurred was inversely related to its body size ($P < 0.1$). Smaller species of each group occur on a greater number of mountain ranges, as expected if population density (and susceptibility to extinction) were related to body size (e.g. Peters & Raelson, 1984). Finally, the overall composition of montane biotas shows progressive changes with species richness, carnivores and mesic forest herbivores being over-represented in richer faunas and under-represented in more depauperate ones, while the converse holds for xeric forest herbivores.

These patterns imply a 'nested subset' relationship among montane biotas, in which depauperate faunas support species which collectively comprise proper subsets of those in richer faunas (Patterson, 1984; Fig. 3). Here, we derive an index for 'nestedness' specifically tailored for relaxing faunas, apply it to the southern Rocky Mountain archipelago, evaluate the non-randomness of faunal structure under realistic constraints using Monte Carlo simulations, and compare nestedness in this fauna, supposedly sculpted by selective extinction, with nestedness in other island systems to ascertain the roles of extinction and colonization in producing nested patterns.

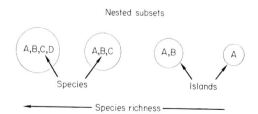

Figure 3. The nested subset hypothesis states that the species comprising a depauperate fauna should constitute a proper subset of those in richer faunas, and that an archipelago of such faunas, ranked by species richness, should present a nested series.

## METHODS

Presence–absence data for 26 terrestrial mammal taxa of boreal or boreocordilleran affinities in the American Southwest were assembled from the primary and secondary literature by Patterson (1984). The number of mammal species comprising the faunas of different mountain ranges varies from 1 to 26, with both median and modal values of seven species. The 28 mountain ranges present 17 classes of species richness (Table 1).

Two ranges of different species richness were considered to be *nested* if each species in the smaller fauna was also represented in the larger. The extent of departure from perfect nestedness ($N$ index) was calculated by: (1) determining the fauna having lowest species richness in which species $i$ occurs; (2) examining all richer faunas for the presence of species $i$; (3) counting the number of

Table 1. Distribution matrix for montane mammals in the American Southwest. Ranges are ranked by species richness and species are ranked by range occurrences (indicated by letters). The tendency for occurrences to cluster in the upper left corner of the table is obvious. Deviations from perfect nestedness, as measured in this study, are indicated by plus (+) symbols ($N = 63$)

| Range | Montane mammal species* | Richness |
|-------|-------------------------|----------|
| 1 | A B C D E F G H I J K L M N O P Q R S T U V W X Y Z | 26 |
| 4 | A B C D E F G H I J K L M N O P Q R S T U V W X | 24 |
| 3 | A B C D E F G H I J K L M N O +Q R S T U V W X | 23 |
| 2 | A B C D E F G H I J K L M N O P Q R S T U + | 21 |
| 5 | A B C D E F G H I J K L M +O P Q R S T + | 19 |
| 8 | A B C D E +G H I J K + +N O P + | 13 |
| 9 | A B C D E +G +I J K + +N O +Q + V | 13 |
| 6 | A B C D E + +H I J K L +N O + + | 12 |
| 24 | A B C D E F G H + +K L + + P + | 11 |
| 10 | A B C D E F G +I J K + + + + + | 10 |
| 11 | A B C D E F G H I J + + + + + | 10 |
| 14 | A B C D E F G + + + +M + R | 9 |
| 23 | A B C D E F +H + + L + + P | 9 |
| 7 | A B C +E + I J + N | 7 |
| 13 | A B C D E F I + | 7 |
| 15 | A B C D E F +M | 7 |
| 17 | A B C D E +G +M | 7 |
| 22 | A B C D E F H + | 7 |
| 25 | A B C D E F H + | 7 |
| 12 | A B C D E F + | 6 |
| 21 | A B C D +F L | 6 |
| 16 | A B C D E + | 5 |
| 20 | A B C + +F L | 5 |
| 27 | A B +D E + | 4 |
| 26 | A B + F† | 3 |
| 28 | A B + | 2 |
| 18 | C | 1 |
| 19 | C | 1 |

* Species are identified by letter in Table 3, ranges by number in Fig. 1.
† This range population is possibly introduced (D. F. Hoffmeister, pers. comm.)

absences of species $i$ in richer faunas; and (4) summing the counts across all species. This provides a single measure of nestedness for the species ensemble; by tallying species separately ($\mathcal{N}_i$), the nestedness of distributions of different species or sets of species (e.g. carnivores, xeric forest herbivores) can be compared *inter se*.

The probability that a perfectly nested relationship among range faunas might arise randomly with respect to species distributions can be estimated from combinatorial mathematics. There are 26! ways that the 26 species could be distributed among ranges in a nested fashion, a rather large number ($c. 4 \times 10^{26}$). However, the total number of possible faunas having the observed distribution of species richnesses, given 26 species and 28 mountain ranges, is staggering; this is equivalent to unordered sampling without replacement, and in this instance is $c. 1 \times 10^{139}$. Thus, the probability that a perfectly nested relationship among faunas could result by chance is about one in $4 \times 10^{112}$. To give perspective to this infinitude, $c. 3 \times 10^{17}$ seconds have elapsed in the history of the Milky Way!

The departure of observed nestedness of montane mammal faunas from randomness was assessed via Monte Carlo simulations. We devised two programs for this purpose (see Appendix) and ran them on the Hewlett–Packard 3000 at AICS Research Inc. Both programs constrained the numbers of species on mountain ranges to those actually observed. The first, RANDOM0, constructed randomized faunas by selecting species from a uniform probability distribution; all species had equal probabilities of assignment. The second program, RANDOM1, used a probability distribution weighted by the actual range occurrences of species; a species found on 10 mountain ranges was twice as likely to be selected for a given random fauna as one distributed on only five mountain ranges. Thus, total occurrences of species were not constrained to observed values, but were based on them in a probabilistic way. Both programs produced 1000 randomized archipelagos, and the following summary statistics of the $\mathcal{N}$ index were determined: overall mean, variance, standard deviation and maximum and minimum values. In addition, means and variances of column scores, $\mathcal{N}_i$ (errors for individual species), were also determined for comparison among species and sets of species. The probability that the observed $\mathcal{N}$ index could have been selected from a statistically normal distribution of simulation scores was assessed by mean of a $t$ test.

Nestedness of the montane mammal faunas was compared to those of other archipelagos to evaluate possible causative factors. Previously unpublished data for the seven most speciose islands in Penobscot Bay, Maine, were generously supplied by K. L. Crowell. Data for Gulf and Pacific islands off Baja California were taken directly from Lawlor (1983).

RESULTS

*Southwestern mountain ranges*

The actual distribution of montane mammals in the American Southwest departs from perfect nestedness. The $\mathcal{N}$ index calculated for the archipelago as a whole equals 63 (Table 1). This is equivalent to 63 range absences that are not consonant with the hypothesis of nested subsets, totaling 8.6% of the presence–absence matrix. If species were distributed on different mountain ranges at random with respect to frequencies of species occurrence or to specific patterns of occurrence, how nested would this archipelago be?

With uniform probabilities of species occurrence (RANDOM0), the average simulated archipelago has an $\mathcal{N}$ index of 270 (Table 2). The observed nested pattern lies 16.6 standard deviations from the simulation mean. Thus, the probability that the observed pattern could have come from the distribution of simulated values is vanishingly small ($P \cong 10^{-30}$). However, species have decidedly unequal distributions on these mountain ranges; some species are limited to a single range, whereas others are found on as many as 26 ranges. If

Table 2. Results of 1000 simulation experiments on each of three archipelagos discussed in the text. Probability values indicate the likelihood that observed $\mathcal{N}$ belongs to the normal distribution of simulated values. See text for differences between RANDOM0 and RANDOM1

| | Mean $\mathcal{N}$ index | S.D. | Min. | Max. | $P \cong$ |
|---|---|---|---|---|---|
| Southern Rocky Mountains (Patterson, 1984), 28 'islands', 1–26 species, $\mathcal{N}$ index = 63 (8.65%) | | | | | |
| RANDOM0 | 270.3 | 12.491 | 233 | 307 | $10^{-30}$ |
| RANDOM1 | 227.9 | 18.135 | 180 | 287 | $9 \times 10^{-20}$ |
| Penobscot Bay, current (Crowell, pers. comm.), 7 islands, 8–17 species, $\mathcal{N}$ index = 10 (8.40%) | | | | | |
| RANDOM0 | 21.9 | 2.290 | 13 | 28 | $8 \times 10^{-9}$ |
| RANDOM1 | 18.5 | 3.133 | 8 | 27 | 0.0034 |
| Penobscot Bay, historic (Crowell, pers. comm.), 7 islands, 9–19 species, $\mathcal{N}$ index = 8 (6.02%) | | | | | |
| RANDOM0 | 23.6 | 2.574 | 15 | 29 | $2 \times 10^{-10}$ |
| RANDOM1 | 20.5 | 3.094 | 9 | 29 | $3 \times 10^{-5}$ |
| Sea of Cortéz, all islands (Lawlor, 1983), 34 islands, 1–13 species, $\mathcal{N}$ index = 147 (16.01%) | | | | | |
| RANDOM0 | 295.5 | 18.925 | 235 | 348 | $10^{-15}$ |
| RANDOM1 | 220.0 | 26.300 | 138 | 304 | 0.0027 |
| Landbridge islands only (Lawlor, 1983), 20 islands, 1–13 species, $\mathcal{N}$ index = 79 (30.38%) | | | | | |
| RANDOM0 | 150.1 | 11.039 | 112 | 185 | $5 \times 10^{-12}$ |
| RANDOM1 | 116.1 | 14.337 | 75 | 157 | 0.0048 |
| Oceanic islands only (Lawlor, 1983), 14 islands, 1–3 species, $\mathcal{N}$ index = 19 (15.08%) | | | | | |
| RANDOM0 | 28.9 | 4.712 | 15 | 42 | 0.0179 |
| RANDOM1 | 21.7 | 5.894 | 5 | 38 | 0.3228 |

the fraction of the 28 mountain ranges that each species actually inhabits is used to weight the probability of selecting species in the randomized faunas, the degree of nestedness ought to increase.

When species are selected from a probability distribution based on their occurrence frequencies (RANDOM1), the $\mathcal{N}$ index of the average archipelago falls to 228 (Table 2). Note that under RANDOM1, the average score decreases but the variance increases. Even against these more realistic constraints, the observed value lies 9.09 standard deviations from the simulation mean, and significantly differs from it ($P \cong 9 \times 10^{-20}$).

The simulations clearly establish the highly non-random nestedness of these Southwestern faunas. The nestedness of individual species distributions are included in Table 3 as partial scores, $\mathcal{N}_i$. Of the 26 species, 12 have distributions

Table 3. List of montane mammal species in the American Southwest, after Patterson (1984). Letters of species correspond to those in Table 1. The number of ranges on which each occurs, a partial nestedness score ($N_i$), and the proportion of non-nested occurrences are tabulated to the right of each entry. Also tabulated are subjective estimates of the correspondence between specific distribution patterns and various extrinsic factors

| Species | Range occurrences | $N_i$ index | $N_i$/R.O. | Trophic-habitat | Richness | Area | Elevation | Geographic | Congeners |
|---|---|---|---|---|---|---|---|---|---|
| A | Sorex monticolus | 26 | 0 | 0 | insectivore | × | | × | × | |
| B | Peromyscus maniculatus rufinus | 26 | 0 | 0 | xeric herbivore | × | | × | | |
| C | Eutamias quadrivittatus group | 25 | 3 | 0.120 | xeric herbivore | × | × | × | | × |
| D | Tamiasciurus hudsonicus | 22 | 2 | 0.091 | xeric herbivore | × | × | × | | |
| E | Microtus longicaudus | 22 | 2 | 0.091 | xeric herbivore | × | | | | |
| F | Sciurus aberti | 18 | 7 | 0.389 | xeric herbivore | | | | | |
| G | Eutamias minimus operarius | 12 | 2 | 0.167 | mesic herbivore | × | × | × | × | |
| H | Spermophilus lateralis | 12 | 3 | 0.250 | xeric herbivore | × | × | | × | × |
| I | Thomomys talpoides complex | 12 | 3 | 0.250 | mesic herbivore | × | | | × | × |
| J | Neotoma cinerea | 11 | 3 | 0.273 | xeric herbivore | | | | × | |
| K | Sorex palustris | 10 | 0 | 0 | insectivore | × | | | × | |
| L | Clethrionomys gapperi | 10 | 12 | 1.200 | mesic herbivore | | | | × | ? |
| M | Sorex nanus | 8 | 7 | 0.875 | insectivore | | × | × | × | |
| N | Marmota flaviventris | 8 | 6 | 0.750 | mesic herbivore | | | | × | |
| O | Zapus princeps | 8 | 0 | 0 | mesic herbivore | × | | | | |
| P | Microtus montanus | 7 | 5 | 0.714 | mesic herbivore | | | | × | × |
| Q | Ochotona princeps | 6 | 0 | 0 | mesic herbivore | × | | | × | |
| R | Mustela erminea | 6 | 6 | 1.000 | carnivore | | | | × | |
| S | Sorex cinereus | 5 | 0 | 0 | insectivore | × | × | | × | |
| T | Lepus americanus | 5 | 0 | 0 | mesic herbivore | × | × | | × | |
| U | Phenacomys intermedius | 4 | 0 | 0 | mesic herbivore | × | | × | × | |
| V | Martes americana | 4 | 2 | 0.500 | carnivore | × | × | | × | |
| W | Gulo gulo | 3 | 0 | 0 | carnivore | × | × | × | | |
| X | Lynx canadensis | 3 | 0 | 0 | carnivore | × | × | × | | |
| Y | Sorex (M.) hoyi | 1 | 0 | 0 | insectivore | × | | | × | |
| Z | Spermophilus elegans | 1 | 0 | 0 | mesic herbivore | × | | | × | |

that are actually perfectly nested — each occurs on every range richer in species than the most depauperate one it occupies. When the deviations from perfect nesting ($N_i$) are scaled by total range occurrences (R.O.), the remaining 14 species exhibit departures from perfect nesting in the range 9–120%.

It is difficult to interpret deviations from perfect nesting. As an example, consider the four trophic-habitat groups considered by Patterson (1984): carnivores, insectivores, mesic forest herbivores and xeric forest herbivores. Two of four carnivores, four of five insectivores and five of 10 mesic forest herbivores exhibit perfectly nested distributions, whereas only one of seven xeric forest forms does so (Table 3). Further, the first three groups show a greater range of values in their $N_i$ scores than do xeric forest herbivores: none of the latter exhibit $N_i$/R.O. values greater than 50%, whereas at least one member of each other group does so. Are these consequences of trophic-habitat affinities having effects on colonization or extinction probabilities, or rather are they simple mathematical artefacts of the generally wider distributions of xeric forest forms? The present analysis sheds no light on this question.

Also included in Table 3 for summary purposes are subjective indications of factors that may govern the distributions of the 26 montane species. These are inferred from three principal sources: (1) $N_i$ indices, yielding an estimate of the predictability of species occurrence based solely on the species richness of the most depauperate fauna it occupies; (2) trivariate plots of presence–absence as a function of area and elevation (cf. Patterson, 1984: fig. 6); and (3) the distribution matrix and map (Table 1, Fig. 3). The possible roles of congeners in determining species distribution are suggested by discussions of food and habitat characteristics in several secondary sources (e.g. Armstrong, 1972; Findley et al., 1975) and by complementary and 'checkerboard' geographic distributions. For most species, patterns of distribution can be clearly correlated with species richness, montane area and elevation of the highest peak. Many species (e.g. Marmota flaviventris, Neotoma cinerea) also exhibit clear regional patterns in range occurrences, being found, for example, only north of a given latitude. Were these very species not recorded as Wisconsinan fossils from the Guadalupe range (range 18; Findley et al., 1975), both geographically and ecologically marginal in this context, one might strongly question the extent of their montane colonizations during glacial episodes. The fossil record substantiates that such distribution patterns are products of postglacial extinction patterns rather than patterns of glacial colonizations (contra Simberloff, 1985).

Finally, it is interesting to note that the effects of competition with congeners on geographic distribution (but not altitudinal distribution or microhabitat utilization) appear evident in only four or five of 26 distribution patterns (Table 3). Significantly, four of the five involve geographic contacts with related forms having centres of distribution in the Sierra Madre Occidental of Mexico. Findley (1969) earlier noted the tendency for northern boreal forms to be replaced by austral equivalents at lower latitudes. The geological recency of these appositions, presumably in direct contact only during glacial episodes of the Pleistocene, would preclude any evolutionary accommodations to competitive relationships. The remaining case involves range complementarity between Clethrionomys and related voles of the genus Microtus. More generally, the geographic distribution of boreal forms on isolated mountain ranges seems explicable by their autecologies.

*Other archipelagos*

To ascertain the generality of the nested subset hypothesis and to evaluate the contributory roles of extinction and colonization in determining such structure, similar simulations were conducted on other mammalian archipelagos with different histories and situations.

Islands studied by Crowell off the Maine coast were subjected to two analyses, the first based on current species composition, the second based on historic records of species occurrence. This approach was deemed fitting for comparative purposes because of the extraordinarily complete records of colonization and local extinction that Crowell has assembled over the last two decades (e.g. Crowell, 1973). Although most, if not all, of these islands were landbridge islands connected to the adjacent mainland during the latest Wisconsinan glacial episode, the islands are relatively small and are close enough to the mainland to approach a colonization–extinction equilibrium (e.g. see Crowell, 1986). The current distributions of mammals on these islands show an $N$ index of 10 (species richness ranging from 8–17), whereas historic records exhibit eight deviations from perfect nestedness (species richness in the range 9–19). These deviations correspond to 8.4 and 6.0% of the distribution matrices, respectively. Both distribution matrices differ significantly from archipelagos produced by either RANDOM0 or RANDOM1 simulations (Table 2), indicating a significant degree of nested structure. It should be noted, however, that these analyses were conducted using only speciose, near-shore islands because only these data were available to us (see discussion in Crowell, 1986).

Mammal faunas on islands off the coast of Baja California also exhibit nested structure. Data are available from 34 islands, with species richness ranging from 1 to 13 species (Lawlor, 1983); the observed $N$ index equals 147, so that 16% of the presence–absence matrix deviates from the expected nested relationship. When RANDOM0 simulations of this archipelago are conducted, the average $N$ index equals 295.5 (Table 2); the actual $N$ value lies 7.85 standard deviations below this mean ($P \ll 0.001$). When Baja faunas are constructed at random using actual species occurrence frequencies (RANDOM1), there is still no reason to believe that observed structure could have been the result of random assortment. The average simulated archipelago had an $N$ index of 220, lying 2.78 standard deviations from the observed value ($P < 0.003$).

However, Lawlor (1983 and elsewhere) has shown that islands in the Sea of Cortéz comprise two rather different sets: landbridge islands and truly oceanic ones. The faunas of the former islands were colonized by continental faunas moving overland through marine trenches exposed by lowered sea-level during Pleistocene glaciations. Oceanic islands, in contrast, were colonized overwater. Thus, one set of islands (landbridge islands) represent faunas thought to be relaxing from higher species number (similar to Southwestern mountain ranges in this respect), whereas others (oceanic islands) have species number determined by both differential colonization and extinction. Are these differences evident in terms of degrees of nestedness?

There are 20 landbridge islands in Lawlor's survey, supporting 1–13 mammal species. Deviations from the expected nested relationship constitute 30.4% of the presence–absence matrix for mammal species. RANDOM0 simulations of only landbridge islands show patterns similar to the archipelago as a whole and to

Southwestern mountain ranges. The average $N$ index of simulated archipelagos (150) deviates greatly from that observed among the islands themselves ($N = 79$). An unexpected degree of structure is evident among the faunas of landbridge islands, even when species are added to the faunas of randomized archipelagos in observed proportions (RANDOM1): the average $N$ score for the latter simulations was 116, still 2.59 standard deviations above the observed value ($P < 0.005$).

These patterns do not hold for the 14 oceanic islands off Baja California. RANDOM0 simulations of the oceanic subarchipelago yield average $N$ values still significantly higher than that observed (28.9 versus 19; $P < 0.02$). While only 15% of the presence–absence matrix deviates from perfect nestedness, this structure may be simply a consequence of species occurrence frequencies. RANDOM1 simulations produce faunas with comparable degrees of nestedness (21.7 versus 19; $P \cong 0.32$). Regrettably, the resolution of both RANDOM0 and RANDOM1 simulations is limited by the low species richness of oceanic islands (one to three species; Lawlor, 1983), so that this cannot be considered a robust test.

The results assembled in Table 2 show that nested structure is apparent in each studied archipelago (RANDOM0 simulations). Only in that archipelago thought to be colonization-limited (i.e. oceanic islands of Baja) can observed nestedness be attributed to species occurrence frequencies (RANDOM1 simulations). For the remaining archipelagos, distributions of individual species must be subject to consistently differential (i.e. selective) colonization or extinction events.

## DISCUSSION

Inferring structure in natural communities, or more generally order in nature, is a once-popular pursuit now considered passé. Increasingly, natural processes once represented as deterministic and simple are treated as stochastic walks through time, space, genetics and/or morphology. By this approach, untested assumptions regarding the importance of this process or that one may be strictly avoided; the literature is replete with examples where deterministic processes (e.g. competition, adaptation, optimization, coevolution) have been uncritically invoked in *post hoc* explanation. However, examples of uncritical science are no justification for wholesale dismissal of such selective processes. If science is the search for repeated patterns (MacArthur, 1972), then we as scientists must do more than simply falsify hypotheses: we must propose testable hypotheses, conduct those tests and (crucially) generalize our results to statements regarding the general processes.

### Montane mammal biogeography

The nested subset hypothesis specifies non-random structure among biotic communities. As formulated for Southwestern montane biotas (Patterson, 1984), such structure was thought to be attributable to selective, apparently deterministic, extinction, culling 'vulnerable' species from a fauna while passing over other species. Evidence that observed patterns have been produced by extinction are by necessity partly inferential, because vagaries of fossil preservation are legion in space, time and taxa. Nevertheless, the abundance and diversity of Wisconsinan fossils now known from a variety of extralimital sites (for tabulations of New Mexican records see Findley *et al.*, 1975) present irrefutable evidence of glacial colonizations. Having established these records, it is not parsimonious to maintain that other species, now inhabiting the same microhabitats in species-rich montane faunas but absent in the available fossil record, did not similarly colonize those mountain ranges, or that fossilized forms did not colonize less isolated mountain ranges where fossil deposits are lacking. The principle of parsimony indicates widespread dispersal during glaciopluvial periods that carried a majority of montane mammal species to a majority of mountain ranges. Grayson (1982), Wells (1983) and Harris (1985) provide more detailed discussions of palynological and palaeontological evidence for Recent extinctions.

An example may serve to illustrate the envisioned mechanism of this process. Montane shrews (*Sorex monticolus*) and deer mice (*Peromyscus maniculatus*) are found on both the Chiricahua and Pinaleño Mountains of SE Arizona (ranges 27 and 28, respectively). While these two species comprise the sole representatives of the boreocordilleran fauna of the Chiricahuas, the larger Pinaleños support two additional boreal species, the red squirrel (*Tamiasciurus hudsonicus*) and the long-tailed vole (*Microtus longicaudus*). The U.S. *Federal Register* (12/30/82) lists Pinaleño populations of both latter species "under Notice of Review" by the U.S. Fish and Wildlife Service for listing as threatened or endangered. Although their formal listing is a consequence of unique taxonomic designations applied to populations from the Pinaleños (*T. hudsonicus grahamensis* and *M. longicaudus leucophaeus*), it is also a consequence of their rarity. Doubtless, both the red squirrel and the long-tailed vole occurred during the Recent past on the adjacent Chiricahuas, where they went extinct sooner because of more restricted areas of suitable habitat and correspondingly more limited population sizes. Viewed in this way, these mountain ranges of differing species richness comprise a 'time-series' of extinction, ranges with smaller faunas representing advanced stages in the course of irreversible local extinctions.

Support for this interpretation may be found not only in patterns of species distribution but also in patterns of evolutionary divergence and ecological abundance. Molecular studies seem particularly well suited to the task. Levels of genetic variability should be directly related to population size: loss of genetic variants through drift should be inversely related to population size. Therefore, rates of genic fixation or overall genetic divergence should be inversely related to montane area. George (1983) described a positive relationship between heterozygosity values of isolated populations of *Sorex monticolus* and area of the mountains they inhabit that seems attributable to such post-glacial restrictions in population size. In a similar vein, Sullivan (1985) recently described significant, positive relations between both number of alleles per locus and percentage polymorphism of isolated populations of least chipmunks (*Eutamias minimus*) with the area they inhabit.

Ecological studies of species abundance might also be used to evaluate the hypothesis of progressive restriction of population size, culminating in selective extinction. Although unit densities of species on isolated mountain ranges can be expected to vary according to the local suitability of habitat, total population size of species on isolated mountain ranges, when ranked, should correlate with the order in which they disappear from faunas. Thus, we predict positive correlations between the total population sizes of species in any large fauna and the number of smaller faunas on which they occur. This would represent a significant refinement over current indices of population size based on body size (e.g. Brown, 1971; Patterson, 1984). The extent of deviations from this pattern (i.e. species found at low abundance in larger faunas but which persist even in depauperate faunas) might be meaningful in evaluating whether the critical factor in such local extinctions is total population size, on the one hand, or temporal variability in population size, on the other (cf. Karr, 1982).

### Nestedness and colonization versus extinction

Although nestedness among Southwestern montane biotas appears to be a consequence of selective extinctions operating on a largely shared 'pluvial' biota, nested structure could also result from largely predictable patterns of insular colonization. Consider species having different colonizing abilities and an adjacent, sterile archipelago which is immune to extinction. Species A might colonize and persist on most islands, species B some fraction of these, species C a fewer number, and species D only the two closest islands (Fig. 4). The archipelago would exhibit complete or nearly complete nestedness, even in the absence of selective extinctions. Undoubtedly, nested structure resulting from predictable, differential colonization should characterize certain taxa on certain island groups.

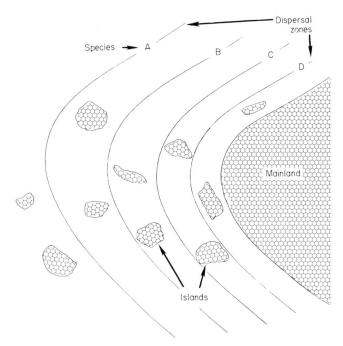

Figure 4. Hypothetical scenario for the production of nested subsets via differential colonization, rather than selective extinction. Although mammal species exhibit a vast range of dispersal capabilities (e.g. bats versus pocket gophers), support for this possible means of faunal structure is unidentified. Probability theory suggests that extinction may be a more potent structural determinant.

Notwithstanding these cases, significant nested structure of natural archipelagos may be more frequently attributed to extinction than to colonization. This follows from probability theory: the variance of stochastic events, such as population changes during the course of colonization or extinction, is inversely proportional to population size. With large population size, stochastic changes will resemble deterministic ones. Because insular colonization involves initially small populations of founders or propagules (whose numbers correspond to the degree of 'insularity'), and because a population size of 0 constitutes an 'absorbing barrier', colonization is more strongly influenced by unpredictable events than is the extinction of an already-established population. Because of 'gambler's ruin', poor men (however skilful) must leave the gaming table first.

Such theoretical expectations may be visible in analyses of Baja California islands. Both RANDOM0 and RANDOM1 simulations of landbridge island faunas produced patterns differing radically from those actually found in nature. However, once the occurrence frequencies of species are taken into account, oceanic islands show no more nested structure than would be expected by species frequencies alone. Different areas may have served as colonization sources for different oceanic islands (colonization rates for most taxa seem to be distance dependent), or else random effects in the initial stages of establishment (operating through competition, predation, disease or abiotic factors) may have swamped species differences in ability to reach an island or to maintain populations there once they arrived.

In generalizing these results, it is important to remember that mammal species are relatively poor overwater colonists, and the islands of most archipelagos may be so isolated (relative to their dispersal capabilities) that extinction effects predominate. A different fauna inhabiting the same islands might exhibit nested structure produced by colonization if colonization rates were high enough to dwarf regional differences in colonization rates or to allow 'rescue effects' (e.g. Brown & Kodric-Brown, 1977). Nesting seabirds might satisfy these conditions for the Baja archipelago.

'Neutral models' or null hypotheses must be specifically tailored to the scientific question at hand. We chose to measure nestedness via counts of 'unexpected extinctions' because differential extinction is thought to be chiefly responsible for patterns of species distribution among isolated mountain ranges (see Brown, 1971, 1978; Patterson, 1982, 1984). An alternative measure of nestedness might have used a least-squares approach. Under our metric, a species is expected to occur in all faunas larger than the smallest in which it occurs; for example, *Marmota flaviventris* is expected to occur on ranges 10, 11, 14, 23 and 24 (where it is absent) because all of these support more species than range 7 (where it occurs). If the primary determinant of species distribution were likely colonization, it might be reasonable to expect marmots to occur in faunas of 10 or more species, that is, to split the error score into both unexpected extinctions and unexpected occurrences (e.g. range 7). Although our null models confer greater weight to extinction as a determinant of species richness, we do not believe an alternative metric would significantly influence our results. The appropriateness of different indices and different null hypotheses to different archipelagos obviated our attempting to derive a universally applicable index of nestedness or set of simulation programs.

## *Implications for the design of natural preserves*

The most obvious implication of this study concerns the optimum size of biological preserves. The question of whether to set aside a single large area or several smaller ones collectively of similar size (i.e. SLOSS) has been widely debated (e.g. McIntyre, Young & King, 1984). Although larger areas support more species, reducing the area results in a less than proportional reduction in the number of species. Thus, smaller areas may, in sum, have more species (Dawson, 1984). This argument is obviously fallacious if each of the smaller areas supports the same set (or subset) of species.

Human encroachments on natural habitats are severe and continuing on a global scale. The earth is now experiencing a wave of extinctions that is unparalleled since at least the Permian, when mass extinctions eliminated more than half the families of marine animals (Sepkoski, 1982). To these extents, the global biota must be in a state of 'faunal relaxation', where extinction rates in habitats, communities, biomes and continents dwarf immigration or speciation rates so as to make them negligible in terms of overall species flux. These considerations suggest that, in the world we are creating, there can be no 'super-tramps' (*sensu* Diamond, 1975), flitting from species-poor habitat to species-poor habitat. Rather, these habitat islands will be either completely isolated from one another by uninhabitable areas or else saturated with species from the interstices, thereby precluding successful colonization. In these respects, faunas produced by Pleistocene fragmentation (habitat islands such as Southwestern mountain ranges or landbridge islands) can serve as valuable models for islands created by 20th century fragmentation. To this extent, the models used here to simulate species composition on Southwestern mountains ranges (Appendix) might have more general application.

The previous analysis has shown that isolated faunas produced by fragmentation show pronounced nestedness. Small islands produced in this way have not only fewer species, but also no additional species. Profound degrees of nesting should be evident in forest islands of different size created from a single patch of forest; this experiment, now under study by Lovejoy and associates in Amazonian Brazil (e.g. Lovejoy *et al.*, 1984), should provide a rigorous test of both the selectivity of extinction (in terms of species autecologies) and of nested faunal composition. While the experiment suffers from its 'unrealistic' design and timescale, being considerably accelerated relative to natural fragmentations, it need not rely on an incomplete fossil record and biogeographic inference to establish the faunas that were present at the time of fragmentation.

Biotic preserves established in different habitat types within a biotic region may ensure that each begins 'relaxation' with different sets of species. However, it is possible that such relaxing faunas may actually converge on a common species composition. Except for endemic and stenotypic taxa, locally abundant species are commonly broadly distributed; species abundance tends to be maximal near the centre of geographic distributions (e.g. Brown, 1984). To this extent, they may be present, if variably abundant, in each of the habitat types. More catholic food or habitat tolerances of these species (by definition) may allow them (1) to sustain their population sizes while other species decline to extinction, or (2) to cross habitat barriers too severe for more specialized species.

Therefore, to the extent that local abundance and geographic range are related, different biotic assemblages have the capacity to converge under selective extinction pressures towards common species composition.

## ACKNOWLEDGEMENTS

We wish to thank D. Simberloff for detailed criticisms of Patterson's (1982) paper which led us to undertake this investigation. The constructive and encouraging comments of J. H. Brown on his (1984) paper actually prompted the search for ways to demonstrate the significance of nested patterns. J. H. Brown, L. R. Heaney, and the other participants in the symposium, especially M. V. Lomolino, all provided useful feedback that improved the manuscript, as did R. F. Inger. Mary Anne Rogers drafted Fig. 1. Research was supported by Field Museum of Natural History and by AICS Research Inc.

## REFERENCES

ABBOTT, I., 1983. The meaning of $z$ in species/area regressions and the study of species turnover in island biogeography. *Oikos, 41:* 385–390.

ARMSTRONG, D. M., 1972. Distribution of mammals in Colorado. *Monograph of the Museum of Natural History, University of Kansas, 3:* 1–415.

BROWN, J. H., 1971. Mammals on mountaintops: nonequilibrium insular biogeography. *American Naturalist, 105:* 467–478.

BROWN, J. H., 1978. The theory of insular biogeography and the distribution of boreal birds and mammals. *Great Basin Naturalist Memoirs, 2:* 209–227.

BROWN, J. H., 1984. On the relationship between abundance and distribution of species. *American Naturalist, 124:* 255–279.

BROWN, J. H. & KODRIC-BROWN, A., 1977. Turnover rates in insular biogeography: effect of immigration on extinction. *Ecology, 58:* 445–449.

CONNOR, E. F. & McCOY, E. D., 1979. The statistics and biology of the species-area relationship. *American Naturalist, 113:* 791–833.

CROWELL, K. L., 1973. Experimental zoogeography: introductions of mice to small islands. *American Naturalist, 107:* 535–558.

CROWELL, K. L., 1986. A comparison of relict versus equilibrium models for insular mammals of the Gulf of Maine. *Biological Journal of the Linnean Society, 28:* 37–64.

DAWSON, D. G., 1984. Principles of ecological biogeography and criteria for reserve design. *Journal of the Royal Society of New Zealand, 14:* 11–15.

DIAMOND, J. M., 1975. Assembly of species communities. In M. L. Cody & J. M. Diamond (Eds), *Ecology and Evolution of Communities:* 342–444. Cambridge: Belknap Press.

FINDLEY, J. S., 1969. Biogeography of Southwestern boreal and desert mammals. In J. K. Jones Jr (Ed.), *Contributions in Mammalogy:* 113–128. Miscellaneous Publications, Museum of Natural History, University of Kansas 51.

FINDLEY, J. S., HARRIS, A. H., WILSON, D. E. & JONES, C., 1975. *Mammals of New Mexico.* Albuquerque: University of New Mexico Press.

GEORGE, S. B., 1983. Genic relationships of Southwestern populations of *Sorex monticolus* and *Sorex cinereus*. *63rd Annual Meeting of the American Society of Mammalogists, Gainesville.* (Abstract only.)

GRAYSON, D. K., 1982. Toward a history of Great Basin mammals during the past 15,000 years. In D. B. Madsen & J. F. O'Connell (Eds), *Man and Environment in the Great Basin:* 82–101. *Society for American Archeology Papers, 2:* 1–242.

HARRIS, A. H., 1985. *Late Pleistocene Vertebrate Paleoecology of the West.* Austin: University of Texas Press.

KARR, J. R., 1982. Population variability and extinction in the avifauna of a tropical land bridge island. *Ecology, 63:* 1975–1978.

KÜCHLER, A. W., 1964. The potential natural vegetation of the conterminous United States, 1:3,168,000. *Special Publications, American Geographical Society, 36:* 1–37.

LAWLOR, T. E., 1983. The mammals. In T. J. Case & M. L. Cody (Eds), *Island Biogeography in the Sea of Cortéz:* 265–289, 482–500. Berkeley: University of California Press.

LAWLOR, T. E., 1986. Comparative biogeography of mammals on islands. *Biological Journal of the Linnean Society, 28:* 99–125.

LOVEJOY, T. E., RANKIN, J. M., BIERREGAARD Jr, R. O., BROWN Jr, K. S., EMMONS, L. H. & VAN DER VOORT, M., 1984. Ecosystem decay of Amazon forest remnants. In M. H. Nitecki (Ed.), *Extinctions:* 295–325. Chicago: University of Chicago Press.

MACARTHUR, R. H., 1972. *Geographical Ecology.* New York: Harper & Row.

MACARTHUR, R. H. & WILSON, E. O., 1967. *The Theory of Island Biogeography.* Princeton: Princeton University Press.

McINTYRE, M. E., YOUNG, E. C. & KING, C. M. (Eds), 1984. Biological reserve design in mainland New Zealand. *Journal of the Royal Society of New Zealand, 14:* 1–45.

PATTERSON, B. D., 1982. Pleistocene vicariance, montane islands, and the evolutionary divergence of some chipmunks (Genus *Eutamias*). *Journal of Mammalogy, 63:* 387–398.

PATTERSON, B. D., 1984. Mammalian extinction and biogeography in the Southern Rocky Mountains. In M. H. Nitecki (Ed.), *Extinctions:* 247–293. Chicago: University of Chicago Press.

PETERS, R. H. & RAELSON, J. V., 1984. Relations between individual size and mammalian population density. *American Naturalist, 124:* 498–517.

SEPKOSKI Jr, J. J., 1982. Mass extinctions in the Phanerozoic oceans. A review. *Geological Society of America Special Paper, 190:* 283–289.

SIMBERLOFF, D., 1985. [Book Review] *Extinctions*, Nitecki, M. H. (Ed.). *The Auk, 102:* 429–431.

SULLIVAN, R. M., 1985. Phyletic, biogeographic, and ecologic relationships among montane populations of least chipmunks (*Eutamias minimus*) in the Southwest. *Systematic Zoology, 34:* 419–448.

WELLS, P. V., 1983. Paleobiogeography of montane islands in the Great Basin since the last glaciopluvial. *Ecological Monographs, 53:* 341–382.

## APPENDIX

RANDOM1 program written in BASIC to create randomized archipelagos having the general form of Lawlor's (1983) landbridge islands, including species richness and proportionate occurrence frequencies. Added lines, representing the added constraints over RANDOM0, are indicated by asterisks (*).

```
      1000 DIM S$[50,50]
      1010 DIM S[50,50]
      1020 DIM R[50],C[50]
      1030 DIM RO[50],CO[50]
      1040 DIM E[50,2]
      1050 MAT S = ZER
      1060 MAT E = ZER
      1070 NO = 25
      1080 IO = 20
      1085 REM INSERT STRING OF SPECIES RICHNESS VALUES (FOR ISLANDS)
      1090 DATA 13,9,7,7,6,5,4,3,3,3,2,2,2,2,2,2,1,1,1,1
      1100 MO = 1E77
      1110 M1 = -1E77
      1120 PRINT
      1130 FOR R = 1 TO IO
      1140 READ R[R]
      1150 NEXT R
     *1160 S = O
      1165 REM INSERT STRING OF ISLAND OCCURRENCE VALUES (FOR SPECIES)
     *1170 DATA 1,1,4,2,1,1,1,1,2,2,1,2,1,9,3,1,8,1,10,2,12,2,1,3,4
     *1180 FOR C = 1 TO NO
     *1190 READ C[C]
     *1200 S = S + C[C]
     *1210 NEXT C
     *1220 FOR C = 1 TO NO
     *1230 C[C] = C[C]/S
     *1240 NEXT C
      1250 PRINT "The first two simulated archipelagos:"
      1260 PRINT
      1270 S1 = S2 = 0
      1280 FOR X = 1 TO 1000
      1290 MAT S = ZER
      1300 FOR R = 1 TO IO
      1310 FOR N = 1 TO R[R]
     *1320 P = RND(0)
     *1330 S = 0
```

```
*1340 FOR C = 1 TO NO
*1350 S = S + C[C]
*1360 IF P < = S THEN 1380
*1370 NEXT C
 1380 IF S[R,C] > 0 THEN 1320
 1390 S[R,C] = C
 1400 NEXT N
 1410 NEXT R
 1420 IF X > 2 THEN 1540
 1430 PRINT "Simulated archipelago no.: ";X
 1440 PRINT
 1450 FOR R = 1 TO IO
 1460 FOR C = 1 TO NO
 1470 IF S[R,C] > 0 THEN PRINT CHR$(S[R,C]+64);
 1480 ELSE PRINT " ";
 1490 NEXT C
 1500 PRINT
 1510 NEXT R
 1520 PRINT
 1530 PRINT
 1540 S = 0
 1550 FOR C = 1 TO NO
 1560 SO = 0
 1570 R = IO
 1580 IF S[R,C] = 0 THEN 1610
 1590 H = R[R]
 1600 GOTO 1640
 1610 R = R−1
 1620 IF R = 0 THEN 1710
 1630 GOTO 1580
 1640 R = R−1
 1650 IF R = 0 THEN 1710
 1660 IF R[R] > H AND S[R,C] = 0 THEN DO
 1670 S = S + 1
 1680 SO = SO + 1
 1690 DOEND
 1700 GOTO 1640
 1710 E[C,1] = E[C,1] + SO
 1720 E[C,2] = E[C,2] + SO**2
 1730 NEXT C
 1740 IF S < MO THEN MO = S
 1750 IF S > M1 THEN M1 = S
 1760 S1 = S1 + S
 1770 S2 = S2 + S**2
 1780 NEXT X
 1790 PRINT "Data Analysis Section"
 1800 PRINT
 1810 PRINT "Max: ";M1
 1820 PRINT "Min: ";MO
 1830 PRINT
 1840 PRINT "Species", "Mean", "Variance"
 1850 FOR C = 1 TO NO
 1860 PRINT CHR$(C+64),E[C,1]/1000,1000/999*(E[C,2]/1000  (E[C,1]/1000)**2)
 1870 NEXT C
 1880 PRINT
 1890 PRINT "Overall mean: ";S1/1000
 1900 PRINT " Variance: ";1000/999*(S2/1000−(S1/1000)**2)
 1910 PRINT " Deviation: ";SQR(1000/999*(S2/1000−(S1/1000)**2))
```

*Biological Journal of the Linnean Society* (1986), *28:* 83–98. With 2 figures

# Species–area relationship and its determinants for mammals in western North American national parks

WILLIAM D. NEWMARK

*School of Natural Resources, University of Michigan, Ann Arbor, Michigan 48109, U.S.A.*

*Accepted for publication 14 February 1986*

The relationship between non-volant mammalian species richness and area in 24 western North American national parks is examined. The exponential and the power function models are concluded to be the 'best' models and account for nearly an identical proportion of the total variance ($\cong 69\%$). Two principal hypotheses, the area *per se* and the habitat diversity hypotheses, have been proposed to explain the species–area relationship. Support exists for both hypotheses based upon partial correlation analysis of non-volant mammalian species richness with area, elevational range, latitude, number of vegetative cover types and index of vegetative cover diversity. I conclude that area *per se* and habitat diversity defined as environmental heterogeneity are the best predictors of non-volant mammalian species richness in western North American national parks. I also conclude that vegetative cover diversity is a poor predictor of mammalian species richness in western North American national parks. Several problems with assessing the area *per se* and habitat diversity hypotheses are noted. These are: (1) the definition of the term 'habitat'; (2) the predictions of these two hypotheses may not be mutually exclusive; and (3) area and habitat diversity tend to be intercorrelated. The slope ($z$) of the power function is equal to 0.12. The hypothesis that variation in the slope of the power function for nature reserves worldwide is a result of the comparative sizes of the nature reserves cannot be excluded. There has been considerable discussion in recent years about the conservation implications of the species–area relationship. Much of this discussion has been concerned with whether a single large reserve contains more species than several small reserves (SLOSS). The answer to SLOSS is heavily dependent upon the objectives of a reserve, the autecology of the species, and the ecological independence of the reserves. It is suggested that particular attention be given to area and elevation when designing nature reserves.

KEY WORDS:—Mammalian species richness – area – elevational range – habitat diversity – western North America – national parks – reserve design.

## CONTENTS

       

## INTRODUCTION

It has been recognized for more than a century that the number of species increases as area increases (De Candolle, 1855; Arrhenius, 1921, 1923; Gleason, 1922, 1925). However, considerable debate still surrounds the biological basis for the species–area relationship (Simberloff, 1978; Connor & McCoy, 1979; McGuiness, 1984), the interpretation of the slope of the power function (Connor & McCoy, 1979; Sugihara, 1981), as well as the conservation implications of the species–area relationship (Diamond, 1975; Gilbert, 1980; Simberloff & Abele, 1976, 1982).

Two principal hypotheses have been proposed to explain the species–area relationship: the habitat diversity hypothesis and the area *per se* hypothesis (Connor & McCoy, 1979). Williams (1943) was the first to propose the habitat diversity hypothesis. He suggested that as larger areas are sampled, an increasing number of habitats will be encountered; thus larger areas contain more species because they contain greater habitat diversity. The area *per se* hypothesis was developed by Preston (1960, 1962) and MacArthur & Wilson (1963, 1967), who suggested that the number of species on an island represents an equilibrium between the rates of extinction and colonization. They assumed that the rate of colonization is dependent upon the distance of an island from a source pool and that the rate of extinction is inversely proportional to population size which in turn depends upon the island area.

In order to corroborate the habitat diversity hypothesis, it must be shown that for islands of equal area, a positive relationship exists between habitat diversity and number of species. Conversely, in order to demonstrate the area *per se* hypothesis, it must be shown that in a homogeneous habitat a positive relationship exists between area and species number (Simberloff, 1978; Connor & McCoy, 1979). Unfortunately, variation in the size and habitat diversity of western North American national parks does not permit a natural experiment, I will therefore use correlation analysis to identify the best predictors of mammalian species richness.

In this paper, I examine the relationship between non-volant mammalian species richness in 24 western North American national parks and area, elevational range, latitude, number of vegetative cover types and index of vegetative cover diversity. I discuss the problems of assessing the area *per se* and habitat diversity hypotheses. In addition, I examine the relationship between number of non-volant mammals and area within western North American national parks and park assemblages and compare it to species–area relationships in Western Australian, and East African reserves. Finally I discuss the conservation implications of the species–area relationship as they apply to the design of nature reserves for mammals.

## METHODS

Twenty-nine national parks and park assemblages in the western U.S. and Canada were included in this study. For purpose of analysis, parks that were contiguous with another park were considered to be a single park assemblage (Bekele, 1980), because of the freedom of movement for the park fauna between the contiguous parks. Thus a total of 24 national parks and park assemblages was included in the analysis (Table 1). All parks are located in the Rocky

## Table 1. Untransformed data used in analysis

| Park—park assemblage | Mammalian species richness | Area (km²) | Latitude (°N) | Elevational range (m) | Number of vegetative cover types | Index of vegetative cover diversity |
|---|---|---|---|---|---|---|
| 1 Wind Caves | 33 | 112 | 43.58 | 365 | 4 | 0.31 |
| 2 Grand Teton—Yellowstone | 55 | 10328 | 44.28 | 2347 | 9 | 0.60 |
| 3 Glacier—Waterton Lakes | 56 | 4627 | 48.71 | 2213 | 9 | 0.79 |
| 4 Kootenay–Banff–Jasper–Yoho | 55 | 20736 | 52.27 | 2887 | 10 | 0.83 |
| 5 Glacier (Canada) | 39 | 1349 | 51.27 | 2535 | 8 | 0.77 |
| 6 Mount Revelstoke | 36 | 262 | 51.09 | 2150 | 7 | 0.72 |
| 7 Manning Provincial | 48 | 712 | 49.11 | 1509 | 6 | 0.54 |
| 8 Olympic | 46 | 3628 | 47.83 | 2428 | 8 | 0.64 |
| 9 Mount Rainier | 40 | 976 | 46.86 | 3897 | 8 | 0.38 |
| 10 Crater Lake | 43 | 641 | 42.77 | 1501 | 6 | 0.67 |
| 11 Lava Beds | 33 | 185 | 41.77 | 457 | 5 | 0.39 |
| 12 Lassen Volcanic | 42 | 426 | 40.50 | 1439 | 7 | 0.68 |
| 13 Yosemite | 57 | 2083 | 37.83 | 3293 | 10 | 0.80 |
| 14 Sequoia—Kings Canyon | 59 | 3389 | 36.77 | 3991 | 9 | 0.73 |
| 15 Wupatki | 30 | 143 | 35.56 | 335 | 3 | 0.40 |
| 16 Grand Canyon | 57 | 4931 | 36.23 | 2275 | 6 | 0.52 |
| 17 Zion | 49 | 588 | 37.32 | 1463 | 5 | 0.68 |
| 18 Bryce Canyon | 33 | 144 | 37.51 | 762 | 5 | 0.56 |
| 19 Capitol Reef | 32 | 979 | 38.08 | 320 | 4 | 0.46 |
| 20 Arches | 33 | 293 | 38.73 | 488 | 4 | 0.50 |
| 21 Dinosaur | 42 | 827 | 40.44 | 1262 | 7 | 0.32 |
| 22 Colorado | 30 | 83 | 39.06 | 670 | 4 | 0.49 |
| 23 Mesa Verde | 44 | 208 | 37.25 | 713 | 3 | 0.43 |
| 24 Rocky Mountain | 44 | 1049 | 40.35 | 1809 | 8 | 0.75 |

Mountains, Sierra-Cascades or Colorado Plateau (Fig 1). The legal size or area ($A$) of the western North American national parks and park assemblages was taken from IUCN (1980).

Non-volant mammalian species richness ($S$) was determined by reviewing the literature and the park sighting records (Newmark, 1986). Species which have been sighted fewer than three times since park establishment were excluded from the analysis, because these species were considered to be transients. All non-volant mammalian exotics were included in the analysis because of their non-transient nature; i.e. in all cases they are species which have established breeding populations within a park.

Elevational range ($E$) has been widely recognized as an indirect indicator of environmental diversity (Hamilton & Armstrong, 1965; Johnson & Raven, 1973; Power, 1976; Patterson, 1980). Most western North American national parks and park assemblages display a large elevational range. Elevational range for each park was taken from U.S. Geological Survey and Canadian Army Survey and Canadian Department of Energy, Mines, and Resources topographical maps.

The inverse relationship between latitude ($L$) and number of species has long been recognized (Wallace, 1878; Fischer, 1960; Simpson, 1964). The latitude of the centre of each reserve was taken from the U.S. and Canadian topographical maps.

The number of vegetative cover types ($N_V$) within each park was calculated. Twenty-five vegetative cover types were identified in the 24 parks and park

W. D. NEWMARK

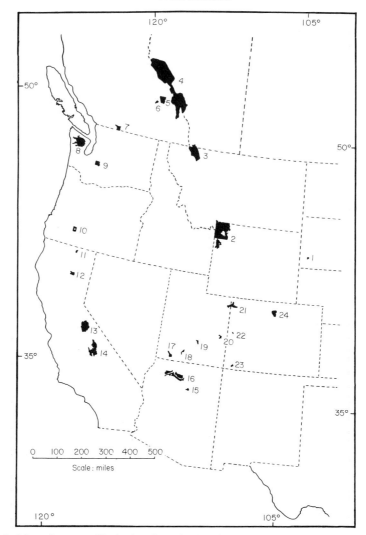

Figure 1. Map of western North American showing location of 24 national parks and park assemblages listed in Table 1.

assemblages from existing National Park Service and Parks Canada vegetative cover type maps (Table 2). The cover types listed in Table 2 are based principally upon the dominant upper story vegetation. The criterion for inclusion was that a given vegetative cover type within a park must cover at least 1% of the park.

An index of vegetative cover diversity ($V_{CD}$) was developed based upon the Shannon–Wiener diversity index. The index of vegetative cover diversity may be described as:

$$V_{CD} = - \sum_{i=1}^{n} p_i \log_e p_i,$$

where $p_i$ is the relative frequency of the $i$th vegetative cover type listed in Table 2.

Table 2. Vegetative cover types in 24 western North American national parks and park assemblages used in analysis. Vegetative cover types were identified from National Park Service and Parks Canada vegetative cover type maps

| | | | | | |
|---|---|---|---|---|---|
| 1 | Alpine | 10 | Douglas fir | 19 | Sagebrush |
| 2 | Engelmann spruce/subalpine fir | 11 | Redwood | 20 | Creosotebrush/saltbrush |
| 3 | Whitebark pine | 12 | Larch | 21 | Blackbrush |
| 4 | Lodgepole pine | 13 | Ponderosa pine/Jefferey pine | 22 | Scrub |
| 5 | Mountain hemlock | 14 | Oak woodland | 23 | Grassland/meadow |
| 6 | Red fir/white fir | 15 | Aspen | 24 | Riparian |
| 7 | Silver fir | 16 | Pinyon pine/juniper | 25 | Barren |
| 8 | Western hemlock | 17 | Chaparral | | |
| 9 | Sitka spruce | 18 | Shrub/brush | | |

Statistical calculations were conducted using the Michigan Interactive Data Analysis System. The least-squares method was used for all regression analyses. Species–area regressions were calculated using the linear (species/area), exponential (species/log area), and power function (log species/log area) models (Connor & McCoy, 1979). The power function model is:

$$S = CA^z,$$

where $S$ is number of species, $A$ is area and $C$ and $z$ are constants. The power function is approximated by the double log transformation:

$$\log S = \log C + z \log A.$$

The exponential model is:

$$S = \log C + z \log A.$$

The linear model is:

$$S = C + zA.$$

Determination of the 'best fit' was identified by examining alternative models for lack of systematic error (Sugihara, 1981). Specifically, I plotted the residuals against the independent terms and examined them for non-linearity and non-constancy of error variance (Neter & Wasserman, 1974). The Lilliefors test (Conover, 1971) was used to test for normality of error terms.

Partial correlation analysis was conducted between non-volant mammalian species richness and area, elevational range, latitude, number of vegetative cover types and index of vegetative cover diversity to identify the 'isolated effects' of each of these variables (Morrison, 1967). Partial correlation analysis was used instead of stepwise multiple regression analysis because of the problems associated with the order in which the independent variables enter the stepwise regression analysis. That is, for variables that are highly correlated, such as area and indices of habitat diversity, the variable that enters the regression equation first will always explain a larger proportion of the total variation of the dependent variable and thus may give a distorted image as to the relative 'importance' of an independent variable. All variables were $\log_{10}$ transformed to normalize their distributions.

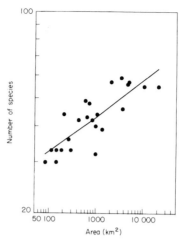

Figure 2. The relationship between $\log_{10}$ number of species of non-volant mammals and $\log_{10}$ area of 24 western North American national parks and park assemblages. Log $S = 1.26 + 0.12$ (log $A$), $r^2 = 0.68$, $P < 0.001$, $N = 24$.

RESULTS

*Species–area relationships*

The exponential and the power function models were considered to be the 'best' models because they did not violate the assumptions of linearity, constancy, or normality of error terms. Species richness was significantly correlated $(P < 0.001)$ with area of the western North American national parks and park assemblages for both the exponential and power function models (Fig. 2). These two models accounted for a nearly identical proportion $(\cong 69\%)$ of the total variance (Table 3).

*Correlation among variables*

Mammalian species richness was positively correlated with area, elevational range, number of vegetative cover types and index of vegetative cover diversity for $\log_{10}$ transformed data (Table 4). This indicates that large parks with a greater elevational range, higher vegetative cover diversity and a large number of vegetative cover types support a greater number of species. Latitude was the only variable not significantly correlated with species richness.

Area was significantly correlated with number of vegetative cover types, elevational range and the index of vegetative cover diversity. This indicates that area and possible indicators of habitat diversity are intercorrelated.

Table 3. Results of species–area regression analysis for 24 western North American national parks and park assemblages

| Regression model | $r^2$ | $F$ test, $P$ | $N$ |
|---|---|---|---|
| Exponential, $S = 7.26 + 12.32$ (log$A$) | 0.69 | <0.001 | 24 |
| Power function, log$S = 1.26 + 0.12$ (log$A$) | 0.68 | < 0.001 | 24 |

Table 4. Correlation matrix of $\log_{10}$ transformed data for 24 western North American national parks and park assemblages

| | $S$ | $A$ | $E$ | $V_{CD}$ | $N_V$ | $L$ |
|---|---|---|---|---|---|---|
| $(S)$ Mammalian species richness | — | | | | | |
| $(A)$ Area | 0.83 | — | | | | |
| $(E)$ Elevational range | 0.79 | 0.72 | — | | | |
| $(V_{CD})$ Index of vegetative cover diversity | 0.57 | 0.54 | 0.65 | — | | |
| $(N_V)$ Number of vegetative cover types | 0.71 | 0.77 | 0.89 | 0.64 | — | |
| $(L)$ Latitude | 0.15 | 0.35 | 0.43 | 0.30 | 0.52 | — |

$P < 0.05$, $r = 0.40$; $P < 0.01$, $r = 0.52$; $P < 0.001$, $r = 0.63$; df = 22.

## Partial correlation analysis

Partial correlation analysis showed that area was significantly correlated with mammalian species richness after holding elevational range, latitude, number of vegetative cover types and the vegetative cover diversity index constant (Table 5). Elevational range was also significantly correlated with species richness after holding area, latitude, number of vegetative cover types and index of vegetative cover diversity constant. Neither latitude, the number of vegetative cover types, nor the index of vegetative cover diversity index were significantly correlated with species richness when the other variables were held constant. These results indicate that both area *per se* and elevational range are significantly correlated with mammalian species richness in western North American national parks when the effects of latitude, vegetative cover and vegetative cover diversity are partialled out, but that latitude, vegetative cover and vegetative cover diversity are not significantly correlated with species richness when the effects of area and elevation are partialled out.

## DISCUSSION

### Area per se *and habitat diversity hypotheses*

Partial correlation analysis indicates that area *per se* is an important predictor of mammalian species richness in western North American national parks. This is consistent with the hypothesis that larger areas normally contain larger populations which in turn have lower probabilities of extinction (MacArthur &

Table 5. Partial correlations between non-volant mammalian species richness and area, elevational range, latitude, index of vegetative cover type diversity and number of vegetative cover types. The partial correlation of each variable with species richness was calculated by holding all other variables constant

| Variable | $r_{partial}$ | $t$ test, $P$ |
|---|---|---|
| Area | 0.67 | < 0.01 |
| Elevational range | 0.54 | < 0.025 |
| Latitude | −0.40 | n.s. |
| Number of vegetative cover types | −0.20 | n.s. |
| Index of vegetative cover diversity | 0.10 | n.s. |

Wilson, 1967; Diamond, 1984a). Additional support for this hypothesis within western North American national parks is twofold.

First, within 14 of the 24 western North American national parks and park assemblages included in this study, a significant inverse relationship exists between number of natural post-establishment extinctions of lagomorphs, carnivores and artiodactyls and park area ($r = 0.72$; $P < 0.01$). Analysis was limited to 14 parks and the orders Lagomorpha, Carnivora and Artiodactyla, because these parks and orders had the most complete historical and current species sighting records. The regression equation describing this relationship is $y = 11.82 - 2.68$ log area (Newmark, 1986). Results will be reported more fully in the future.

Second, for populations of lagomorphs, carnivores and artiodactyls that have gone extinct since park establishment in western North American national parks and park assemblages, estimated initial population size is the most consistent predictor of the log of the ratio of the odds of persistence/extinction. This result is based upon regressing persistence/extinction of populations of lagomorphs, carnivores and artiodactyls on park age, initial population size, body weight, index of ecological specialization, age of maturity and successional stage affinity using multiple logistic regression analysis (Newmark, 1986). These results also will be reported more fully in the future.

Partial correlation annysis also indicates that elevational range is an important predictor of mammalian richness in western North American national parks. This result is consistent with findings by Patterson (1984) who reported a significant relationship between number of montane mammals and elevation in the southern Rocky Mountains.

It has been recognized since before the turn of the century that many mammals in western North America are distributed along elevational gradients (Merriam, 1890; Grinnell & Storer, 1924; Hall, 1946). In addition, Simpson (1964) has shown that for North America, the mountainous regions are the centres of highest mammalian species diversity.

Elevational range is an important predictor of mammalian species richness in western North American national parks, because an increase in elevational range is most likely associated with an increase in environmental heterogeneity. It is well known that elevation is correlated with temperature, precipitation, humidity, wind speed, evaporation and insolation in western North America (Whittaker, 1960; Marr, 1967). Thus greater elevational range should reflect greater climatic and substrate diversity. It is most likely that this increase in climatic and substrate diversity is responsible for the observed increase in mammalian species richness. An increase in climatic and substrate diversity should increase the opportunity for the ecological segregation of species as a result of behavioural and physiological differences between species (Terborgh, 1971; Brown, 1971; Heller & Gates, 1971; Diamond, 1973). Heller (1971) and Heller & Gates (1971) have demonstrated for four species of chipmunks (*Eutamias* spp.) in the Sierra Nevadas in California, that individual physiological tolerances of the species as well as their relative competitive abilities are important determinants affecting their elevational distribution. These results are further supported by Brown (1971) who has shown that two species of chipmunks (*Eutamias umbrinus* and *E. dorsalis*) in the Great Basin are segregated along elevational gradients as a result of interspecific competition.

Partial correlation analysis indicates that habitat diversity, defined as either the number of vegetative cover types or as an index of vegetative cover diversity, is a poor predictor of mammalian species richness in western North American national parks. I propose several explanations for the insignificant correlations between mammalian species richness and vegetative cover diversity in western North American national parks.

First, it is possible that the dominant upper-story vegetation, upon which the two vegetative cover diversity indices are based, is less important in defining the habitat requirements for mammals than the middle and ground-level vegetation. However, many of the vegetative cover types that were used in the analysis are single strata. While little work has been conducted on the importance of vegetative strata on mammalian richness, there has been considerable work done on the importance of vertical height diversity on avian richness (e.g. MacArthur & MacArthur, 1961; Karr, 1968; Rotenberry & Wiens, 1980). Lynch & Whigham (1984) have shown that individual bird species in the eastern deciduous forests of the U.S. respond differentially to specific structural and floristic characteristics of the forest. It is possible that mammals respond similarly.

A second possible explanation for the insignificant correlation between number of mammalian species and vegetative cover diversity is that vegetative cover diversity may not be important in defining habitat diversity with regard to mammalian richness. While this explanation runs counter to the widely accepted definition of habitat as being the vegetative cover of an environment (Ricklefs, 1979; Karr, 1980), it is consistent with the findings of several other workers (Brown, 1978; Lawlor, 1983). Brown (1978) reported an insignificant correlation between number of montane mammals on mountaintops in the Great Basin and an index of habitat diversity, developed by Johnson (1975), based upon the number of coniferous tree species and three mesic vegetative cover types. Additionally, Lawlor (1983) reported an insignificant correlation between number of mammals and number of plant species on landbridge islands in the Sea of Cortéz off Mexico.

To my knowledge, only two studies have concluded that habitat diversity, as estimated by vegetative cover diversity, is the principal predictor of mammalian richness in western North America when both area and habitat diversity area included in the analysis; however, both of these studies are inconclusive. Lawlor (1983) reported that distance to the mainland and number of plant species were the best predictors of number of mammals on oceanic islands in the Sea of Cortéz and concluded that isolation and environmental complexity as estimated by number of plant species are the principal determinants of mammalian richness on these islands. However, it is possible that the number of plant species is intercorrelated with some third variable, such as annual precipitation, which is affecting both numbers of species of mammals and plants either directly or indirectly. Abramsky & Rosenzweig (1984) have shown that annual precipitation, which they suggest reflects productivity, is a good predictor of number of rodent species in rocky and sandy habitats in Israel and in sandy habitats in the deserts of southwestern U.S. Secondly, Bekele (1980) reported the number of potential natural vegetation types (Küchler, 1966) to be the best predictor of number of large mammals in 14 western U.S. national parks.

The obvious contradiction between results presented here and those of Bekele (1980) deserves further comment. First, it is questionable whether the number of potential natural vegetation types (Küchler, 1966) should reflect 'more truly' habitat diversity than an index based upon existing vegetative cover types. Secondly, using a more recent edition of the vegetation map (Küchler, 1975), I calculated a different number of potential natural vegetation types for many of the same 14 western U.S. national parks that Bekele (1980) included in his analysis. Using these more recent data, I found an insignificant partial correlation ($P > 0.1$) between number of species of mammals and number of potential natural vegetation types in 20 western U.S. national parks when area, elevational range and latitude were held constant (20 instead of 24 western North American parks and park assemblages were included in the analysis because Küchler's potential natural vegetation classification system is limited to the contiguous U.S.). Further detailed studies of the relationship between vegetative diversity and mammalian richness are needed.

A third possible explanation for the insignificant correlation between species richness and vegetative cover diversity is that vegetative cover diversity may be more important for local or alpha diversity than for regional or beta diversity (MacArthur, 1965; Ricklefs, 1979). Given the large geographic expanse of the 24 national parks and park assemblages included in this study, it is quite possible that vegetative cover diversity is not reflective of regional or beta diversity. Elevational range is possibly a better measurement of regional or beta diversity.

It is apparent that several factors complicate the assessment of the relative importance of area *per se* and habitat diversity in explaining species–area relationships in western North American national parks. First is the inadequacy of existing definitions of the term 'habitat' to explain mammalian species richness in western North American national parks. The definition of the term 'habitat' as the vegetative cover of an environment (Ricklefs, 1979; Karr, 1980) is unsatisfactory because of the poor correlation of numbers of non-volant mammals with vegetative cover diversity in western North American national parks. In addition, the definition of habitat as a *m*-dimensional space in which a species exists (Whittaker, Levin & Root, 1973) is unsatisfactory because it is too broad to be of any predictive value.

A second factor which makes it difficult to assess the relative importance of area *per se* and habitat diversity in western North American national parks is that the predictions of the area *per se* and habitat diversity hypotheses may not be mutually exclusive (Simberloff, 1978; Connor & McCoy, 1979; Gilbert, 1980). Support for both hypotheses exists. Simberloff (1976) and Rey (1984) have confirmed experimentally the importance of area *per se* as a predictor of number of arboreal arthropods on small mangrove and *Spartina* islands off the coast of Florida. Harman (1972) and Abele (1974) have provided support for the importance of habitat diversity in predicting number of species of aquatic invertebrates in marine and fresh water environments, and MacArthur & MacArthur (1961) have demonstrated the importance of habitat diversity in predicting avian species richness in eastern North America. It is quite possible that in one region or for one taxon, area may be an important predictor of number of species while in another region or for another taxon, habitat diversity may be an important predictor. Finally, it is possible that both area *per se* and habitat diversity may be important predictors in the same region or for the same taxon as it appears to be with non-volant mammals in western North American national parks.

A third factor which complicates the assessment of the relative importance of area *per se* and habitat diversity is that area and indices of habitat diversity tend to be intercorrelated (e.g. Power, 1972, 1976; Brown, 1978; Kitchener *et al.*, 1980; Reed, 1983; Lynch & Whigham, 1984). An examination of the correlation matrix (Table 4) indicates that within western North American national parks, area and possible indicators of habitat diversity (elevational range, number of vegetative cover types, and index of vegetative cover diversity) are positively correlated.

Partial correlation analysis shows that both area *per se* and elevational range are important predictors of mammalian species richness in western North American national parks. Area *per se* is probably important because larger areas contain larger populations which in turn have a higher probability of persistence. Elevational range is important because an increase in elevational range is most likely associated with an increase in environmental heterogeneity which in turn allows for greater ecological segregation of species. Finally, vegetative cover diversity is a poor predictor of mammalian richness in western North American national parks.

## Interpretation of the species–area slope (z)

Although western North American national parks are becoming increasingly isolated as a result of disturbance on lands adjacent to the parks, they are not yet true habitat islands. The slope of the power function for the species–area relationship ($z = 0.12$) indicates that western North American national parks and park assemblages are more similar to non-isolated continental samples than to true isolates. MacArthur & Wilson (1967) and Lawlor (1986) report that the slope for most non-isolated continental samples is between 0.12 and 0.17 and the slope for true isolates is between 0.20 and 0.35.

The slope of the power function for the species–area relationship for western North American national parks differs from the reported slopes for other groups of nature reserves worldwide. Kitchener *et al.* (1980) report a slope of 0.39 for non-volant mammals in nature reserves in Western Australia. Miller & Harris (1977) did not find a significant species–area relationship for large mammals in East African national parks. However, Western & Ssemakula (1981), when comparing East African parks by habitat type, found a significant species–area relationship with a slope ($z$) of 0.04–0.08. The variation in the slope of the species–area regression of nature reserves worldwide may be related to the relative isolation of the parks, the relative transience of the species or the comparative sizes of the reserves. Unfortunately, quantitative data are unavailable to examine the first two hypotheses; however, from general qualitative descriptions in the literature of Western Australian and East African reserves, it appears that Western Australian reserves are much more isolated than either western North American or East African reserves.

Martin (1981) has shown that the slope of the power function will vary according to the size of the islands forming an archipelago. Archipelagos with small islands tend to have steeper slopes than archipelagos with large islands.

Martin (1981) suggested that this empirical relationship is a result of the asymptotic nature of the species–area relationship. This hypotheses cannot be rejected based upon the comparative slopes and sizes of the Western Australian, western North American and East African parks. Western Australian parks are the smallest group of parks($\bar{x} = 10$ km$^2$) and have the steepest slope ($z = 0.39$), followed by western North American parks which are intermediate in size ($\bar{x} = 2446$ km$^2$) and slope ($z = 0.12$), followed by the East African parks which are the largest parks ($\bar{x} = 5643$ km$^2$) and have the shallowest slope ($z = 0.04$–$0.08$).

### *Implications of the species–area relationship for conservation of mammals*

There has been considerable discussion in recent years as to the conservation implications of the species–area relationship. Much of this discussion has been concerned with the utility of the species–area relationship in developing guide-lines for reserve design (Diamond, 1972, 1975; Simberloff & Abele, 1976, 1982; Gilbert, 1980; Reed, 1983). A general consensus now exists that a single large reserve will contain initially more species and lose fewer species over time than a single small reserve. This relationship holds as long as the species–area curve does not flatten out. The positive relationship between non-volant mammalian species richness and area for western North American national parks as well as the inverse relationship between number of post-establishment extinctions of lagomorphs, carnivores and artiodactyls and park area provides further support for this relationship (Newmark, 1986).

A more contentious question has been whether a single large reserve will contain more species than several small reserves of equivalent size, referred to by the acronym SLOSS (e.g Simberloff & Abele, 1976, 1982; Wilcox & Murphy, 1985). In large part the answer to SLOSS depends upon the reserve objectives, the ecological independence of the reserves (Shaffer & Samson, 1985), as well as the autecology of the species being protected.

If the primary objective of a nature reserve is to maximize species richness, then the answer to SLOSS is largely contingent upon the slope of the regression curve and the similarity of species composition between reserves (Simberloff & Abele, 1976). It is now generally agreed that two small reserves in different habitats will normally contain more *total* species than a single large reserve (Higgs & Usher, 1980; Gilpin & Diamond, 1980; Simberloff & Abele, 1982; Soulé & Simberloff, 1986).

If on the other hand the primary objective of a nature reserve is to minimize species extinctions, then the answer to SLOSS is strongly dependent upon the autecology of the species being protected as well as the ecological independence of the reserves to stochastic extinction events (Shaffer & Samson, 1985). As has been frequently stated, species are not equal (e.g. Diamond, 1976). Humphrey & Kitchener (1982) have shown that in Western Australian nature reserves, a single reserve contains more vertebrate species that cannot use habitat adjacent to the reserve than two small reserves of equivalent size, while two small reserves contain more total vertebrate species that can use habitat adjacent to the reserves than a single large reserve. These results are similar to those of Blake & Karr (1984) who have reported that a single large forest in Illinois contains more long-distance avian migrants than two small forests of equivalent size, but that two small forests contain more short-distance avian migrants, residents and total species than a single large reserve.

The importance of recognizing the autecology of the species being protected when designing nature reserves is further dramatized by the results of Patterson & Atmar (1986) who have shown that the loss of species of montane mammals in the southern Rocky Mountains follows a nested subset pattern. They explain this phenomena as a result of smaller areas containing smaller populations which have higher probabilities of extinction. Support for this hypothesis is provided by the significant inverse relationship between the log of the ratio of the odds of persistence/extinction and estimated initial population size of lagomorphs and carnivores in western North American national parks (Newmark, 1986). This implies that there is a critical area requirement for most montane mammals in western North America. Nature reserves can be expected in the long run to support only those species that have an area requirement smaller than the reserve.

The issue of minimum critical size for nature reserves is particularly important for mammals because as a group, mammals are comparatively poor colonizers (Newmark, 1986; Lawlor, 1983, 1986; Heaney, 1986; Morgan & Woods, 1986). Heaney (1986) estimates that the rate of colonization for mammals in the Philippines across saltwater barriers less than 15 km is approximately one successful colonization per 250 000–500 000 years. Morgan & Woods (1986) estimate the rate of colonization for non-volant mammals into the West Indies across saltwater barriers as one colonization for every 1.5–3.1 million years. The poor colonizing ability of mammals is further reflected in the low relative turnover of mammals (Crowell, 1986) in comparison with other invertebrate and vertebrate taxa (Schoener, 1983) on oceanic islands.

While most nature reserves are not surrounded on all sides by saltwater barriers, it is quite likely in the future that the habitat adjacent to most nature reserves will become increasingly inhospitable to mammalian dispersal. Approximately 85% of the lands adjoining the western North American national parks are public lands (Newmark, 1986). Yet within 14 of the 24 western North American national parks included in this study with the best historical current species sighting records (park age, $\bar{x} = 75.1$ years), there have been only three post-establishment natural colonizations by species of lagomorphs, carnivores and artiodactyls not previously found within the parks (Newmark, 1986). This is equivalent to a rate of one colonization per 350 years.

Corridors between nature reserves should enhance the potential for colonization by non-volant mammals (Diamond, 1975; Harris, 1984). Yet the benefits of promoting colonization must be weighed against the risks of introducing disease and exotic species. The impacts of disease and introduced species upon isolated populations can be severe and have been identified as two of the most important factors responsible for the historical extinction of most isolated vertebrate species (Diamond, 1984b; Frankel & Soulé, 1981). Thus, given the poor colonizing ability of most mammals and the problems associated with corridors, it is critical that particular emphasis be placed upon maximizing reserve area when designing nature reserves for mammals.

It is widely recognized that reserve area and elevation are normally only two of several criteria that are considered when designing a reserve. Issues such as acquisition and maintenance costs, introduction of exotic species, poaching and promotion of rural development are also frequently of equal concern when planning nature reserves (McNeeley & Miller, 1984). Nonetheless, there are several additional practical reasons why special attention should be given to variables such as reserve area and elevation. First, area and elevation are relatively easy to measure in comparison to habitat diversity and can be taken readily from topographic maps. Secondly, area and to a lesser degree elevation have been shown to be consistently correlated with species richness for a wide variety of taxa. In contrast, most indices of habitat diversity tend to be taxon-specific. That is, most indices of habitat diversity which have proven to be successful in predicting species richness for one taxon are generally poor in predicting species richness for another taxon (e.g. Brown, 1978). Thus, given the limited resources facing most conservation organizations, it would be prudent if particular attention be given to such easily measured variables as area and elevation in the selection and design of nature reserves.

## ACKNOWLEDGEMENTS

I would like to thank G. E. Belovsky, K. R. Miller, M. E. Soulé, B. S. Low and B. J. Rathcke for their valuable assistance throughout this study. I also would like to thank L. R. Heaney and B. D. Patterson for their comments on this manuscript. Special thanks are given to M. Kinnaird for drawing Figure 1. Finally, I would like to acknowledge the outstanding assistance I received from the many scientists and resource managers of the National Park Service and Parks Canada who so generously provided information and reviewed species checklists. Support was provided by two Rackham dissertation enhancement grants.

## REFERENCES

ABELE, L. G., 1974. Species diversity of decapod crustaceans in marine habitats. *Ecology, 55:* 156–161.
ABRAMSKY, Z. & ROSENZWEIG, M. L., 1984. Tilman's predicted productivity-diversity relationship shown by desert rodents. *Nature, 309:* 150–151.
ARRHENIUS, O., 1921. Species and area. *Journal of Ecology, 9:* 95–99.
ARRHENIUS, O., 1923. On the relation between species and area—a reply. *Ecology, 4:* 90–91.
BEKELE, E., 1980. *Island biogeography and guidelines for the selection of conservation units for large mammals.* Unpublished Ph.D. dissertation, University of Michigan, Ann Arbor, Michigan.
BLAKE, J. G. & KARR, J. R., 1984. Species composition of bird communities and the conservation benefit of large versus small forests. *Biological Conservation, 30:* 173–187.
BROWN, J. H., 1971. Mechanisms of competitive exclusion between two species of chipmunks. *Ecology, 52:* 305–311.
BROWN, J. H., 1978. The theory of insular biogeography and the distribution of boreal birds and mammals. *Great Basin Naturalist Memoirs, 2:* 209–227.
DE CANDOLLE, A., 1855. *Géographie botanique raisonnée: ou, exposition des faites principaux et des lois concervant la distribution géographique des plantes de l'époque actuelle.* Paris: V. Maisson.
CONNOR, E. F. & McCOY, E. D., 1979. The statistics and biology of the species-area relationship. *American Naturalist, 133:* 791–833.
CONOVER, W. J., 1971. *Practical Nonparametric Statistics.* New York: John Wiley and Sons Inc.
CROWELL, K. L., 1986. A comparison of relict versus equilibrium models for insular mammals of the Gulf of Maine. *Biological Journal of the Linnean Society, 28:* 37–64.
DIAMOND, J. M., 1972. Biogeographic kinetics: estimation of relaxation times for avifaunas of southwest Pacific islands. *Proceedings of the National Academy of Sciences of the U.S.A., 69:* 3199–3203.
DIAMOND, J. M., 1973. Ecological consequences of island colonization by southwest Pacific birds, I. Types of niche shifts. *Proceedings of the National Academy of Sciences of the U.S.A., 67:* 529–536.
DIAMOND, J. M., 1975. The island dilemma: lessons of modern biogeographic studies for the design of natural reserves. *Biological Conservation, 7:* 129–146.

DIAMOND, J. M., 1976. Island biogeography and conservation: strategy and limitations. *Science, 193:* 1027–1029.

DIAMOND, J. M., 1984a. "Normal" extinctions of isolated populations. In M. H. Nitecki (Ed.), *Extinctions:* 191–246. Chicago: University of Chicago Press.

DIAMOND, J. M., 1984b. Historic extinctions: a Rosetta Stone for understanding prehistoric extinctions. In P. S. Martin & R. G. Klein (Eds), *Quaternary Extinctions:* 824–862. Tucson: University of Arizona Press.

DRAPER, N. R. & SMITH, H., 1981. *Applied Regression Analysis.* New York: John Wiley and Sons Inc.

FISCHER, A. G., 1960. Latitudinal variation in organic diversity. *Evolution, 14:* 64–81.

FRANKEL, O. H. & SOULÉ, M. E., 1981. *Conservation and Evolution.* Cambridge: Cambridge University Press.

GILBERT, F. S., 1980. The equilibrium theory of island biogeography: fact or fiction? *Journal of Biogeography, 7:* 209–235.

GILPIN, M. E. & DIAMOND, J. M., 1980. Subdivision of nature reserves and the maintenance of species diversity. *Nature, 285:* 567–568.

GLEASON, H. A., 1922. On the relation between species and area. *Ecology, 3:* 158–162.

GLEASON, H. A., 1925. Species and area. *Ecology, 6:* 66–74.

GRINNELL, J. & STORER, T. I., 1924. *Animal Life in the Yosemite.* Berkeley: University of California Press.

HALL, E. R., 1946. *Mammals of Nevada.* Berkeley: University of California Press.

HAMILTON, T. H. & ARMSTRONG, N. E., 1965. Enviromental determination of insular variation in bird species abundance in the Gulf of Guinea. *Nature, 207:* 148–151.

HARMAN, W. N., 1972. Benthic substrates: their effect on fresh-water mollusca. *Ecology, 53:* 271–277.

HARRIS, L. D., 1984. *The Fragmented Forest: Island Biogeography Theory and the Preservation of Biotic Diversity.* Chicago: University of Chicago Press.

HEANEY, L. R., 1986. Biogeography of mammals in SE Asia: estimates of rates of colonization, extinction and speciation. *Biological Journal of the Linnean Society, 28:* 127–165.

HELLER, H. C., 1971. Altitudinal zonation of chipmunks (*Eutamias*): interspecific aggression. *Ecology, 52:* 312–319.

HELLER, H. C. & GATES, D. M., 1971. Altitudinal zonation of chipmunks (*Eutamias*): energy budgets. *Ecology, 52:* 424–433.

HIGGS, A. J. & USHER, M. B., 1980. Should nature reserves be large or small. *Nature, 285:* 568–569.

HUMPHREYS, W. F. & KITCHENER, D. J., 1982. The effect of habitat utilization on species-area curves: implications for optimal reserve area. *Journal of Biogeography, 9:* 391–396.

IUCN COMMISSION ON NATIONAL PARKS AND PROTECTED AREAS, 1980. *1980 United Nations List of National Parks and Equivalent Reserves.* Gland: IUCN.

JOHNSON, M. P. & RAVEN, P. H., 1973. Species number and endemism: the Galápagos revisited. *Science, 179:* 893–895.

JOHNSON, N. K., 1975. Controls of number of bird species on montane islands in the Great Basin. *Evolution, 29:* 545–567.

KARR, J. R., 1968. Habitat and avian diversity on strip-mined land in east-central Illinois. *Condor, 70:* 348–357.

KARR, J. R., 1980. History of the habitat concept in birds and the measurement of avian habitats. In R. Nohring (Ed.), *Acta XVII Congressus Internationalis Ornithologici:* 991–997. Berlin: Deutsche Ornithologen-Gesellschaft.

KITCHENER, D. J., CHAPMAN, A., MUIR, B. G. & PALMER, M. 1980. The conservation value for mammals of reserves in the Western Australian wheatbelt. *Biological Conservation, 18:* 179–207.

KÜCHLER, A. W., 1966. Potential natural vegetation of the coterminous United States. Scale 1 : 3,168,000. *American Geographical Society of New York, Special Publications, 36.*

KÜCHLER, A. W., 1975. Potential natural vegetation of the coterminous United States, 2nd edition Scale 1 : 3,168,000. *American Geographical Society of New York, Special Publications, 36.*

LACK, D., 1973. The numbers of species of hummingbirds in the West Indies. *Evolution, 23:* 193–209.

LAWLOR, T., 1983. The mammals. In T. J. Case & M. C. Cody (Eds), *Island Biogeography in the Sea of Cortéz:* 265–289. Berkeley: University of California Press.

LAWLOR, T. E., 1986. Comparative biogeography of mammals on islands. *Biological Journal of the Linnean Society, 28:* 99–125.

LYNCH, J. F. & WHIGHAM, D. F., 1984. Effects of forest fragmentation on breeding bird communities in Maryland, U.S.A. *Biological Conservation, 28:* 287–324.

MACARTHUR, R. H., 1965. Patterns of species diversity. *Biological Reviews, Cambridge Philosophical Society, 40:* 510–533.

MACARTHUR, R. H. & MACARTHUR, J., 1961. On bird species diversity. *Ecology, 42:* 594–598.

MACARTHUR, R. M. & WILSON, E. O., 1963. An equilibrium theory of insular zoogeography. *Evolution, 17:* 373–387.

MACARTHUR, R. M. & WILSON, E. O., 1967. *The Theory of Island Biogeography.* Princeton: Princeton University Press.

McGUINNESS, K. A., 1984. Equations and explanations in the study of species-area curves. *Biological Reviews, Cambridge Philosophical Society, 59:* 423–440.

McNEELEY, J. A. & MILLER, K. R. (Eds), 1984. *National Parks, Conservation, and Development: The Role of Protected Areas in Sustaining Society*. Washington, D.C.: Smithsonian Institution Press.

MARR, J. W., 1967. Ecosystems of the east slope of the Front Range in Colorado. *University of Colorado Studies, Series in Biology, 8.*

MARTIN, T. E., 1981. Species-area slopes and coefficients: a caution on their interpretation. *American Naturalist, 118:* 823–837.

MERRIAM, C. H., 1890. Results of a biological survey of the San Francisco Mountain region and Desert of the Little Colorado in Arizona, I. General results...with special reference to the distribution of species. *North American Fauna, 3:* 5–34.

MILLER, R. I. & HARRIS, L. D., 1977. Isolation and extirpation in wildlife reserves. *Biological Conservation, 12:* 311–315.

MORGAN, G. S. & WOODS, C. A., 1986. Extinction and the zoogeography of West Indian land mammals. *Biological Journal of the Linnean Society, 28:* 167–203.

MORRISON, D. F., 1967. *Multivariate Statistical Methods*. New York: McGraw-Hill.

NETER, J. & WASSERMAN, W., 1974. *Applied Linear Statistical Models: Regression, Analysis of Variance and Experimental Designs*. Homewood: Richard D. Irwin, Inc.

NEWMARK, W. D., 1986. *Mammalian richness, colonization, and extinction in western North American national parks*. Unpublished Ph.D. dissertation, University of Michigan, Ann Arbor, Michigan.

PATTERSON, B. D., 1980. Montane mammalian biogeography in New Mexico. *Southwestern Naturalist, 25:* 33–40.

PATTERSON, B. D., 1984. Mammalian extinctions and biogeography in the southern Rocky Mountains. In M. H. Nitecki (Ed.), *Extinctions:* 247–293. Chicago: University of Chicago Press.

PATTERSON, B. D. & ATMAR, W., 1986. Nested subsets and the structure of insular mammalian faunas and archipelagos. *Biological Journal of the Linnean Society, 28:* 65–82.

POWER, D. M., 1972. Numbers of bird species on the California Islands. *Evolution, 26:* 451–463.

POWER, D. M., 1976. Avifauna richness of the California Channel Islands. *Condor, 78:* 394–398.

PRESTON, F. W., 1960. Time and space and the variation of species. *Ecology, 41:* 611–627.

PRESTON, F. W., 1962. The canonical distribution of commonness and rarity. *Ecology, 43:* 185–215, 410–432.

REED, T. M., 1983. The role of species-area relationships in reserve choice: a British example. *Biological Conservation, 25:* 263–271.

REY, J. R., 1984. Experimental tests of island biogeography theory. In D. R. Strong, D. S. Simberloff, L. G. Abele & A. B. Thistle (Eds), *Ecological Communities: Conceptual Issues and the Evidence:* 101–112. Princeton: Princeton University Press.

RICKLEFS, R. E., 1979. *Ecology*, 2nd edition. New York: Chiron Press.

ROTENBERRY, J. T. & WIENS, J. A., 1980. Habitat structure, patchiness, and avian communities in North American steppe vegetation: a multivariate analysis. *Ecology, 61:* 1228–1250.

SCHOENER, T. W., 1983. Rate of species turnover decreases from lower to higher organisms: a review of the data. *Oikos, 41:* 372–377.

SHAFFER, M. L. & SAMSON, F. B., 1985. Populations size and extinction: a note on determining critical population sizes. *American Naturalist, 125:* 144–152.

SIMBERLOFF, D. S., 1976. Experimental zoogeography of islands: effects of island size. *Ecology, 57:* 629–642.

SIMBERLOFF, D. S., 1978. Colonization of islands by insects: immigration, extinction, and diversity. *Symposia, Royal Entomological Society of London, 9:* 139–153.

SIMBERLOFF, D. S. & ABELE, L. G., 1976. Island biogeography theory and conservation practice. *Science, 191:* 285–286.

SIMBERLOFF, D. S. & ABELE, L. G., 1982. Refuge design and island biogeographic theory: effects of fragmentation. *American Naturalist, 120:* 41–50.

SOULÉ, M. E. & SIMBERLOFF, D. S., 1986. What do genetics and ecology tell us about the design of nature reserves? *Biological Conservation, 35:* 19–40.

SIMPSON, G. G., 1964. Species density of North American Recent mammals. *Systematic Zoology, 13:* 57–73.

SUGIHARA, G., 1981. $S = CA^Z$, $Z = 1/4$: A reply to Connor and McCoy. *American Naturalist, 117:* 790–793.

TERBORGH, J., 1971. Distribution on environmental gradients: theory and a preliminary interpretation of distributional patterns in the avifauna of the Cordillera Vilacamba, Peru. *Ecology, 52:* 23–40.

WALLACE, A. R., 1878. *Tropical Nature and Other Essays*. New York: Macmillan.

WESTERN, D. & SSEMAKULA, J., 1981. The future of the savannah ecosystems: ecological islands or faunal enclaves? *African Journal of Ecology, 19:* 7–19.

WHITTAKER, R. H., 1960. Vegetation of the Siskiyou Mountains, Oregon and California. *Ecological Monographs, 30:* 279–338.

WHITTAKER, R. H., LEVIN, S. A. & ROOT, R. B., 1973. Niche, habitat, and ecotope. *American Naturalist, 107:* 321–338.

WILCOX, B. A. & MURPHY, D. D., 1985. Conservation strategy: the effects of fragmentation on extinction. *American Naturalist, 125:* 879–887.

WILLIAMS, C. B., 1943. Area and number of species. *Nature, 152:* 264–267.

*Biological Journal of the Linnean Society* (1986), *28:* 99–125. With 9 figures

# Comparative biogeography of mammals on islands

TIMOTHY E. LAWLOR

*Department of Biological Sciences, Humboldt State University, Arcata, California 95521, U.S.A.*

*Accepted for publication 14 February 1986*

Insular faunas of terrestrial mammals and bats are examined on a worldwide basis to test the adequacy of equilibrium and historical legacy models as explanations for species–area relationships. Species numbers of bats on islands conform to predictions from equilibrium theory, whereby recurrent immigrations and extinctions influence species richness. By contrast, species numbers of terrestrial mammals on islands result from a historical legacy of very low immigration rates on oceanic islands (the faunas are colonization-limited) and by the fragmentation of once contiguous continental faunas to form relictual populations, which subsequently undergo extinctions, on landbridge islands (the faunas are extinction-limited). This explanation is supported by several lines of evidence: (1) $z$ values (slopes of species–area curves) are lower for non-volant mammals on oceanic islands than for those on landbridge islands, but are the opposite for bats; (2) $z$ values for non-volant mammals are lower than those for bats on oceanic islands, but are higher than those for bats on landbridge islands; and (3) landbridge island faunas are attenuated mainland faunas, whereas those on oceanic islands are ecologically incomplete. No support is found for alternative hypotheses to explain low species–area slopes for terrestrial mammals on oceanic islands.

KEY WORDS:—Equilibrium theory – historical legacy model – mammals – island biogeography – $z$ values.

CONTENTS

## INTRODUCTION

Worldwide occurrences of mammals on islands attest to the fact that non-volant mammals occur infrequently and exhibit much greater endemism on well-isolated islands than do other terrestrial vertebrates (for example, lizards) and volant forms (birds, bats) (Brown & Gibson, 1983). For example, non-volant mammals are absent or rare on New Zealand, the Greater and Lesser Antilles and many other oceanic island systems. Many islands, such as

99

Madagascar and Sulawesi, are noteworthy for their peculiar indigenous mammal faunas. These facts suggest either that non-volant mammals are poor overwater dispersers and that colonization events are rare, that they have very poor success rates on oceanic islands which they do reach, or both. That terrestrial mammals exhibit high degrees of endemism on oceanic islands which they do successfully invade is *prima facie* evidence of their poor vagility. The question thus arises as to whether equilibrium theory, depending as it does on recurrent colonization and extinction, can adequately explain distributions of terrestrial mammals in insular settings.

Equilibrium theory (MacArthur & Wilson, 1963, 1967) predicts that species numbers on islands are due to balances between rates of colonization and extinction. Different equilibria can be expected on islands of different sizes and relative isolation. Large islands should have relatively large numbers of species because rates of extinction are low compared to those of small islands. Islands near the mainland should also have relatively large numbers of species because rates of colonization are higher than on isolated distant islands. Frequent turnovers of species composition are expected, but species numbers should remain more or less constant. Slopes of species–area curves should be steeper for distant (oceanic) island faunas ($z$ values should be higher) than those for near (landbridge) island faunas in the same archipelago because of the combined effects of extinction and low colonization rates on well-isolated islands and because the impact of the two is greater on small islands (see slopes depicted in Fig. 1).

However, differences in species numbers, species composition and degree of endemicity of terrestrial mammals on oceanic and landbridge islands suggest that non-equilibrial processes also may be influential in determining species numbers. Two types of non-equilibrial situations are depicted by the species–area curves in Fig. 2. One has been described by Brown (1971, 1978; see also Patterson, 1980) for relictual non-volant mammals occupying montane

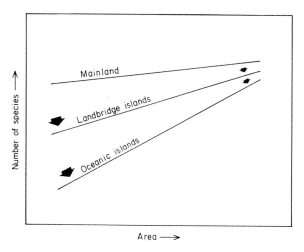

Figure 1. Equilibrial effects of isolation and differing rates of colonization and extinction on species–area curves for non-volant mammals occurring on islands in a hypothetical archipelago. Arrows identify the relative impact of extinctions on slopes of species–area curves for landbridge and oceanic islands.

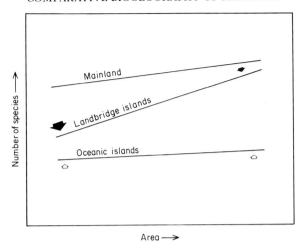

Figure 2. Non-equilibrial effects of different colonization histories and extinction on species–area curves for non-volant mammals occurring on islands in a hypothetical archipelago. Arrows identify the relative impact of extinction (filled) and immigration (open) on the slope of species–area curves for landbridge and oceanic islands.

islands in the Great Basin of western North America. Mammals occur as relicts in insular habitats created by fragmentation of once extensive boreal forests since the Pleistocene. On landbridge islands like these, species numbers are attained from above via relaxation of formerly widespread continental faunas (Diamond, 1972). Such faunas are said to be 'supersaturated' when initially formed. With time, species numbers dwindle because the islands are too small to support the original continental faunas inhabiting them and extinction rates are initially high. But because extinction rates are higher on small than on large islands, disproportionately fewer species survive on small islands, and the species–area curve gradually steepens (high $z$ values are attained; see slope for landbridge islands, Fig. 2). Up to this point the relaxation of such faunas resembles that of typical landbridge islands undergoing gradual reduction in species numbers before reaching a new equilibrium value. However, for organisms that also have poor dispersal capabilities, island invasions may effectively be prevented (except over long geologic time spans). The result is a non-equilibrial condition in which the species–area relationship is determined solely by extinctions of species originally present before island separation occurred, and ultimately the species–area curve may become quite steep.

By contrast, species numbers of non-volant mammals on oceanic islands are attained from below via waif (overwater) dispersal. These 'undersaturated' islands (oceanic islands, Fig. 2) are depauperate but have relatively *flat* species–area curves ($z$ values are low) because colonization events are very rare. Undersaturation is most common on large oceanic islands, probably because as distances from mainland source areas increase, the advantage of large islands over small ones effectively disappears. Large remote islands simply never attain the species richness predicted for them on the basis of their size. This explanation evidently accounts for the depauperate nature of freshwater fish faunas in North American lakes—land barriers inhibit migration to these insular habitats (lakes and ponds) and few colonizations occur (Barbour &

Brown, 1974). Increases in species richness of poor dispersers on large remote islands (or lakes) are attained chiefly by speciation over long periods, an exceedingly slow process. This non-equilibrial condition is established almost entirely by (low) rates of colonization. Species numbers on oceanic islands are therefore colonization-limited.

Recently I described what appeared to be non-equilibrial species–area relationships for non-volant mammal faunas on oceanic and landbridge islands in the Gulf of California, Mexico (Lawlor, 1983). Here I examine distributions of insular terrestrial mammals and bats on a worldwide basis to test the generality of these patterns. If non-equilibrial conditions determine species–area relationships of non-volant mammals on islands and if equilibrial conditions are responsible for those of volant ones, four predictions should be borne out, as follows.

(1) For any set of islands with a common source area, the $z$ value for non-volant mammals should be lower on oceanic islands than on landbridge islands ($z_o < z_{lb}$). The underlying basis for this prediction is simply that terrestrial mammals are poor overwater dispersers so that greater isolation should greatly depress rates of colonization, and hence species numbers, on oceanic islands. Non-volant mammals should be more poorly represented on oceanic islands of varying sizes than on equivalently sized landbridge islands.

(2) For any set of islands with a common source fauna, the $z$ value for volant mammals should be higher on oceanic islands than on landbridge islands ($z_o > z_{lb}$). Because bats are more vagile than terrestrial mammals, their insular distributions should be more strongly influenced by ongoing processes of colonization and extinction. Consequently, rates of extinction should exceed rates of immigration to a greater degree on small oceanic islands than on small landbridge islands where local extinctions are partly offset by recurrent immigration, and the species–area curve should be steeper ($z$ values should be higher) for bats on oceanic islands. As Lomolino (1984) noted, isolation should be an important determinant of species numbers for more vagile mammals only on very distant islands. Indeed, I expect species–area relationships of bats to resemble those of birds, which of course formed the initial basis for equilibrium theory (MacArthur & Wilson, 1963, 1967).

(3) For any set of oceanic islands with a common source area, the $z$ value for non-volant mammals should be lower than that for volant ones (bats) ($z_{nv} < z_v$). The reasons for this proposal stem from arguments for the preceeding two predictions.

(4) For any set of landbridge islands, the $z$ value for non-volant mammals should be higher than that for volant ones ($z_{nv} > z_v$). This prediction also follows from the preceeding arguments. Because species numbers of non-volant mammals on landbridge islands are relaxed from former higher levels because of extinctions (especially on small islands), the species–area curve should steepen (obtain a higher $z$ value) with time. However, bats are much more vagile than terrestrial mammals; consequently, frequent colonizations of landbridge islands by bats should more readily offset extinctions and the species–area curve for bats should have a gentle slope.

The first and third predictions are not expected outcomes of equilibrium theory, but are expected if species occurrences of non-volant mammals on islands are due to a historical legacy of exceedingly low colonization rates and high extinction rates on islands. The second and fourth predictions are compatible with either equilibrial or non-equilibrial processes.

## MATERIALS AND METHODS

The species–area relationship is usually described by the equation $S = CA^z$, where $S$ is species number, $A$ is island area, $C$ is the intercept (all in logarithms), and $z$ is the slope of the line defined by the linear transposition of the equation (Preston, 1962; MacArthur & Wilson, 1963, 1967). Here I emphasize comparative values of $z$ in order to evaluate predicted differences in species–area curves. Unless otherwise noted, only species–area relationships that yielded significant $z$ values were used in analyses that follow.

Landbridge islands were defined as those that had a mainland connection at the end of the Pleistocene and that subsequently became isolated owing to eustatic sea-level changes. An island separated from the mainland by a water depth of 120 m or less was considered landbridge. Oceanic islands were defined as those having had no certain connection in the past to (or at least a very long separation from) a mainland source area. Those islands separated from a source area by water depths exceeding 120 m were classified as oceanic.

Species numbers were obtained from published sources for all island systems for which adequate data were available. Measures for island areas and distances of islands from mainland source regions were obtained from published sources or were taken from maps produced by the Defense Agency Mapping Service.

Use of species–area curves and $z$ values for testing equilibrium theory has definite limitations (Haas, 1975; Connor & McCoy, 1979; Gilbert, 1980; Wright, 1981). For example, it is virtually impossible to distinguish equilibrial and non-equilibrial conditions based upon a single curve, and there is some question as to whether $z$ values by themselves have much biological meaning. Consequently, only comparative analyses of insular mammal faunas having the same source pool of species are attempted here. Further, species–area curves for sets of islands in different parts of the world will differ in varying degrees according to source pool size, taxonomic and ecologic composition of the source pool, ages of islands, island locations relative to the mainland and differences in environmental diversity among islands. In addition, intertaxa comparisons of $z$ values may lead to spurious inferences about colonization histories because different taxa have dissimilar equilibrium values and they approach these values at different rates (Wright, 1981). Finally, $z$ values obtained by use of simple linear regressions may be misleading (Wright, 1981). These difficulties are avoided or minimized in this study because, except where noted, differences in species–area curves for insular faunas having the same source pool are compared. Still, certain limitations remain (see Martin, 1981), and these considerations should be kept in mind.

Several other potential sources of error exist in the data sets. Unfortunately, literature sources represent surveys of all known historical records of mammals on the islands. Extended census periods probably artificially inflate species numbers because some turnover has doubtless occurred on the islands. Another source of error stems from inadequacy of sampling. For example, mammalian faunas on islands in Malaysia and off New Guinea are more poorly known than most of the other island sets. Although these problems should not be ignored, neither is serious enough to alter overall patterns of species–area relationships.

I ignored extinct species unless their extirpation occurred within historical time. Clearly this is a somewhat arbitrary determination, but it is necessary in order to assure consistency of data sets used for comparative purposes. Inclusion of fossil forms tends to inflate species numbers on large islands because fossil localities are biased in favour of those islands. Also, inferences based on differences among sets of islands could be misleading if extinct species are recorded for some islands but not for others. More important, inclusion of fossil data expands the time period over which species numbers are tallied. This may result in spuriously high numbers of species, especially if turnover is common at all on islands. However, I want to emphasize that, by omitting fossil forms, I was not attempting to ignore extinction as an important factor influencing species occurrences; I simply wanted to remove it as a potential source of error when calculating current species numbers and making comparisons among islands. Omission of fossil records from some archipelagos results in species numbers and species–area curves that are considerably different than ones previously published (e.g. Bass Strait islands (Hope, 1973), West Indies

Table 1. Summary of biogeographic measures for non-volant (and volant) mammals from landbridge and oceanic islands used in this study. All $z$ values are significant ($P < 0.05$). For sources of data, see Appendix

| Island | $N$ | $z$ value | Area (km²) | Average distance (km) | |
|---|---|---|---|---|---|
| | | | | To mainland | To mainland or island* |
| Landbridge | | | | | |
| British Columbia | 75 | 0.211 | 706.1 | 86.0 | 4.1 |
| Baja California | 20 | 0.284 | 128.3 | 6.1 | 4.8 |
| Panama | 13 | 0.333 | 78.2 | 18.2 | 10.9 |
| British Isles | 64 | 0.227 | 5109.6 | 609.3 | 14.9 |
| British Channel Islands | 5 | 0.289 | 38.8 | 30.6 | 20.3 |
| Japan | 15 | 0.347 | 28810.8 | 278.5 | 41.3 |
| | (7) | (0.231) | (60931.7) | (168.0) | (42.9) |
| Sunda Shelf | 27 | 0.252 | 50438.0 | 180.8 | 70.4 |
| Northern Australia | 11 | 0.305 | 1071.8 | 17.5 | 8.2 |
| Kimberley Islands | 18 | 0.369 | 37.4 | 9.4 | 6.6 |
| Western Australia | 11 | 0.316 | 100.0 | 38.2 | 38.2 |
| Southern Australia | 17 | 0.295 | 306.8 | 25.5 | 19.4 |
| Bass Strait Islands | 21 | 0.345 | 3561.6 | 167.8 | 53.8 |
| Oceanic | | | | | |
| California Channel Is. | 12 | 0.168 | 75.5 | 45.5 | 24.3 |
| Baja California | 14 | 0.100 | 88.0 | 20.5 | 11.5 |
| West Indies | 9 | 0.122 | 22396.2 | 352.8 | 197.8 |
| | (21) | (0.210) | (10204.8) | (570.0) | (144.9) |
| Philippines | 12 | 0.189† | 15973.0 | 793.8 | 97.6 |
| Western New Guinea | 17 | 0.174 | 3044.1 | 264.7 | 83.9 |
| | (23) | (0.320) | (2494.0) | (260.0) | (78.2) |
| Eastern New Guinea | 27 | 0.135 | 2830.2 | 316.0 | 117.8 |
| | (47) | (0.227) | (1819.8) | (530.0) | (96.2) |

*Minimum distance to mainland or nearest larger island.

†This value is 0.204 when islands in the Palawan chain (Palawan, Busuanga, Balabac, Culion) are excluded. Heaney (1986) considers them to be landbridge islands.

(Wright, 1981; Lomolino, 1984); see Table 1 and Appendix). I also ignored introduced and commensal species and marine mammals. Included among commensal species were *Suncus murinus*, *Rattus rattus*, *R. norvegicus*, *R. exulans*, and *Mus musculus*. Inclusion of commensal species especially inflates species numbers on small islands, because the addition of one or two of these widespread species to island faunas results in a much greater increase in the logarithms of small numbers of species than large ones. Also, river otters (*Lutra canadensis*) and mink (*Mustela vison*) were omitted from consideration because, although they are not strictly marine, they commonly inhabit coastal waters.

On landbridge islands in the Lesser Antilles, Koopman (1958) detected marked differences in species numbers of bats that were independent of island area; the differences were attributed to disparities in the ecological diversity of the islands he surveyed. I avoided this problem in part by trying to ensure that all island combinations had the same continental source area and, where possible, by evaluating the ecological character of each island.

Seven unusual sets of islands were omitted from this study, some of which are in inland lakes, as follows: Basswood Lake, Minnesota (Beer, Lukens & Olson, 1954); Great Salt Lake, Utah (Marshall, 1940; Bowers, 1982); Lake Michigan (Hatt *et al.*, 1948); Thousand Islands, St. Lawrence River (Lomolino, 1982); coastal Maine (Crowell, 1986); and islands south of Funen, Denmark (Ursin, 1950). All of these islands have had recent and periodic connections to mainland areas owing to reduced water levels (Great Salt Lake), man-made connections (Maine and Denmark islands), or seasonal ice formation (the remaining islands). Consequently, I am suspicious of the accuracy of their species–area relationships, at least in the present context, for they do not fit the criteria I established for identifying landbridge and oceanic islands. That movements are common between islands of this sort was confirmed by Beer *et al.* (1954), Crowell (1986), and Lomolino (1986) for islands they investigated.

## RESULTS

A summary of significant $z$ values and other measures for all sets of islands is presented in Table 1. Raw data for individual sets of islands are provided in the Appendix. Two sets of islands reported in other studies (e.g. Lomolino, 1984) proved to have non-significant $z$ values and are not included: Virginia Barrier Islands (Dueser *et al.*, 1979); and islands off Venezuela (Koopman, 1958).

*Prediction 1:* Figure 3 summarizes ranges of $z$ values for non-volant mammals on landbridge and oceanic islands. There is no overlap of $z$ values for terrestrial mammals on 12 landbridge and six oceanic islands. A Mann–Whitney $U$ test of the null hypothesis that these values do not differ must be rejected ($P < 0.001$). Values of $z$ for terrestrial mammals on oceanic islands are invariably lower than those for faunas on landbridge islands.

This relationship was further investigated by examining non-volant mammals on landbridge and oceanic islands occurring in the same archipelago. Data are available from three sets of islands: Baja California, Malaysia (including the Philippines) and the West Indies (Fig. 4). In each comparison, there are more non-volant mammals on landbridge than on oceanic islands and, as expected, the slope of the species–area curve for oceanic islands is flatter than that for landbridge islands. Although $z$ values do not differ significantly ($P > 0.05$) for

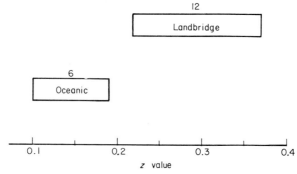

Figure 3. Bar graph summarizing the range of $z$ values for non-volant mammal faunas occurring on landbridge and oceanic islands. Only significant $z$ values ($P < 0.05$) are included (see Table 1). The number of island sets is indicated above each bar.

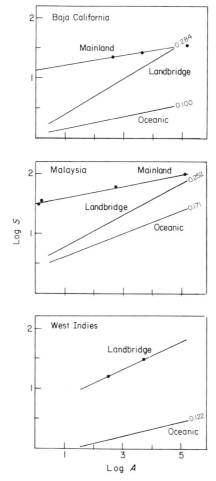

Figure 4. Species–area curves for non-volant mammal faunas occurring on three archipelagos containing both landbridge and oceanic islands. Numbers refer to $z$ values. Mainland species numbers were obtained from Heaney (1984) for Malaysia and from Hall (1981) and Woloszyn & Woloszyn (1984) for Baja California. Landbridge islands depicted in the graph for the West Indies are Trinidad and Tobago; species numbers are taken from Morgan & Woods (1986).

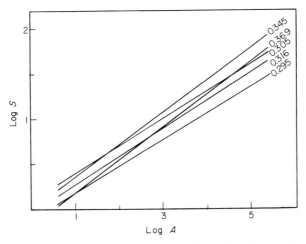

Figure 5. Suite of species–area curves for five sets of landbridge islands off the continent of Australia. Numbers refer to $z$ values.

any pair of slopes, the difference between slopes is in the predicted direction in each of the three cases. The West Indies comparison is less than convincing, however, because there are only two landbridge islands (Trinidad and Tobago) containing habitats comparable to the oceanic West Indies.

Values of $z$ for oceanic islands of the West Indies and the Philippines are noteworthy for two reasons. Because these two sets of islands are older and more isolated than oceanic islands off Baja California (Table 1), I expect them to have higher $z$ values. In both cases, *in situ* speciation, especially on large islands, has evidently caused the species–area slope to steepen. Actually, the species–area relation for non-volant mammals on islands in the West Indies is artificially steep because 11 well-surveyed islands that support no species (see Appendix) had to be excluded from the analysis (the logarithm of zero is undefined).

Figure 5 shows a suite of species–area curves for terrestrial mammals on

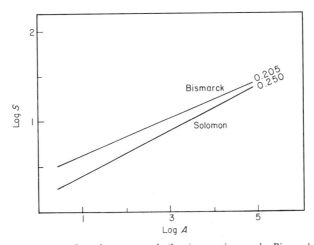

Figure 6. Species–area curves for volant mammals (bats) occurring on the Bismarck and Solomon islands off eastern New Guinea. Numbers refer to $z$ values.

landbridge islands off the continent of Australia. Of interest is the similarity of slopes and intercepts for all five sets of islands.

*Prediction 2:* Bat faunas from islands are poorly known. Figure 6 depicts a single available comparison between volant mammals, in this case from islands off eastern New Guinea. The data are for oceanic islands only, but these are separable into near islands (Bismarck Archipelago) and distant islands (Solomon Islands). Species numbers are lower on the Solomon Islands and, although the difference in slopes is slight, $z$ values for the two island faunas differ in the predicted fashion: the Solomon Island bats exhibit the higher value.

*Prediction 3:* Three intra-archipelago comparisons were made to test the prediction that $z$ values of non-volant mammals should be less than those of volant ones on oceanic islands: the West Indies and islands off eastern and western New Guinea (Fig. 7). The prediction is confirmed in all three examples. Terrestrial mammals exhibit a lower $z$ value than bats. This relationship is further supported by the fact that $z$ values for terrestrial mammals are also

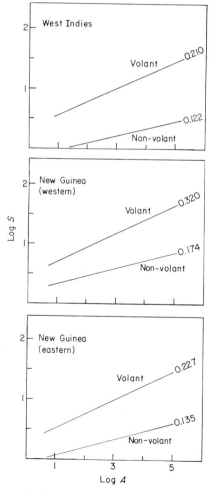

Figure 7. Species–area curves for three sets of oceanic islands containing both volant and non-volant mammals. Numbers refer to $z$ values.

lower than those for birds, which are biogeographic equivalents of bats, on oceanic islands in the West Indies and off Baja California (Wright, 1981; Cody, 1983).

*Prediction 4:* The single comparison (Japan; Fig. 8) is consistent with the prediction that non-volant mammals should have higher $z$ values than volant ones on landbridge islands. This relationship is again supported by comparisons of terrestrial mammals and birds on four sets of landbridge islands for which data are available (Bass Strait, British Channel Islands, British Isles and Baja California; Wright, 1981; Cody, 1983).

From predictions 1–4, there are 13 intra-archipelago comparisons in which one $z$ value is expected to be greater than another (comparisons of non-volant mammals and birds are included). The predictions are vindicated in all cases, which would occur by chance with a probability of less than 0.001 (sign test).

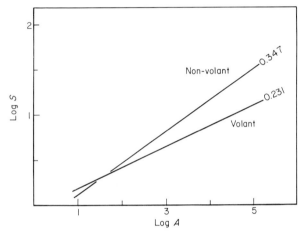

Figure 8. Species–area curves for a set of landbridge islands (Japan) containing both volant and non-volant mammals. Numbers refer to $z$ values.

In order to test directly the influence of isolation on $z$ values, I conducted correlation analyses of species numbers of non-volant mammals and distance of islands from source areas. The results are mixed. There is a slightly negative but non-significant relationship $(P > 0.05)$ between $z$ values and mean island distances to potential mainland source areas for combined sets of islands (for values used, see Table 1). However, there is a significant negative correlation of $z$ values with mean distance between island and mainland or nearest larger island. Of course, the negative function is expected because $z$ values for non-volant mammal faunas on oceanic islands (which are more isolated on average than landbridge islands) are lower than those on landbridge islands (see Table 1). No significant relationships were revealed in the same two analyses for volant mammal faunas, but sample sizes are small. When landbridge and oceanic islands are considered separately, there is a non-significant relationship between $z$ values and measures of isolation.

There is not an obvious relationship between species numbers and island isolation for individual sets of islands. Only four of 18 (two of 12 landbridge; two of six oceanic) non-volant and one of four (no landbridge; one of three oceanic) volant faunas exhibit significant negative correlations $(P<0.05)$ of species numbers and island–mainland distances. Only one non-volant fauna shows such a relationship when distance is measured as the minimum distance between an island and the mainland or nearby large island. However, a significant positive relationship $(P<0.05)$ between species numbers and species–area residuals was found in 14 of 18 non-volant and two of four volant faunas. Species–area residuals represent the portion of variation in species numbers left unexplained after the effect of area has been removed (Lomolino, 1982; Heaney, 1984).

## DISCUSSION

The results are consistent with the hypothesis that distributions of non-volant mammals on islands are a historic consequence of few colonization events on isolated oceanic islands and considerable extinction of relict populations on landbridge islands. Species numbers on oceanic islands are low largely because colonization events via overwater dispersal are very rare; large oceanic islands simply never attain the species numbers expected on the basis of their size, and $z$ values are low. On the other hand, because non-volant mammal faunas on landbridge islands are remnants of formerly contiguous continental faunas, they are characterized by high $z$ values, which are attributable to disproportionately higher rates of extinction of species on small islands than on large ones and to the absence of new colonizers to offset the losses. These conclusions are further supported by the facts that: (1) bats (and birds) exhibit $z$ values that are higher on oceanic islands and lower on landbridge islands than those for non-volant mammals; and (2) water barriers have had a pronounced inhibitory effect on immigrations of terrestrial mammals, but not bats, to oceanic islands.

By contrast, bats, presumably because they are more vagile, seem strongly influenced by frequent and ongoing episodes of colonization and extinction. Their species–area relationships are consistent with predictions of equilibrium theory: species–area slopes are higher on oceanic islands than they are on landbridge islands.

Additional evidence supporting a historical-legacy hypothesis for terrestrial mammal distributions comes from analyses of compositional differences of insular mammal faunas (Simpson, 1956; Lawlor, 1983, in prep.; Heaney, 1986). Oceanic islands (e.g. those in the Philippines, West Indies and off Baja California) are composed of depauperate faunas. They contain mostly rodents; insectivores, lagomorphs, carnivores and large herbivores (primates, artiodactyls) vary from few to none. Endemic terrestrial species are also much more common on oceanic islands than on landbridge islands (Simpson, 1956; Lawlor, 1983; Heaney, 1986). Faunas on landbridge islands, by contrast, comprise nested subsets of groups also present in source areas (Patterson & Atmar, 1986). In short, faunas on landbridge islands are attenuated mainland faunas, whereas those on oceanic islands are ecologically incomplete. These compositional differences are explicable only in terms of the greatly reduced capacity of terrestrial mammals other than rodents to successfully invade and persist on distant, well-isolated islands. Extinctions cannot explain the relative absence of these mammals on oceanic islands that have areas and complexities similar to nearby species-rich landbridge islands and that otherwise have relatively diverse rodent and bat faunas.

An explanation of the distribution of non-volant mammals based on colonization histories applies to archipelagos in which immigration potential is high and isolation effects are low as well as it does to ones in which immigration potential is low and isolation effects are high. For example, predicted differences between $z$ values characterize non-volant faunas on the near-shore archipelagos off Baja California as well as those on the distant islands of Malaysia (the Philippines and Sunda Shelf islands).

Lomolino (1984) reported that species–area relationships for terrestrial mammal faunas on islands were in accord with predictions of equilibrium theory. He found that $z$ values for the faunas he examined, most of which were also investigated in the present study, were not significantly different from 0.26, the $z$ value established by Preston (1962) and MacArthur & Wilson (1967) as typical of insular faunas based upon the canonical lognormal distribution of species abundances on islands of different sizes. However, Lomolino's (1984) analysis did not distinguish landbridge and oceanic islands; instead, all islands were considered together as 'oceanic'. Consequently, systematic effects of different island histories and colonizing abilities on the mammal faunas of these two types of islands were obscured.

Wright (1981) was unable to detect any obvious or consistent effects of colonization histories on species–area relationships of several vertebrate groups for 10 sets of islands he examined. Unfortunately, his comparisons were limited in number because of a paucity of data for oceanic island systems.

The absence of consistent overall patterns in analyses of species–isolation relationships may be explained in two ways. The systematic effects of different colonization histories of landbridge and oceanic islands may mask any potential influence of isolation on species numbers. Although this interpretation is consistent with the hypothesis proposed herein, it may be spurious. Distance between islands and source areas conceivably can be determined in at least three different ways: (1) as the shortest distance between a given island and the mainland; (2) as the distance between a given island and the mainland or nearby large island, whichever is least; and (3), for all islands in a set of islands that are oceanic with respect to the source area but landbridge with respect to one another, as the distance between the island located nearest the mainland and the mainland. Each of these measures has been used at one time or another (e.g. see Brown, 1971, 1978; Diamond, 1972; Cody, 1983; Lawlor, 1983; Heaney, 1984; Lomolino, 1984). Cogent arguments can be put forth to justify each one (and perhaps others as well), yet the resulting distance values are very different. The particular choice of measure might depend, for example, on the orientation of the archipelago to the source area (that is, whether the islands are more or less equidistant from, or arranged as stepping-stones at right-angles to, the mainland).

A simple example is instructive. For the two sets of islands in Fig. 9, mean distances are 10 and 28 km for near and far islands, respectively, when calculated according to the first method described above. However, when calculated according to the second method, mean distances are identical (10 km). Obvious differences in relative isolation are obscured by the second method; on the other hand, an unrealistic measure of isolation is introduced by the first method because, after all, insular faunas ultimately owe their origins to invasions from mainland source populations.

Near islands

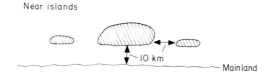

Far islands

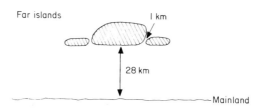

Figure 9. Two sets of three islands arranged in different positions and with different degrees of isolation relative to one another and to the mainland. Average minimum distances to the mainland are 10 and 28 km for near and far islands, respectively, whereas average minimum distances to the mainland or nearby larger islands are identical (10 km) for the two sets of islands. For discussion, see text.

Use of species–area residuals is also problematical. Other influences on species numbers besides distance may also contribute to residual variation. Nevertheless, the fact that species numbers correlate positively with species–area residuals for the majority of insular mammal faunas suggests that much of the variation in species numbers remains to be explained.

The point I am trying to make is that I am not sure any important conclusions can be drawn from analyses of species numbers and measures of isolation, despite having relied on them myself in the recent past (Lawlor, 1983). Generally, there is a lack of consistent negative correlations between species numbers and distance for island systems examined in this study and elsewhere (Koopman, 1958; Brown, 1971, 1978; Dueser & Brown, 1980; Lawlor, 1983; Heaney, 1984; but see Lomolino, 1982). And, although Lomolino (1984) reported a significant negative relationship between $z$ values and mean island distances for a large number of insular mammal faunas, the correlation disappears when $z$ values are calculated according to the criteria used in the present study. These analyses suggest that, if there is an impact of isolation that transcends distinctions between types of islands, we have not yet designed an appropriate or reliable way to measure it.

Impacts of isolation on species occurrences are further complicated by speciation occurring on well-isolated islands over time. The positive correlation between species numbers of non-volant mammals and distance on oceanic islands is explained, in large part, by the large number of endemic species and genera (even families) on the Philippines and West Indies. These archipelagos are, simultaneously, two of the most isolated sets of islands examined and among the oldest sets of islands geologically. Consequently, the association of species numbers and island isolation is more likely attributable to differences in rates of species formation—high on distant, old islands and low on near-shore, young islands—than it is to differential rates of colonization and extinction.

Three alternative hypotheses are available to also explain the low $z$ values for non-volant mammal faunas on oceanic islands. First, extinction rates ("relaxation times"; Diamond, 1972) may differ between oceanic and landbridge island faunas. Low extinction rates on oceanic islands would yield a flat species–area curve. However, I know of no reason to expect that oceanic islands should exhibit reduced extinction rates compared to landbridge islands, and there is evidence that this is not the case. The most depauperate oceanic island faunas are on large islands, not small ones (see Fig. 4), especially when compared to faunas on landbridge islands; that is, the species–area curve for oceanic island faunas is most depressed at its upper end. Species numbers of terrestrial mammal faunas on small oceanic and landbridge islands are much more similar. The opposite relationship would be the expected one. This contradictory evidence leads me to reject this hypothesis.

Secondly, the species-abundance distributions underlying species–area relationships on oceanic islands may be more skewed than lognormal (Sugihara, 1981). Although there are differences among island faunas with regard to the precise form of the species–area relationship, I know of no examples of a systematic difference between oceanic and landbridge islands with respect to distribution of species abundances. Still, this remains a possibility.

Thirdly, species may not experience islands as isolated universes. Diamond & Mayr (1976) and Schoener (1974) showed that high intra-archipelago immigration rates of bird species may yield species–area curves with low slopes. Extensive evidence weighs against this hypothesis for explaining mammal species occurrences. Non-volant mammals do not experience islands in such a fine-grained fashion. Many lines of evidence here (see above) and elsewhere indicate that bodies of water consitute imposing barriers to mainland–island and island–island movements of terrestrial mammals. Moreover, if mammal faunas were to show decreased $z$ values owing to increased colonization rates, I would expect to see evidence of it on the less isolated landbridge islands, but I do not; extinction clearly plays a major role on these islands.

## SUMMARY

Patterns of occurrences of mammals on islands suggest that the ways in which terrestrial mammal faunas are established and maintained on oceanic islands are fundamentally different from those on landbridge islands and that these differences are more pronounced in terrestrial mammals than in bats. Species richness of bats on both types of islands is determined primarily by ongoing equilibrial processes of differential colonization and extinction, whereas species richness of terrestrial mammals is governed by historical influences of exceedingly low invasion rates on oceanic islands (the faunas are colonization-limited), and by the fragmentation of widespread continental populations to form relictual faunas, which subsequently undergo extinctions, on landbridge islands (the faunas are extinction-limited). Several lines of evidence support the hypothesis: (1) $z$ values are lower for non-volant mammals on oceanic islands than for those on landbridge islands, but are just the opposite for bats; (2) $z$ values for non-volant mammals are lower than those for bats on oceanic islands, but are higher than those for bats on landbridge islands; and (3) landbridge island faunas are attenuated mainland faunas, whereas those on oceanic islands are ecologically incomplete. No support is found for alternative hypotheses to explain low species–area slopes for terrestrial mammals on oceanic islands.

## ACKNOWLEDGEMENTS

I am grateful to Larry Heaney and Bruce Patterson for their constructive comments made on an earlier draft of this paper. I have benefitted greatly from discussions of my ideas with them and with others, notably many graduate students at Humboldt State University. Fred Ellison aided immeasurably by helping to gather data on island areas and distances. Statistical analyses were made possible by use of the facilities and expertise available at the Computer Center, Humboldt State University.

## REFERENCES

ANDREWARTHA, H. G. & BARKER, S., 1969. Introduction to a study of the ecology of the Kangaroo Island wallaby, Protemnodon eugenii (Desmerest) within Flinders Chase, Kangaroo Island, South Australia. *Transactions of the Royal Society of South Australia, 93:* 127–133.

ANONYMOUS, 1968. Mammals of the Pellew Islands. *Mimag*, June 1968: 19–21.

BAKER, R. J. & GENOWAYS, H. H., 1978. Zoogeography of Antillean bats. In F. B. Gill (Ed.), *Zoogeography of the Caribbean:* 53–97. Special Publication, Academy of Natural Sciences of Philadelphia, Vol. 13.

BAKER, R. J., GENOWAYS, H. H. & PATTON, J. C., 1978. Bats of Guadeloupe. *Occasional Papers, The Museum, Texas Tech University, 50:* 1–16.

BARBOUR, C. D. & BROWN, J. H., 1974. Fish species diversity in lakes. *American Naturalist, 108:* 473–489.

BEER, J. R., LUKENS, P. & OLSON, D., 1954. Small mammal populations on the islands of Basswood Lake, Minnesota. *Ecology, 35:* 437–445.

BOWERS, M. A., 1982. Insular biogeography of mammals in the Great Salt Lake. *Great Basin Naturalist, 42:* 589–596.

BROWN, J. H., 1971. Mammals on mountaintops: nonequilibrium insular biogeography. *American Naturalist, 105:* 467–478.

BROWN, J. H., 1978. The theory of insular biogeography and the distribution of boreal birds and mammals. *Great Basin Naturalist Memoirs, 2:* 209–227.

BROWN, J. H. & GIBSON, A. C., 1983. *Biogeography.* St. Louis: C. V. Mosby Co.

BURBRIDGE, A. A., 1971. The fauna and flora of the Monte Bello Islands. *Report of the Department of Fisheries and Fauna, Western Australia, 9:* 1–18.

BURBRIDGE, A. A. & McKENZIE, N. L., 1978. The islands of the north-west Kimberley, Western Australia. *Wildlife Research Bulletin Western Australia, 7:* 1–47.

BUTLER, W. H., 1970. A summary of the vertebrate fauna of Barrow Island, Western Australia. *Western Australia Naturalist, 11:* 149–160.

CHASEN, F. N., 1940. A handlist of Malaysian mammals. A systematic list of the mammals of the Malay Peninsula, Sumatra, Borneo and Java, including the adjacent small islands. *Bulletin of the Raffles Museum, Singapore, 15:* 1–209.

CODY, M. L., 1983. The land birds. In T. J. Case & M. L. Cody (Eds), *Island Biogeography in the Sea of Cortéz:* 210–245, 455–473. Berkeley: University of California Press.

CONNOR, E. F. & McCOY, E. D., 1979. The statistics and biology of the species–area relationship. *American Naturalist, 113:* 791–833.

CORBET, G. B., 1971. Provisional distribution maps of British mammals. *Mammal Review, 1:* 95–142.

CORBET, G. B., 1978. *The Mammals of the Palaearctic Region: a Taxonomic Review.* London and Ithaca, New York: British Museum (Natural History) and Cornell University Press.

CORBET, G. B. & SOUTHERN, H. N. (Eds), 1977. *The Handbook of British Mammals*, 2nd edition. Oxford: Blackwell Scientific Publications.

COWAN, I. McT. & GUIGUET, C. J., 1975. *The Mammals of British Columbia.* Victoria: British Columbia Provincial Museum.

CROWELL, K. L., 1986. A comparison of relict versus equilibrium models for insular mammals of the Gulf of Maine. *Biological Journal of the Linnean Society, 28:* 37–64.

DIAMOND, J. M., 1972. Biogeographic kinetics: estimation of relaxation times for avifaunas of southwest Pacific islands. *Proceedings of the National Academy of Sciences of the U.S.A., 69:* 3199–3203.

DIAMOND, J. M. & MAYR, E., 1976. Species-area relation for birds of the Solomon Archipelago. *Proceedings of the National Academy of Sciences of the U.S.A., 73:* 262–266.

DUESER, R. D. & BROWN, W. C., 1980. Ecological correlates of insular species diversity. *Ecology, 61:* 50–56.

DUESER, R. D., BROWN, W. C., HOGUE, G. S., McCAFFREY, C., McCUSKEY, S. A. & HENNESSEY, G. J., 1979. Mammals of the Virginia Barrier Islands. *Journal of Mammalogy, 60:* 425–429.

ELLERMAN, J. R. & MORRISON-SCOTT, T. C. S., 1951. *Checklist of Palaearctic and Indian Mammals.* London: British Museum (Natural History).

FOSTER, J. B., 1965. The evolution of the mammals of the Queen Charlotte Islands, British Columbia. *Occasional Papers, British Columbia Provincial Museum, 14:* 1–130.

GILBERT, F. S., 1980. The equilibrium theory: fact or fiction? *Journal of Biogeography, 7:* 209–235.

GOLDMAN, E. A., 1920. Mammals of Panama. *Smithsonian Miscellaneous Collections, 69*(5): 1–309.

HAAS, P. H., 1975. Some comments on the use of the species–area curve. *American Naturalist, 109:* 371–373.

HALL, E. R., 1981. *The Mammals of North America,* 2nd edition. New York: John Wiley.

HANDLEY Jr, C. O., 1966. Checklist of mammals of Panama. In R. L. Wenzel & V. J. Tipton (Eds), *Ectoparasites of Panama:* 753–795. Chicago: Field Museum of Natural History.

HATT, R. T., VAN TYNE, J., STUART, L. C. & POPE, C. H., 1948. Island life in Lake Michigan. *Bulletin of the Cranbrook Institute of Science, 27:* 1–175.

HEANEY, L. R., 1984. Mammalian species richness on islands on the Sunda Shelf, Southeast Asia. *Oecologia, 61:* 11–17.

HEANEY, L. R., 1986. Biogeography of mammals in SE Asia: estimates of rates of colonization, extinction and speciation. *Biological Journal of the Linnean Society, 28:* 127–165.

HEANEY, L. R. & RABOR, D. S., 1982. Mammals of Dinagat and Siargao islands, Philippines. *Occasional Papers, Museum of Zoology, University of Michigan, 699:* 1–30.

HILL, J. E., 1961. Indo-Australian bats of the genus *Tadarida. Mammalia, 25:* 29–56.

HILL, J. E., 1968. Notes on mammals from the islands of Rennell and Bellona. In *The Natural History of Rennell Island, British Solomon Islands, 5:* 53–60.

HILL, J. E., 1971. Bats from the Solomon Islands. *Journal of Natural History, 5:* 573–581.

HILL, J. E., 1983. Bats (Mammalia: Chiroptera) from Indo-Australia. *Bulletin of the British Museum (Natural History), Zoology, 45:* 103–208.

HONACKI, J. H., KINMAN, K. E. & KOEPPL, J. W. (Eds), 1982. *Mammal Species of the World.* Lawrence, Kansas: Allen Press & Association of Systematic Collections.

HOPE, J. H., 1973. Mammals of the Bass Strait Islands. *Proceedings of the Royal Society of Victoria, 85:* 163–195.

JOHNSON, D. H., 1964. Mammals. In R. L. Sprecht (Ed.), *Records of the American–Australian scientific expedition to Arnhem Land, 4:* 327–415.

JONES Jr, J. K. & BBKER, R. J., 1979. Notes on a collection of bats from Montserrat, Lesser Antilles. *Occasional Papers, The Museum, Texas Tech University, 60:* 1–6.

KELLOGG, R., 1946a. Three new mammals from the Pearle Islands, Panama. *Proceedings of the Biological Society of Washington, 59:* 57–62.

KELLOGG, R., 1946b. Mammals of San Jose Island, Bay of Panama. *Smithsonian Miscellaneous Collections, 106*(7): 1–4.

KELLY, P. A., 1981. Fieldmice and other mammals on islands off Galway and Mayo. *Irish Naturalist Journal, 20:* 352–353.

KOOPMAN, K. F., 1958. Land bridges and ecology in bat distribution on islands off the northern coast of South America. *Evolution, 12:* 429–439.

KOOPMAN, K. F., 1979. Zoogeography of mammals from islands off the northeastern coast of New Guinea. *American Museum Novitates, 2690:* 1–17.

KOOPMAN, K. F., 1982. Results of the Archbold expeditions. No. 109. Bats from eastern Papua and the East Papuan islands. *American Museum Novitates, 2747:* 1–34.

KURODA, N., 1922. Notes on the mammals fauna of Tsushima and Iki islands. *Journal of Mammalogy, 3:* 42–45.

KURODA, N., 1939. Distribution of mammals in the Japanese empire. *Journal of Mammalogy, 20:* 37–50.

LAURIE, E. M. O. & HILL, J. E., 1954. *List of the Land Mammals of New Guinea, Celebes, and Adjacent Islands.* London: British Museum (Natural History).

LAWLOR, T. E., 1983. The mammals. In T. J. Case & M. L. Cody (Eds), *Island Biogeography in the Sea of Cortéz:* 265–289, 482–500. Berkeley: University of California Press.

LOMOLINO, M. V., 1982. Species–area and species–distance relationships of terrestrial mammals in the Thousand Island region. *Oecologia, 54:* 72–75.

LOMOLINO, M. V., 1984. Mammalian island biogeography: effects of area, isolation, and vagility. *Oecologia, 61:* 376–382.

LOMOLINO, M. V., 1986. Mammalian community structure on islands: the importance of immigration, extinction and interactive effects. *Biological Journal of the Linnean Society, 28:* 1–21.

MACARTHUR, R. H. & WILSON, E. O., 1963. An equilibrium theory of insular biogeography. *Evolution, 17:* 373–387.

MACARTHUR, R. H. & WILSON, E. O., 1967. *The Theory of Island Biogeography.* Princeton, New Jersey: Princeton University Press.

MAIN, A. R., 1961. The occurrence of Macropodidae on islands and its climatic and ecological implications. *Transactions of the Royal Society of Western Australia, 44:* 84–89.

116 T. E. LAWLOR

MARSHALL, W. H., 1940. A survey of the mammals of the islands in Great Salt Lake, Utah. *Journal of Mammalogy, 21:* 144–149.
MARTIN, T. E., 1981. Species–area slopes and coefficients: a caution on their interpretation. *American Naturalist, 118:* 823–837.
McCABE, T. T. & COWAN, I. M., 1945. *Peromyscus maniculatus macrorhinus* and the problem of insularity. *Transactions of the Royal Canadian Institute, 25:* 172–215.
McKEAN, J. L., 1972. Notes on some collections of bats (Order Chiroptera) from Papua-New Guinea and Bougainville Island. *Technical Paper, Division of Wildlife Research, C.S.I.R.O., 26:* 1–35.
MEDWAY, L., 1977. *Mammals of Borneo.* Monograph of the Malaysian Branch, Royal Asiatic Society, No. 7.
MORGAN, G. S. & WOODS, C. A., 1986. Extinction and zoogeography of West Indian land mammals. *Biological Journal of the Linnean Society, 28:* 167–203.
OTTENWALDER, J. A. & GENOWAYS, H. H., 1982. Systematic review of the Antillean bats of the *Natalus micropus*-complex (Chiroptera: Natalidae). *Annals of the Carnegie Museum, 51:* 17–38.
PARKER, S. A., 1973. An annotated checklist of the native land mammals of the Northern Territory. *Records of the Australian Museum, 16:* 1–57.
PATTERSON, B. D., 1980. Montane mammalian biogeography in New Mexico. *Southwestern Naturalist, 25:* 33–40.
PATTERSON, B. D. & ATMAR, W., 1986. Nested subsets and the structure of insular mammalian faunas and archipelagos. *Biological Journal of the Linnean Society, 28:* 65–82.
PETERSEN, R. L., 1981. Systematic variation in the *tristus* group of the bent-winged bats of the genus *Miniopterus* (Chiroptera: Vespertilionidae). *Canadian Journal of Zoology, 59:* 828–843.
PHILLIPS, C. J., 1966. A new species of bat of the genus *Melonycteris* from the Solomon Islands. *Journal of Mammalogy, 47:* 23–27.
PHILLIPS, C. J., 1968. Systematics of megachiropteran bats in the Solomon Islands. *University of Kansas Publications, Museum of Natural History, 16:* 777–837.
PRESTON, F. W., 1962. The canonical distribution of commonness and rarity. *Ecology, 43:* 185–215, 410–432.
REDFIELD, J. A., 1976. Distribution, abundance, size, and genetic variation of *Peromyscus maniculatus* on the gulf islands of British Columbia. *Canadian Journal of Zoology, 54:* 463–474.
ROBINSON, A. C. & SMYTHE, M. E. B., 1976. The vertebrate fauna of Nuyts Archipelago, South Australia. *Transactions of the Royal Society of South Australia, 100:* 171–176.
ROOKMAAKER, L. C. & BERGMANS, W., 1981. Taxonomy and geography of *Rousettus amplexicaudatus* (Geoffroy, 1810) with comparative notes on sympatric congeners (Mammalia: Megachiroptera). *Beaufortia, 31:* 1–29.
SCHMITT, L. H., 1975. Genetic evidence for the existence of two separate populations of Rattus fuscipes greyi on Pearson Island, South Australia. *Transactions of the Royal Society of South Australia, 99:* 35–38.
SCHOENER, T. W., 1974. The species–area relation within archipelagos: models and evidence from island land birds. In H. J. Frith & J. H. Calaby (Eds), *Proceedings of the 16th International Ornithological Congress:* 629–642. Canberra: Australian Academy of Sciences.
SILVA TABOADA, G., 1979. *Los murciélagos de Cuba.* Havana: Academia Ciencias de Cuba.
SIMPSON, G. G., 1956. Zoogeography of West Indian land mammals. *American Museum Novitates, 1759:* 1–28.
SMITH, J. D. & HOOD, C. S., 1981. Preliminary notes on bats from the Bismarck Archipelago (Mammalia: Chiroptera). *Science in New Guinea, 8:* 81–121.
SMITH, J. D. & HOOD, C. S., 1983. A new species of tube-nosed fruit bat (Nyctimene) from the Bismarck Archipelago, Papua New Guinea. *Occasional Papers, The Museum, Texas Tech University, 81:* 1–14.
SUGIHARA, G., 1981. Minimal community structure: an explanation of species abundance patterns. *American Naturalist, 116:* 770–787.
TATE, G. H. H., 1945. The marsupial genus *Phalanger.* Results of the Archbold expeditions. No. 52. *American Museum Novitates, 1323:* 1–31.
TAYLOR, E. H., 1934. *Philippine Land Mammals.* Manila: Monograph, Bureau of Science, Department of Agriculture and Commerce, No. 30.
TAYLOR, J. M., CALABY, J. H. & VAN DEUSEN, H. M., 1982. A revision of the genus *Rattus* (Rodentia, Muridae) in the New Guinean region. *Bulletin of the American Museum of Natural History, 173:* 177–336.
THOMAS, O., 1906. A list of further collections of mammals from Western Australia, including a series from Bernier Island, obtained for Mr. W. E. Balston; with field-notes by the collector, Mr. G. C. Shortridge. *Proceedings of the Zoological Society of London, 1906:* 763–767.
THOMAS, O., 1914. On mammals from Manus Island, Admiralty Group, and Ruk Island, Bismarck Archipelago. *Annals and Magazine of Natural History, Series 8, 13:* 434–439.
URSIN, E., 1950. Zoogeographical remarks on the mammals occurring on the islands south of Funen (Denmark). *Dansk Naturhistorisk Forening, Videnskabelige Meddelelser, 112:* 35–62.
VAN DUESEN, H. M., 1957. Results of the Archbold expeditions. No. 76. A new species of wallaby (*Dorcopsis*) from Goodenough Island, Papua. *American Museum Novitates, 1826:* 1–25.
VARONA, L. S., 1974. *Catalogo de los mamíferos vivientes y extinguidos de las Antillas.* Havana: Academia Ciencias de Cuba.
VON BLOEKER Jr, J. C., 1967. The land mammals of the southern California islands. In R. N. Philbrick

(Ed.), *Proceedings of a Symposium on the Biology of the California Islands:* 245–263. Santa Barbara, California: Santa Barbara Botanical Garden.

WAITE, E. R. & WOOD JONES, F., 1927. Fauna of Kangaroo Island, South Australia. No. 2. The mammals. *Transactions of the Royal Society of South Australia, 51:* 322–325.

WALLIN, L., 1969. The Japanese bat fauna. *Zoologiska Bidrag fran Uppsala, 37:* 223–440.

WATTS, C. H. S. & ASLIN, H. J., 1981. *The Rodents of Australia.* London: Angus & Robertson.

WOLOSZYN, D. & WOLOSZYN, B. W., 1982. *Los mamíferos de la Sierra de la Laguna Baja California Sur.* La Paz, Mexico: Consejo Nacional Ciencia Technologica.

WRIGHT, S. J., 1981. Intra-archipelago vertebrate distributions: the slope of the species-area relation. *American Naturalist, 118:* 726–748.

Appendix. Species numbers and biogeographic variables for mammal faunas on landbridge and oceanic islands. Literature sources of species numbers are listed for each island set. Measures of island areas and distances to source areas were obtained from those references, from standard geographic references and gazetteers, or from maps

| Island | Area (km²) | Distance (km) To mainland | To mainland or island* | No. of species Terrestrial mammals | Bats |
|---|---|---|---|---|---|
| *Landbridge Islands* | | | | | |
| *British Columbia* | | | | | |
| Vancouver | 33 800.0 | 2.5 | 2.5 | 16 | — |
| Graham | 6436.0 | 77.0 | 77.0 | 6 | — |
| Moresby | 2745.0 | 134.0 | 0.5 | 5 | — |
| Princess Royal | 2270.0 | 1.0 | 1.0 | 10 | — |
| Pitt | 1370.0 | 0.5 | 0.5 | 9 | — |
| Banks | 1005.0 | 25.0 | 3.0 | 4 | — |
| King | 839.0 | 1.0 | 1.0 | 2 | — |
| Porcher | 545.0 | 8.0 | 2.0 | 5 | — |
| Aristazabal | 385.0 | 40.0 | 2.5 | 4 | — |
| Hunter | 335.0 | 3.0 | 3.0 | 6 | — |
| Swindle | 310.0 | 12.0 | 0.5 | 8 | — |
| McCauley | 280.0 | 15.0 | 0.5 | 7 | — |
| Calvert | 260.0 | 6.0 | 6.0 | 5 | — |
| Hecate | 260.0 | 5.5 | 5.5 | 3 | — |
| Louise | 250.0 | 144.0 | 0.5 | 3 | — |
| Kunghit | 215.0 | 177.0 | 1.5 | 3 | — |
| Saltspring | 181.0 | 28.0 | 1.0 | 8 | — |
| Campbell | 166.0 | 8.0 | 8.0 | 8 | — |
| Lyell | 150.0 | 152.0 | 1.5 | 2 | — |
| Campania | 127.0 | 23.0 | 2.0 | 5 | — |
| Yeo | 90.0 | 0.5 | 0.5 | 6 | — |
| North Estevan | 70.0 | 35.0 | 5.0 | 1 | — |
| Horsfall | 60.0 | 3.0 | 0.5 | 6 | — |
| Lulu | 55.0 | 79.0 | 11.5 | 3 | — |
| Nigei | 55.0 | 16.0 | 1.5 | 2 | — |
| Talunkwan | 55.0 | 155.0 | 0.2 | 2 | — |
| Hope | 50.0 | 21.0 | 1.0 | 3 | — |
| Hibben | 50.0 | 172.0 | 0.5 | 2 | — |
| Langara | 50.0 | 161.0 | 1.5 | 1 | — |
| Dufferin | 40.0 | 3.0 | 0.4 | 5 | — |
| Chatfield | 40.0 | 2.0 | 1.0 | 4 | — |
| Tanu | 40.0 | 158.0 | 1.5 | 2 | — |
| Chaatl | 40.0 | 159.0 | 0.4 | 2 | — |
| West Estevan | 40.0 | 41.0 | 0.8 | 2 | — |
| Saturna | 28.0 | 18.5 | 18.5 | 4 | — |
| Vargas | 28.0 | 123.0 | 1.0 | 2 | — |

*Minimum distance to mainland or nearest larger island.

## Appendix. Continued

| Island | Area (km²) | Distance (km) | | No. of species | |
|---|---|---|---|---|---|
| | | To mainland | To mainland or island* | Terrestrial mammals | Bats |
| Pender | 26.0 | 22.5 | 2.0 | 4 | — |
| Bowen | 26.0 | 2.0 | 2.0 | 4 | — |
| Goose | 25.0 | 35.0 | 14.5 | 3 | — |
| Spider | 24.0 | 24.0 | 1.0 | 4 | — |
| Cox | 20.0 | 68.0 | 10.0 | 3 | — |
| Ramsay | 20.0 | 159.0 | 0.4 | 1 | — |
| Hippa | 10.0 | 191.0 | 0.5 | 3 | — |
| Frederick | 10.0 | 181.0 | 1.0 | 2 | — |
| Stuart | 8.0 | 32.5 | 5.0 | 4 | — |
| Kunga | 7.0 | 154.0 | 5.0 | 1 | — |
| Balaclava | 6.0 | 15.5 | 2.5 | 2 | — |
| Maude | 5.0 | 153.0 | 0.5 | 2 | — |
| Moore | 5.0 | 64.0 | 9.0 | 1 | — |
| Reef | 5.0 | 144.0 | 6.0 | 1 | — |
| Hurst | 4.0 | 15.0 | 2.5 | 3 | — |
| Wathus | 3.0 | 158.0 | 2.0 | 1 | — |
| Helgeson | 2.0 | 183.0 | 1.0 | 2 | — |
| Anthony | 2.0 | 165.0 | 2.5 | 1 | — |
| Harrison | 2.0 | 152.0 | 1.0 | 1 | — |
| Bell | 1.5 | 13.0 | 3.0 | 2 | — |
| Saunders | 1.5 | 185.0 | 0.5 | 2 | — |
| Bischoff | 1.0 | 171.0 | 0.5 | 2 | — |
| Bolkus | 1.0 | 197.0 | 2.0 | 2 | — |
| Lina | 1.0 | 155.0 | 0.2 | 2 | — |
| Heard | 1.0 | 12.0 | 5.0 | 2 | — |
| Duncan | 1.0 | 15.0 | 1.5 | 2 | — |
| Doyle | 1.0 | 14.0 | 4.0 | 2 | — |
| Triangle | 1.0 | 95.0 | 31.0 | 2 | — |
| Marble | 1.0 | 187.0 | 4.0 | 1 | — |
| Gordon | 1.0 | 190.0 | 0.8 | 1 | — |
| Hotspring | 1.0 | 162.0 | 1.0 | 1 | — |
| East Copper | 1.0 | 195.0 | 2.0 | 1 | — |
| George | 1.0 | 196.0 | 3.5 | 1 | — |
| Rankine | 1.0 | 144.0 | 1.5 | 1 | — |
| Table | 1.0 | 2.0 | 2.0 | 1 | — |
| Pine | 1.0 | 12.0 | 12.0 | 1 | — |
| Ogilvie | 0.8 | 191.0 | 1.0 | 1 | — |
| Queens | 0.8 | 191.0 | 0.8 | 1 | — |
| MacKenzie | 0.8 | 193.0 | 1.0 | 1 | — |

Sources: Cowan & Guiguet (1975), Foster (1965), Hall (1981), McCabe & Cowan (1945), Redfield (1976).

*Baja California*

| | | | | | |
|---|---|---|---|---|---|
| Tiburon | 1208.0 | 2.0 | 2.0 | 13 | — |
| Cedros | 348.0 | 24.0 | 24.0 | 5 | — |
| Magdalena | 290.0 | 1.0 | 1.0 | 9 | — |
| Santa Margarita | 205.0 | 1.0 | 1.0 | 7 | — |
| San Jose | 194.0 | 5.0 | 5.0 | 7 | — |
| Carmen | 151.0 | 6.0 | 6.0 | 4 | — |
| Espiritu Santo | 99.0 | 6.0 | 6.0 | 6 | — |
| San Marcos | 32.0 | 5.0 | 5.0 | 2 | — |
| Coronados | 8.5 | 2.0 | 2.0 | 3 | — |
| Natividad | 7.2 | 7.0 | 7.0 | 1 | — |
| Danzante | 4.9 | 1.0 | 1.0 | 2 | — |
| Smith | 4.5 | 5.0 | 5.0 | 2 | — |
| Turner | 4.0 | 22.0 | 2.0 | 3 | — |
| San Francisco | 2.6 | 8.0 | 2.5 | 2 | — |
| San Martin | 2.3 | 5.0 | 5.0 | 3 | — |

## Appendix. Continued

| Island | Area (km²) | Distance (km) | | No. of species | |
| | | To mainland | To mainland or island* | Terrestrial mammals | Bats |
| --- | --- | --- | --- | --- | --- |
| Willard | 2.0 | 1.0 | 1.0 | 2 | — |
| Asuncion | 1.2 | 2.0 | 2.0 | 1 | — |
| Todos Santos | 1.2 | 6.0 | 6.0 | 2 | — |
| San Roque | 0.8 | 3.0 | 3.0 | 1 | — |
| San Geronimo | 0.4 | 9.0 | 9.0 | 1 | — |
| Source: Lawlor (1983). | | | | | |
| *Panama* | | | | | |
| Coiba | 450.0 | 24.0 | 24.0 | 3 | — |
| San Miguel | 270.0 | 36.0 | 36.0 | 7 | — |
| San Jose | 80.0 | 63.0 | 12.0 | 2 | — |
| Cebaco | 70.0 | 6.0 | 6.0 | 9 | — |
| Sevilla | 30.0 | 3.0 | 3.0 | 6 | — |
| Brava | 25.0 | 1.0 | 1.0 | 4 | — |
| Pedro Gonzales | 20.0 | 51.0 | 13.0 | 1 | — |
| Parida | 18.0 | 15.0 | 10.0 | 3 | — |
| Insoleta | 15.0 | 1.0 | 1.0 | 2 | — |
| Gobernador | 12.0 | 3.0 | 3.0 | 4 | — |
| Espartal | 12.0 | 1.0 | 1.0 | 1 | — |
| Almijas | 10.0 | 1.0 | 1.0 | 1 | — |
| Saboga | 4.0 | 31.0 | 31.0 | 1 | — |
| Sources: Goldman (1920), Handley (1966), Kellogg (1946a,b). | | | | | |
| *British Isles* | | | | | |
| Britain | 229 850.0 | 30.0 | 30.0 | 26 | — |
| Ireland | 85 114.0 | 565.0 | 34.0 | 11 | — |
| Lewis | 2137.0 | 700.0 | 35.0 | 5 | — |
| Skye | 1738.0 | 680.0 | 0.8 | 13 | — |
| Shetland | 984.0 | 345.0 | 169.0 | 2 | — |
| Mull | 910.0 | 725.0 | 1.0 | 8 | — |
| Anglesey | 708.0 | 470.0 | 0.8 | 14 | — |
| Islay | 603.0 | 755.0 | 1.0 | 9 | — |
| Isle of Man | 575.0 | 550.0 | 28.0 | 4 | — |
| Rousay | 524.0 | 474.0 | 1.0 | 3 | — |
| Orkney | 490.0 | 460.0 | 28.0 | 3 | — |
| South Uist | 434.0 | 772.0 | 26.5 | 4 | — |
| Arran | 427.0 | 680.0 | 4.0 | 10 | — |
| Wight | 380.0 | 96.0 | 2.0 | 16 | — |
| Jura | 356.0 | 735.0 | 6.0 | 7 | — |
| North Uist | 274.0 | 764.0 | 10.0 | 5 | — |
| Hoy | 145.0 | 508.0 | 13.0 | 4 | — |
| Achill | 144.0 | 703.0 | 0.8 | 1 | — |
| Bute | 125.0 | 705.0 | 2.0 | 9 | — |
| Rhum | 94.0 | 738.0 | 13.0 | 5 | — |
| Tiree | 86.0 | 786.0 | 23.0 | 3 | — |
| Coll | 78.0 | 763.0 | 9.0 | 3 | — |
| Benbecula | 70.0 | 770.0 | 2.0 | 4 | — |
| Barra | 63.0 | 806.0 | 4.0 | 1 | — |
| Raasay | 63.0 | 705.0 | 1.0 | 6 | — |
| Sanday | 55.0 | 446.0 | 64.0 | 1 | — |
| South Ronaldsay | 55.0 | 474.0 | 10.0 | 3 | — |
| Colonsay | 51.0 | 765.0 | 8.0 | 4 | — |
| Westray | 39.0 | 464.0 | 7.0 | 1 | — |
| Stronsay | 35.0 | 450.0 | 52.0 | 1 | — |
| Shapinsay | 31.0 | 464.0 | 2.0 | 3 | — |
| Scalpay | 27.0 | 610.0 | 0.8 | 7 | — |
| Lismore | 27.0 | 710.0 | 2.0 | 5 | — |

## Appendix. Continued

| Island | Area (km²) | Distance (km) | | No. of species | |
|---|---|---|---|---|---|
| | | To mainland | To mainland or island* | Terrestrial mammals | Bats |
| Ulva | 23.0 | 745.0 | 2.0 | 4 | — |
| Walney | 23.0 | 478.0 | 0.8 | 2 | — |
| Luing | 20.0 | 745.0 | 2.0 | 5 | — |
| Kerrera | 18.0 | 716.0 | 1.0 | 1 | — |
| Scarba | 16.0 | 740.0 | 2.0 | 6 | — |
| Canna | 16.0 | 752.0 | 4.0 | 2 | — |
| Seil | 16.0 | 730.0 | 0.8 | 4 | — |
| Clare | 16.0 | 684.0 | 3.0 | 1 | — |
| Foula | 14.0 | 407.0 | 21.0 | 1 | — |
| Gigha | 12.0 | 750.0 | 3.0 | 5 | — |
| South Rona | 12.0 | 646.0 | 76.0 | 3 | — |
| Lundy | 12.0 | 242.0 | 18.0 | 1 | — |
| North Ronaldsay | 12.0 | 450.0 | 81.0 | 2 | — |
| Soay | 10.0 | 730.0 | 1.0 | 4 | — |
| Inishman | 9.2 | 602.0 | 2.0 | 2 | — |
| Flotta | 9.0 | 485.0 | 2.0 | 3 | — |
| Iona | 9.0 | 766.0 | 1.0 | 3 | — |
| Skomer | 8.0 | 324.0 | 2.0 | 4 | — |
| Pabbay | 8.0 | 756.0 | 6.0 | 4 | — |
| Cape Clear | 8.0 | 469.0 | 3.0 | 2 | — |
| Ramsey | 7.0 | 137.0 | 1.5 | 3 | — |
| Mingulay | 7.0 | 825.0 | 24.0 | 1 | — |
| South Shuna | 6.0 | 720.0 | 1.0 | 4 | — |
| Tory | 6.0 | 752.0 | 11.0 | 2 | — |
| Muck | 6.0 | 733.0 | 8.0 | 3 | — |
| Inisheer | 4.7 | 596.0 | 6.0 | 1 | — |
| Handa | 4.0 | 670.0 | 50.0 | 1 | — |
| Ailsa Craig | 3.0 | 645.0 | 10.0 | 1 | — |
| Garvellachs | 2.0 | 748.0 | 4.0 | 2 | — |
| Inishmore | 1.9 | 607.0 | 12.0 | 1 | — |
| Inishbofin | 1.2 | 676.0 | 5.0 | 1 | — |

Sources: Corbet (1971), Corbet & Southern (1977), Kelly (1981).

*British Channel Islands*
| | | | | | |
|---|---|---|---|---|---|
| Jersey | 116.3 | 21.0 | 21.0 | 7 | — |
| Guernsey | 63.5 | 44.0 | 27.0 | 5 | — |
| Alderney | 7.9 | 14.0 | 14.0 | 3 | — |
| Sark | 5.2 | 34.0 | 34.0 | 2 | — |
| Herm | 1.3 | 40.0 | 5.5 | 2 | — |

Sources: Corbet (1971), Corbet & Southern (1977).

*Japan*
| | | | | | |
|---|---|---|---|---|---|
| Honshu | 212 380.0 | 170.0 | 170.0 | 31 | 21 |
| Hokkaido | 78 511.0 | 290.0 | 18.0 | 27 | 13 |
| Sakhalin | 74 056.0 | 8.0 | 8.0 | 32 | 8 |
| Kyushu | 41 971.0 | 185.0 | 1.0 | 24 | 13 |
| Shikoku | 18 765.0 | 340.0 | 6.0 | 24 | 6 |
| Shantar | 1900.0 | 29.0 | 29.0 | 7 | — |
| Quelpart | 1829.0 | 82.0 | 82.0 | 8 | — |
| Tsushima | 702.0 | 48.0 | 48.0 | 12 | 8 |
| Dogo | 630.0 | 340.0 | 72.0 | 6 | — |
| Yakushima | 539.0 | 510.0 | 58.0 | 7 | — |
| Tanegashima | 456.0 | 520.0 | 32.0 | 6 | — |
| Rishiri | 190.0 | 260.0 | 19.0 | 2 | — |
| Iki | 137.0 | 135.0 | 49.0 | 4 | 2 |
| Oshima | 91.0 | 870.0 | 23.0 | 2 | — |
| Okinoshima | 5.0 | 390.0 | 4.5 | 1 | — |

Sources: Corbet (1978), Ellerman & Morrison-Scott (1951), Hill (1983), Honacki *et al.* (1982), Kuroda (1922, 1939), Wallin (1969).

## Appendix. Continued

| Island | Area (km$^2$) | Distance (km) | | No. of species | |
|---|---|---|---|---|---|
| | | To mainland | To mainland or island* | Terrestrial mammals | Bats |
| *Sunda Shelf* | | | | | |
| Borneo | 743 244.0 | 500.0 | 500.0 | 120 | — |
| Sumatra | 473 607.0 | 65.0 | 65.0 | 110 | — |
| Java | 125 628.0 | 830.0 | 25.0 | 61 | — |
| Bangka | 11 964.0 | 15.0 | 15.0 | 37 | — |
| Bungaran | 1594.0 | 500.0 | 221.0 | 23 | — |
| Bintang | 1075.0 | 21.0 | 21.0 | 20 | — |
| Lingga | 860.0 | 84.0 | 84.0 | 16 | — |
| Singkep | 740.0 | 37.0 | 37.0 | 12 | — |
| Langkawi | 525.0 | 18.0 | 18.0 | 12 | — |
| Banggi | 450.0 | 1060.0 | 12.0 | 17 | — |
| Batam | 340.0 | 16.0 | 16.0 | 15 | — |
| Penang | 285.0 | 4.0 | 4.0 | 15 | — |
| Kundur | 270.0 | 42.0 | 42.0 | 18 | — |
| Ko Samui | 240.0 | 16.0 | 16.0 | 7 | — |
| Jemaja | 194.0 | 202.0 | 202.0 | 13 | — |
| Terutao | 150.0 | 18.0 | 18.0 | 14 | — |
| Karimata Besar | 130.0 | 350.0 | 65.0 | 19 | — |
| Ko Pennan | 120.0 | 47.0 | 8.0 | 7 | — |
| Tioman | 114.0 | 38.0 | 38.0 | 22 | — |
| Siantan | 113.0 | 265.0 | 265.0 | 14 | — |
| Sugi | 60.0 | 48.0 | 23.0 | 7 | — |
| Sirhassan | 46.0 | 515.0 | 66.0 | 15 | — |
| Redang | 25.0 | 26.0 | 26.0 | 7 | — |
| Mapor | 20.0 | 67.0 | 17.0 | 5 | — |
| Penebangan | 13.0 | 16.0 | 16.0 | 12 | — |
| Aur | 10.0 | 61.0 | 61.0 | 5 | — |
| Perhentian Besar | 8.0 | 20.0 | 20.0 | 6 | — |

Sources: Chasen (1940), Heaney (1984, 1986), Medway (1977).

| | | | | | |
|---|---|---|---|---|---|
| *Northern Australia* | | | | | |
| Melville | 6215.0 | 24.0 | 24.0 | 14 | — |
| Groote Eylandt | 2460.0 | 42.0 | 42.0 | 21 | — |
| Bathurst | 2035.0 | 54.0 | 1.0 | 13 | — |
| Elcho | 290.0 | 1.0 | 1.0 | 5 | — |
| Vanderlin | 250.0 | 6.0 | 6.0 | 6 | — |
| West | 130.0 | 4.0 | 4.0 | 5 | — |
| Bentinck | 120.0 | 25.0 | 5.0 | 5 | — |
| Southwest | 100.0 | 1.0 | 1.0 | 9 | — |
| Centre | 80.0 | 7.5 | 1.0 | 8 | — |
| Crocodile | 60.0 | 3.0 | 3.0 | 2 | — |
| North | 50.0 | 25.0 | 2.0 | 5 | — |

Sources: Anonymous (1968), Johnson (1964), Parker (1973), Waite & Wood Jones (1927), Watts & Aslin (1981).

| | | | | | |
|---|---|---|---|---|---|
| *Kimberley Islands* (Including Osborn and Kingfisher Islands, and Bonaparte and Buccaneer Archipelagos) | | | | | |
| Augustus | 179.5 | 2.0 | 2.0 | 7 | — |
| Bigge | 171.9 | 4.0 | 4.0 | 6 | — |
| Boongaree | 48.8 | 1.0 | 1.0 | 5 | — |
| Darcy | 48.0 | 18.0 | 12.0 | 2 | — |
| Coronation | 38.3 | 7.0 | 7.0 | 1 | — |
| Uwins | 33.0 | 1.0 | 1.0 | 3 | — |
| Sir Graham Moore | 26.6 | 12.0 | 12.0 | 2 | — |
| Middle Osborn | 23.0 | 2.0 | 2.0 | 1 | — |
| Katers | 17.6 | 2.0 | 2.0 | 2 | — |
| St. Andrew | 14.1 | 2.5 | 2.5 | 2 | — |
| South West Osborn | 13.7 | 3.0 | 3.0 | 1 | — |
| Champagny | 13.3 | 28.0 | 20.0 | 1 | — |
| Kingfisher | 10.1 | 31.0 | 31.0 | 1 | — |

## Appendix. Continued

| Island | Area (km²) | Distance (km) | | No. of species | |
|---|---|---|---|---|---|
| | | To mainland | To mainland or island* | Terrestrial mammals | Bats |
| Wollaston | 8.5 | 1.5 | 1.5 | 3 | — |
| Melomys | 8.5 | 31.0 | 2.0 | 1 | — |
| Heywood | 7.6 | 20.0 | 12.0 | 2 | — |
| Borda | 6.0 | 2.0 | 2.0 | 2 | — |
| Carlia | 4.8 | 1.0 | 1.0 | 2 | — |
| Source: Burbridge & McKenzie (1978). | | | | | |
| *Western Australia* | | | | | |
| Dirk Hartog | 610.0 | 1.5 | 1.5 | 3 | — |
| Barrow | 207.0 | 53.0 | 53.0 | 12 | — |
| Dorre | 130.0 | 52.0 | 52.0 | 4 | — |
| Bernier | 100.0 | 44.0 | 44.0 | 6 | — |
| Rottnest | 16.0 | 18.0 | 18.0 | 1 | — |
| Garden | 12.0 | 2.0 | 2.0 | 1 | — |
| Hermite | 9.5 | 80.0 | 80.0 | 3 | — |
| Wallaby West | 6.0 | 36.0 | 36.0 | 2 | — |
| Trimouille | 5.0 | 75.0 | 75.0 | 1 | — |
| Wallaby East | 3.6 | 38.0 | 38.0 | 2 | — |
| Thevernard | 2.0 | 21.0 | 21.0 | 1 | — |
| Sources: Burbridge (1971), Butler (1970), Main (1961), Thomas (1906), Watts & Aslin (1981). | | | | | |
| *Southern Australia* (Including Recherche and Nuyts Archipelagos) | | | | | |
| Kangaroo | 5100.0 | 40.5 | 40.5 | 17 | — |
| Flinders | 50.0 | 28.0 | 28.0 | 1 | — |
| Middle | 11.0 | 8.0 | 8.0 | 1 | — |
| Gambier | 10.0 | 32.0 | 32.0 | 1 | — |
| St. Francis | 10.0 | 31.0 | 30.0 | 2 | — |
| Mondrain | 9.0 | 10.0 | 10.0 | 1 | — |
| Christmas | 3.5 | — | — | 1 | — |
| Salisbury | 3.4 | 40.0 | 39.0 | 1 | — |
| Pearson | 3.3 | 62.0 | 24.0 | 3 | — |
| North Twin Peaks | 2.9 | 10.0 | 10.0 | 1 | — |
| Woody | 2.0 | — | — | 1 | — |
| St. Peters | 2.0 | 6.0 | 6.0 | 1 | — |
| Franklin | 2.0 | 18.0 | 14.5 | 1 | — |
| Dog | 2.0 | — | — | 1 | — |
| Masillon | 2.0 | 38.0 | 3.0 | 1 | — |
| Wilson | 1.3 | 14.0 | 14.0 | 1 | — |
| Combe | 1.0 | 19.0 | 13.0 | 1 | — |
| Sources: Andrewartha & Barker (1969), Main (1961), Robinson & Smythe (1976), Schmitt (1975), Waite & Wood Jones (1927), Watts & Aslin (1981). | | | | | |
| *Bass Strait* | | | | | |
| Tasmania | 67 900.0 | 223.0 | 223.0 | 25 | — |
| Flinders | 1330.0 | 141.0 | 141.0 | 12 | — |
| King | 1100.0 | 89.0 | 89.0 | 12 | — |
| Cape Barren | 445.0 | 194.0 | 8.0 | 7 | — |
| Clarke | 115.0 | 213.0 | 3.0 | 6 | — |
| Robbins | 110.0 | 230.0 | 223.0 | 4 | — |
| Three Hummock | 80.0 | 205.0 | 75.0 | 7 | — |
| Hunter | 70.0 | 200.0 | 68.0 | 4 | — |
| Deal | 20.0 | 86.0 | 86.0 | 3 | — |
| Badger | 10.1 | 177.0 | 10.0 | 2 | — |
| Prime Seal | 8.9 | 156.0 | 5.5 | 3 | — |
| Vansittart | 8.1 | 203.0 | 1.0 | 2 | — |
| Erith-Dover | 7.8 | 82.0 | 82.0 | 2 | — |
| West Sister | 6.1 | 141.0 | 50.0 | 4 | — |
| Babel | 4.4 | 187.0 | 1.5 | 1 | — |
| East Sister | 4.0 | 146.0 | 7.0 | 1 | — |

## Appendix. Continued

| Island | Area (km²) | Distance (km) | | No. of species | |
| --- | --- | --- | --- | --- | --- |
| | | To mainland | To mainland or island* | Terrestrial mammals | Bats |
| Waterhouse | 3.7 | 210.0 | 3.0 | 1 | — |
| Great Dog | 3.3 | 197.0 | 2.0 | 1 | — |
| Preservation | 3.0 | 204.0 | 2.0 | 1 | — |
| Long | 3.0 | 191.0 | 1.0 | 2 | — |
| Hogan | 2.0 | 49.0 | 49.0 | 1 | — |
| Source: Hope (1973). | | | | | |
| | | *Oceanic Islands* | | | |
| *California Channel Islands* | | | | | |
| Santa Cruz | 249.0 | 30.0 | 30.0 | 4 | — |
| Santa Rosa | 217.0 | 44.0 | 9.0 | 3 | — |
| Santa Catalina | 194.0 | 32.0 | 32.0 | 5 | — |
| San Clemente | 145.0 | 79.0 | 34.0 | 2 | — |
| San Nicholas | 58.0 | 98.0 | 84.0 | 2 | — |
| San Miguel | 37.0 | 42.0 | 5.0 | 2 | — |
| Santa Barbara | 2.6 | 61.0 | 39.0 | 1 | — |
| West Anacapa | 2.3 | 20.0 | 20.0 | 1 | — |
| Middle Anacapa | 0.3 | 19.0 | 19.0 | 1 | — |
| East Anacapa | 0.3 | 18.0 | 18.0 | 1 | — |
| Prince | 0.2 | 42.0 | 1.0 | 1 | — |
| Sutil | 0.05 | 61.0 | 1.0 | 1 | — |
| Source: von Bloeker (1967). | | | | | |
| *Baja California* | | | | | |
| Angel de la Guarda | 895.0 | 13.0 | 13.0 | 3 | — |
| Cerralvo | 160.0 | 11.0 | 11.0 | 2 | — |
| San Esteban | 43.0 | 37.0 | 9.0 | 1 | — |
| Santa Catalina | 43.0 | 24.0 | 24.0 | 1 | — |
| San Lorenzo Sur | 35.0 | 18.0 | 18.0 | 2 | — |
| Montserrate | 19.4 | 13.0 | 13.0 | 2 | — |
| Santa Cruz | 14.0 | 17.0 | 14.0 | 1 | — |
| San Lorenzo Norte | 7.5 | 20.0 | 0.1 | 2 | — |
| Tortuga | 6.3 | 37.0 | 37.0 | 1 | — |
| San Pedro Nolasco | 3.2 | 10.0 | 10.0 | 2 | — |
| Mejia | 3.0 | 24.0 | 1.6 | 2 | — |
| San Diego | 1.3 | 17.0 | 7.0 | 1 | — |
| Salsipuedes | 1.2 | 19.0 | 3.0 | 1 | — |
| Granito | 0.4 | 27.0 | 0.8 | 1 | — |
| Source: Lawlor (1983). | | | | | |
| *West Indies* | | | | | |
| Cuba | 111 463.0 | 220.0 | 220.0 | 5 | 27 |
| Hispaniola | 73 147.0 | 575.0 | 85.0 | 2 | 17 |
| Jamaica | 11 526.0 | 625.0 | 145.0 | 2 | 21 |
| Puerto Rico | 8860.0 | 710.0 | 114.0 | 0 | 13 |
| Isla de Pinos | 3061.0 | 395.0 | 47.0 | 2 | 14 |
| Guadeloupe | 1510.0 | 580.0 | 573.0 | 0 | 11 |
| Martinique | 1106.0 | 425.0 | 395.0 | 1 | 9 |
| Dominica | 790.0 | 500.0 | 41.0 | 0 | 12 |
| St. Lucia | 604.0 | 345.0 | 318.0 | 1 | 8 |
| Barbados | 430.0 | 365.0 | 145.0 | 0 | 6 |
| St. Vincent | 345.0 | 275.0 | 255.0 | 1 | 9 |
| Grenada | 311.0 | 140.0 | 140.0 | 2 | 12 |
| Antigua | 282.0 | 705.0 | 73.0 | 0 | 7 |
| St. Croix | 213.0 | 785.0 | 107.0 | 0 | 6 |
| St. Kitts | 176.0 | 725.0 | 82.0 | 0 | 4 |
| Barbuda | 162.0 | 760.0 | 41.0 | 0 | 6 |
| Montserrat | 101.0 | 665.0 | 52.0 | 0 | 8 |
| Anguilla | 90.7 | 835.0 | 91.0 | 0 | 5 |

## Appendix. Continued

| Island | Area (km²) | Distance (km) | | No. of species | |
|---|---|---|---|---|---|
| | | To mainland | To mainland or island* | Terrestrial mammals | Bats |
| St. Martin | 90.7 | 815.0 | 73.0 | 0 | 6 |
| St. Eustatius | 19.9 | 755.0 | 18.0 | — | 5 |
| Saba | 13.0 | 770.0 | 27.0 | — | 3 |
| Swan | 2.6 | 175.0 | 175.0 | 1 | — |

Sources: Baker & Genoways (1978), Baker *et al.* (1978), Jones & Baker (1979), Morgan & Woods (1986), Ottenwalder & Genoways (1982), Silva Toboada (1979), Varona (1974).

*Philippines*

| Island | Area (km²) | To mainland | To mainland or island* | Terrestrial mammals | Bats |
|---|---|---|---|---|---|
| Luzon | 108 171.0 | 410.0 | 410.0 | 28 | — |
| Mindanao | 99 078.0 | 905.0 | 204.0 | 25 | — |
| Negros | 13 670.0 | 890.0 | 154.0 | 8 | — |
| Samar | 13 429.0 | 880.0 | 18.0 | 10 | — |
| Palawan | 11 650.0 | 600.0 | 181.0 | 23 | — |
| Mindoro | 9735.0 | 720.0 | 15.0 | 15 | — |
| Leyte | 7213.0 | 930.0 | 1.0 | 14 | — |
| Bohol | 3864.0 | 975.0 | 25.0 | 9 | — |
| Basilan | 1282.0 | 910.0 | 18.0 | 8 | — |
| Busuanga | 938.0 | 695.0 | 49.0 | 16 | — |
| Dinagat | 670.0 | 1055.0 | 4.0 | 15 | — |
| Biliran | 498.0 | 930.0 | 3.0 | 10 | — |
| Culion | 400.0 | 700.0 | 54.0 | 9 | — |
| Siargao | 347.0 | 1080.0 | 24.0 | 7 | — |
| Balabac | 306.0 | 575.0 | 456.0 | 10 | — |
| Camiguin | 265.0 | 445.0 | 30.0 | 2 | — |
| Maripipi | 25.0 | — | 14.0 | 5 | — |

Sources: Heaney (1986), Heaney & Rabor (1982), Taylor (1934)

*Western New Guinea*

| Island | Area (km²) | To mainland | To mainland or island* | Terrestrial mammals | Bats |
|---|---|---|---|---|---|
| Halmahera | 17 400.0 | 282.0 | 282.0 | 2 | 9 |
| Ceram | 16 720.0 | 140.0 | 140.0 | 7 | 19 |
| Buru | 8786.0 | 514.0 | 63.0 | 6 | 17 |
| Biak | 2644.0 | 111.0 | 111.0 | 4 | 2 |
| Morotai | 2218.0 | 435.0 | 18.0 | 3 | 7 |
| Batchian | 2133.0 | 344.0 | 14.0 | 4 | 11 |
| Obi | 1962.0 | 308.0 | 125.0 | 3 | 1 |
| Great Kei | 682.0 | 132.0 | 132.0 | 6 | 19 |
| Amboina | 597.0 | 408.0 | 7.0 | 3 | 19 |
| Kei | 512.0 | 169.0 | 7.0 | 5 | 19 |
| Numfor | 512.0 | 67.0 | 67.0 | 1 | 2 |
| Gebe | 256.0 | 196.0 | 196.0 | 1 | 2 |
| Ternate | 171.0 | 450.0 | 14.0 | 3 | 9 |
| Saparua | 85.0 | 364.0 | 6.0 | 2 | 1 |
| Goram | 40.0 | 128.0 | 128.0 | 1 | 5 |
| Manowoka | 40.0 | 158.0 | 8.0 | — | 1 |
| Rau | 40.0 | 480.0 | 2.0 | — | 1 |
| Kur | 40.0 | 191.0 | 70.0 | — | 1 |
| Watubela | 25.0 | 135.0 | 135.0 | — | 1 |
| Banda | 20.0 | 309.0 | 103.0 | 3 | 5 |
| Panjang | 15.0 | 143.0 | 14.0 | 1 | 1 |
| Keffing | 5.0 | — | — | — | 1 |
| Arsilulu | 5.0 | — | — | — | 1 |

Sources: Hill (1983), Laurie & Hill (1954), Rookmaaker & Bergmans (1981).

*Eastern New Guinea*
  Near-shore Islands

| Island | Area (km²) | To mainland | To mainland or island* | Terrestrial mammals | Bats |
|---|---|---|---|---|---|
| Umboi | 938.0 | 49.0 | 23.0 | 4 | 10 |
| Long | 391.0 | 50.0 | 50.0 | — | 4 |

## Appendix. Continued

| Island | Area (km²) | Distance (km) | | No. of species | |
|---|---|---|---|---|---|
| | | To mainland | To mainland or island* | Terrestrial mammals | Bats |
| Karkar | 368.0 | 16.0 | 16.0 | 3 | 8 |
| Sakar | 35.0 | 89.0 | 13.0 | 1 | 7 |
| Tolokiwa | 30.0 | 70.0 | 21.0 | 1 | 5 |
| Bagabag | 25.0 | 44.0 | 21.0 | 4 | 7 |
| Crown | 10.0 | 72.0 | 11.0 | — | 4 |
| Kadovar | 5.0 | 23.0 | 23.0 | — | 2 |
| **Bismarck Islands** | | | | | |
| New Britain | 36 674.0 | 88.0 | 88.0 | 9 | 30 |
| New Ireland | 8651.0 | 550.0 | 30.0 | 3 | 29 |
| Manus | 1554.0 | 280.0 | 280.0 | 1 | 9 |
| Mussan | 341.0 | 598.0 | 239.0 | 1 | 8 |
| Tabar | 251.0 | 590.0 | 25.0 | — | 6 |
| Lihir | 170.0 | 625.0 | 45.0 | — | 4 |
| Duke of York | 25.0 | 560.0 | 13.0 | 3 | 13 |
| Emirau | 20.0 | 628.0 | 15.0 | 1 | 10 |
| Bat | 1.0 | 214.0 | 198.0 | 1 | — |
| **Solomon Islands** | | | | | |
| Bougainville | 8591.0 | 610.0 | 203.0 | 4 | 13 |
| Guadacanal | 5281.0 | 970.0 | 510.0 | 5 | 19 |
| Malaita | 4307.0 | 1085.0 | 550.0 | 1 | 11 |
| Santa Isabel | 4095.0 | 870.0 | 297.0 | — | 11 |
| San Cristobal | 3090.0 | 1154.0 | 52.0 | 1 | 11 |
| Choiseul | 2966.0 | 715.0 | 55.0 | — | 14 |
| New Georgia | 2044.0 | 730.0 | 53.0 | — | 3 |
| Kolombangara | 704.0 | 712.0 | 175.0 | — | 7 |
| Rennell | 684.0 | 1028.0 | 178.0 | — | 12 |
| Vella Lavella | 640.0 | 670.0 | 112.0 | — | 5 |
| Mendora (=Rendova) | 381.0 | 710.0 | 36.0 | 1 | — |
| Florida | 368.0 | 1017.0 | 29.0 | 1 | 7 |
| Shortland | 232.0 | 665.0 | 9.0 | — | 6 |
| Russell | 176.0 | 905.0 | 82.0 | — | 10 |
| San Jorge | 150.0 | 971.0 | 1.0 | — | 5 |
| Fauro | 71.0 | 621.0 | 12.0 | — | 11 |
| Ugi | 42.2 | 1200.0 | 2.0 | — | 4 |
| Ghizo | 35.2 | 690.0 | 11.0 | — | 3 |
| Simbo (=Naravo) | 13.0 | 650.0 | 35.0 | — | 2 |
| Ndai | 12.0 | 1075.0 | 96.0 | — | 1 |
| Rubiana (=Roviana) | 10.0 | 739.0 | 2.0 | 1 | 5 |
| Ontong Java | 9.6 | 1040.0 | 247.0 | — | 1 |
| Mono | 8.0 | 620.0 | 50.0 | — | 2 |
| Alu | 7.0 | 3.0 | 685.0 | — | 6 |
| **East Papuan Islands** | | | | | |
| Ferguson | 1342.0 | 41.0 | 41.0 | 5 | 10 |
| Normanby | 1036.0 | 11.0 | 11.0 | 2 | 6 |
| Woodlark | 1036.0 | 222.0 | 185.0 | 2 | 12 |
| Tagula | 803.0 | 286.0 | 286.0 | 2 | 11 |
| Goodenough | 681.0 | 27.0 | 27.0 | 4 | 7 |
| Rossel | 341.0 | 373.0 | 32.0 | 1 | 5 |
| Kiriwina | 264.0 | 151.0 | 77.0 | 2 | 13 |
| Misima | 259.0 | 184.0 | 184.0 | 2 | 13 |

Sources: Hill (1961, 1968, 1971, 1983), Koopman (1979, 1982), Laurie & Hill (1954), McKean (1972), Peterson (1981), Phillips (1966, 1968), Rookmaaker & Bergmans (1981), Smith & Hood (1981, 1983), Tate (1945), Taylor *et al.* (1982), Thomas (1914), Van Duesen (1957).

*Biological Journal of the Linnean Society* (1986), *28*, 127–165. With 8 figures

# Biogeography of mammals in SE Asia: estimates of rates of colonization, extinction and speciation

LAWRENCE R. HEANEY

*Museum of Zoology and Division of Biological Sciences, University of Michigan, Ann Arbor, Michigan 48109, U.S.A.*

*Accepted for publication 14 February 1986*

Four categories of islands in SE Asia may be identified on the basis of their histories of landbridge connections. Those islands on the shallow, continental Sunda Shelf were joined to the Asian mainland by a broad landbridge during the late Pleistocene; other islands were connected to the Sunda Shelf by a middle Pleistocene landbridge; some were parts of larger oceanic islands; and others remained as isolated oceanic islands. The limits of late Pleistocene islands, defined by the 120 m bathymetric line, are highly concordant with the limits of faunal regions. Faunal variation among non-volant mammals is high between faunal regions and low within the faunal regions; endemism of faunal regions characteristically exceeds 70%. Small and geologically young oceanic islands are depauperate; larger and older islands are more species-rich. The number of endemic species is correlated with island area; however, continental shelf islands less than 125 000 km² do not have endemic species, whereas isolated oceanic islands as small as 47 km² often have endemic species. Geologically old oceanic islands have many endemic species, whereas young oceanic islands have few endemic species. Colonization across sea channels that were 5–25 km wide during the Pleistocene has been low, with a rate of about 1–2/500 000 years. Comparison of species–area curves for mainland areas, late Pleistocene islands, and middle Pleistocene islands indicates that extinction occurs rapidly when landbridge islands are first isolated, with the extent of extinction dependent upon island size; extinction then slows to an average rate of 1–2%/10 000 years. The great majority of the non-volant Philippine mammals arrived from the Sunda Shelf, the geographically closest of the possible source areas. Speciation within the Philippines has contributed substantially to species richness, perhaps exceeding colonization by a factor of two or more as a contributor to species number. Colonization, extinction and speciation rates differ among taxonomic groups, with murid rodents being most successful and carnivores least successful. In order for any model of island biogeography to be widely applicable to insular faunas, the model must include speciation as a major variable. It is suggested that insular mammalian faunas typically are not in equilibrium, because geological and climatic changes can occur as rapidly as colonization and speciation.

KEY WORDS:—Island biogeography – mammals – SE Asia – Philippines – extinction – colonization – speciation – equilibrium biogeography.

## CONTENTS

0024–4066/86/050127 + 39 $03.00/0

## INTRODUCTION

For the past twenty years, the theory of island biogeography developed by MacArthur & Wilson (1963, 1967; MacArthur, 1972) has provided a framework within which to investigate the ecological and evolutionary dynamics of the processes that control patterns of species richness. This general theory, with its component equilibrium model, serves as a structured set of predictions that allows an investigator to ask biologically important questions. By approaching the topic of island biogeography in a systematic way, investigators are often able to judge their data in the context of similar, comparable data sets, and so may draw conclusions and make predictions that may be generalized over a wide taxonomic and geographic range.

Both the general theory and the equilibrium model of MacArthur and Wilson have been controversial (e.g. see critical reviews by Gilbert, 1980; Williamson, 1981). Some critics have, in effect, stated that the simplicity and rigidity of the equilibrium model have allowed it to be falsified, and that it should be discarded. Given MacArthur's view of a model as "a lie that allows you to see the truth" (cited by Crowell, 1986), this narrow view of the role of falsification may be an inappropriate criticism. The model appears to be most effectively used in much the same way as the Hardy–Weinberg model of population genetics: equilibrium is not assumed or even expected; rather, it is the reason for the presence or lack of equilibrium that is of interest (e.g. Lack, 1976).

Other criticism of the model has focused on its failure to allow for historical factors, especially speciation (e.g. Heaney, 1984a). Although some parts of the theory address long-term processes, most of MacArthur and Wilson's discussion centres on variables that operate over 'ecological time'. This may be appropriate for highly vagile organisms, and for less vagile organisms in a system encompassing short distances, but it restricts the usefulness of the theory. Unfortunately, much of the research conducted with the framework of the MacArthur and Wilson model has utilized species that are highly vagile relative to the distances involved in the study, so that the importance of long-term processes remains problematic.

Recent studies of the island biogeography of mammals (Brown, 1971, 1978; Patterson, 1980, 1984; Lawlor, 1983; Heaney, 1984a) have concluded that, with the possible exception of bats, mammals are very poor colonizers across significant habitat and geographic barriers; none of these studies could detect any current colonization. These studies also provided evidence that the rate of extinction for any given island fauna is influenced by two major variables. First, extinction is more rapid, and much more extensive, on progressively smaller islands. Secondly, extinction is temporally variable, apparently being high soon after the island is isolated from the mainland, but falling to a low level thereafter. Islands isolated for 12 000–15 000 years often have rich faunas in which current extinction is undetectable. Thus, there is little evidence for isolated insular mammalian faunas that are in dynamic equilibrium (i.e. that show evidence of turnover). Finally, limited data indicate that speciation may occur within the same time-frame as extinction and colonization, and probably should be considered in models of mammalian species richness (Heaney, 1984a; Patterson, 1984).

Unfortunately, the evidence at hand does not provide direct estimates of the rates of extinction, immigration or speciation for any isolated insular mammal faunas; with a few exceptions, such data are available only for the small mammal faunas on islands that are often bridged by ice (Williamson, 1981; Lomolino, 1982, 1986; Crowell, 1986; Hanski, 1986).

Thus, attempts to model the dynamics of species richness of non-volant mammals on islands have left four questions unanswered. (1) What are the actual rates of colonization and extinction among these species? (2) Are the rates effectively equal? (3) What role does speciation play in determining species richness? and (4) How is speciation affected by colonization and extinction?

The SE Asian archipelago is the largest aggregation of islands in the world, and affords an excellent opportunity to investigate problems in mammalian island biogeography. Over 7000 islands are said to be enclosed within the boundaries of the Republic of the Philippines alone. The archipelago is especially unusual in that it contains islands of widely differing sizes, and geological evidence indicates that several historical groups exist: some islands are strictly oceanic, some are fragments of once-larger islands, and some had landbridge connections to the Asian mainland.

The mammalian fauna of the region is also remarkably diverse. The Philippine islands support at least 17 endemic genera of rodents, two of insectivores and four of bats, as well as many endemic species of more widespread genera. Many of these endemics are restricted to one or a few islands and short distances separate faunas that are quite distinct (Heaney, 1985b). This is unlike the pattern of the mammalian fauna on the islands of the adjacent Sunda Shelf. On this vast continental shelf the proportion of endemics is much lower, and widely separated islands support very similar faunas (Medway, 1972, 1977; Heaney, 1984a).

The purpose of this paper is to review the biogeography of the mammalian faunas found on the islands of the Sunda Shelf and the Philippines in the light of current theoretical problems in island biogeography. In order to accomplish this, it is necessary to summarize current knowledge of the faunas of the islands in the Philippines because previous summaries are badly out of date (Dickerson, 1928; Taylor, 1934). To provide the necessary perspective, I will first briefly summarize the geological history of the area and describe general patterns of mammalian distribution, and then present data that allow direct estimation of rates of colonization, extinction and speciation. I have, with regret, omitted bats from this study; their distributions on nearly all small islands and many large islands in the region are poorly documented and records are widely scattered. Introduced, commensal mammals are not included in any of the analyses that follow.

## METHODS

Data on Sunda Shelf mammals are from Heaney (1984a), except that recent taxonomic changes (Jenkins, 1982; Musser & Newcomb, 1983) have been incorporated. Mainland species–area data are those used by Heaney (1984a), plus data from Harrison (1969) and Lim, Muul & Chai (1977). Although the faunas of Java and Sumatra are often cited by zoogeographers, there are no current, complete lists of their mammalian faunas; therefore, I have included checklists as an Appendix.

I have provided summaries of the mammalian faunas on most Philippine islands because they are not available elsewhere. Specimens of Philippine mammals were examined in all major collections in North America and in several collections in the Philippines. Records of occurrence that were not previously noted in published literature are documented in Tables 1–5 by inclusion of the acronym for the collection that houses them. The following acronyms are used: AMNH (American Museum of Natural History, New York); DMNH (Delaware Museum of Natural History, Greenville); FMNH (Field Museum of Natural History, Chicago); UMMZ (University of Michigan, Museum of Zoology, Ann Arbor); USNM (U.S. National Museum of Natural History, Washington, D.C.); VISCA (Visayas State College of Agriculture, Baybay, Leyte); ZMB (Zoologisches Museum der Humboldt-Universitat, Berlin).

It has been necessary to make several taxonomic judgements in order to complete this paper. I have generally taken a conservative approach, i.e. species are recognized only where they are likely to be valid; in other cases I have indicated that the taxa are members of species groups that need revision (e.g. *Bullimus* species group). In no case do these judgements significantly affect the conclusions drawn here.

Cluster analyses of faunal similarity indices were based on the unweighted pair-group method of analysis, using a program developed by R. Strauss. Standard errors were estimated at each cluster node from all possible pairs of between-group distances, where the groups are the two clusters that are joined at the node, calculated as the standard deviation of the distances divided by the number of distances. Regression lines were calculated using the least-squares method.

## GEOLOGICAL SETTING

South and east of the continent of Asia lie most of the world's largest islands: Borneo, Sumatra, Java, New Guinea and Australia, each surrounded by a constellation of lesser islands. New Guinea lies on the continental shelf of Australia and shares much of its fauna with that island-continent. Likewise, Borneo, Sumatra and Java lie on the continental shelf of Asia that is called the Sunda Shelf. Between these two continental shelves are the oceanic islands of Wallacea, which originated primarily as island arcs at pressure points between sliding oceanic plates; these tectonic forces have caused geological uplift and volcanism (Hamilton, 1979; Divis, 1980; Ollier, 1985). This paper deals with only a part of this vast complex of islands: the islands of the Sunda Shelf and those of the Philippines, one of the oceanic island constellations of Wallacea.

## Table 1. List of mammal species known to occur on selected islands in the Palawan faunal region

| Island | Palawan | Busuanga | Culion | Balabac |
|---|---|---|---|---|
| Area (km²) | 11 785 | 938 | 400 | 306 |
| Elevation (m) | 2 084 | 695 | 495 | 605 |
| Depth to Palawan (m) | – | 73 | 73 | 91 |
| Distance to Palawan (km) | – | 86 | 55 | 31 |
| Insectivora | | | | |
| Crocidura palawanensis** | T | — | — | USNM |
| Suncus murinus* | T | — | — | — |
| Tupaia palawanensis** | T | S | S | USNM |
| Primates | | | | |
| Macaca fascicularis | T | S | S | USNM |
| Pholidota | | | | |
| Manis javanicus | T | — | — | — |
| Rodentia | | | | |
| Sundasciurus steerii group** | T | S | S | USNM |
| Sundasciurus rabori** | H | — | — | — |
| Hylopetes nigripes** | T | — | — | — |
| Chiropodomys calamianensis** | $M_1$ | T | — | $M_1$ |
| Haeromys sp. nov.** | $M_2$ | $M_2$ | — | — |
| Maxomys panglima** | T | S | S | USNM |
| Palawanomys furvus** | $M_3$ | — | — | — |
| Rattus exulans* | T | S | S | USNM |
| Rattus norvegicus* | T | — | — | — |
| Rattus rattus* | T | USNM | S | — |
| Rattus tiomanicus | MC | S | — | — |
| Sundamys muelleri | MN | MN | S | MN |
| Hystrix pumilus** | T | S | — | — |
| Carnivora | | | | |
| Felis bengalensis | T | T | — | — |
| Mydaus marchei** | USNM | S | — | — |
| Aonyx cinerea | T | — | — | — |
| Herpestes brachyurus | T | T | — | — |
| Herpestes urva | W | — | — | — |
| Paguma larvata | W | — | — | — |
| Paradoxurus hermaphroditus | T | FMNH | S | USNM |
| Viverra tangalunga | USNM | USNM | USNM | — |
| Artiodactyla | | | | |
| Sus barbatus | T | S | S | T |
| Cervus porcinus | — | — | S | — |
| Tragulus napu | — | — | — | T |
| Total non-volant species | 27 | 17 | 11 | 11 |
| Total indigenous species | 23 | 15 | 9 | 10 |

*Introduced commensal species.
**Species endemic to faunal region.
H = Heaney, 1979; $M_1$ = Musser, 1979; $M_2$ = Musser, pers. comm.; $M_3$ = Musser, 1981a; MC = Musser & Califia, 1982; MN = Musser & Newcomb, 1983; S = Sanborn, 1952; T = Taylor, 1934, W = Wozencraft, pers. comm.

### Pleistocene conditions

The growth and recession of continental glaciers during the Pleistocene were associated on a global basis with changes in sea level and temperature. At the end of the Pleistocene, about 18 000 years ago, sea level was about 120 m below

Table 2. List of mammal species known to occur on selected islands in the Mindanao Faunal Region

| Island | Mindanao | Samar | Leyte | Bohol | Basilan | Dinagat | Siargao | Biliran | Marippi |
|---|---|---|---|---|---|---|---|---|---|
| Area (km$^2$) | 99 078 | 13 429 | 7213 | 3864 | 1282 | 670 | 347 | 498 | 22 |
| Elevation (m) | 2954 | 850 | 1349 | 878 | 1012 | 929 | 274 | 1340 | 924 |
| Depth to Mindanao (m) | — | 80 | 80 | 80 | 82 | 64 | 26 | 80 | 80 |
| Distance to Mindanao (km) | — | 138 | 50 | 85 | 17 | 14 | 31 | 205 | 245 |
| **Insectivora** | | | | | | | | | |
| Podogymnura aureospinula** | | — | — | — | — | 1 | — | — | — |
| Podogymnura truei** | 1 | — | — | — | — | — | — | — | — |
| Crocidura beatus** | T | — | DMNH | — | — | — | — | — | UMMZ |
| Crocidura grandis** | T | — | — | — | — | — | — | — | — |
| Crocidura parvacauda** | T | — | UMMZ | — | — | — | — | — | — |
| Suncus murinus* | T | — | UMMZ | — | — | — | — | — | — |
| Urogale everetti** | T | — | — | — | — | — | — | — | — |
| **Dermoptera** | | | | | | | | | |
| Cynocephalus volans** | T | T | T | T | T | H | H | 1 | 1 |
| **Primates** | | | | | | | | | |
| Tarsius syrichta** | T | T | T | T | L | H | H | 1 | — |
| Macaca fascicularis | T | T | T | FMNH | T | — | — | UMMZ | UMMZ |
| **Rodentia** | | | | | | | | | |
| Exilisciurus concinnus** | 1 | 1 | 1 | 1 | 1 | 1 | 1 | 1 | — |
| Petinomys crinitus (1)** | T | — | — | — | L | H | H | — | — |
| Sundasciurus philippinensis group** | T | T | DMNH | FMNH | T | H | H | UMMZ | — |
| Apomys hylocetes** | 1 | — | — | — | — | — | — | — | — |
| Apomys insignis** | 1 | — | — | — | — | — | — | — | — |

1 = Heaney & Morgan, 1982
1 = reported to Heaney; no specimens
1 = reported to Heaney; no specimens
1 = Heaney, 1985a
1 = inc. Hylopetes mindanensis Rabor
1 = Musser, 1982b
1 = Musser, 1982b

| Species | C1 | C2 | C3 | C4 | C5 | C6 | C7 | C8 | C9 | Reference |
|---|---|---|---|---|---|---|---|---|---|---|
| Apomys littoralis | 1 | — | — | — | — | — | — | UMMZ | — | 1 = Musser, 1982b |
| Apomys microdon | S | — | — | — | — | — | — | UMMZ | — | 1 = Musser, 1982b |
| Batomys salomonseni** | — | — | DMNH | — | — | — | — | — | — | — |
| Batomys sp. nov.** | T | — | DMNH | — | — | H | H | — | — | 1 = Johnson, 1946 |
| Bullimus bagobus group | — | 1 | — | FMNH | — | H | H | — | — | 1 = Musser et al., 1985 |
| Crateromys australis** | 1 | — | — | — | — | H | — | — | — | 1 = Musser, 1982c |
| Crunomys melanius** | — | — | — | — | — | — | — | — | — | 1 = Musser, 1982c |
| Crunomys rabori** | 1 | — | 1 | — | — | — | — | — | — | 1 = Musser, 1977b |
| Limnomys sibuanus** | T | — | DMNH | — | — | — | — | — | — | — |
| Mus castaneus* | T | 1 | DMNH | FMNH | — | H | H | UMMZ | UMMZ | 1 = Johnson, 1946 |
| Rattus everetti group | 1 | FMNH | DMNH | FMNH | L | H | — | UMMZ | — | 1 = Musser, 1977a |
| Rattus exulans* | 1 | T | DMNH | — | L | — | — | — | — | — |
| Rattus norvegicus* | T | 1 | 1 | FMNH | L | H | H | UMMZ | UMMZ | 1 = Musser, 1977a |
| Rattus rattus* | DMNH | 1 | — | — | — | H | — | — | — | — |
| Rattus sp. nov.** | T | — | 1 | FMNH | — | — | — | — | — | — |
| Tarsomys apoensis** | T | — | — | — | — | — | — | — | — | — |
| **Carnivora** | | | | | | | | | | |
| Paradoxurus hermaphroditus | T | T | T | VISCA | L | H | — | — | 1 | 1 = reported to Heaney; no specimens |
| Viverra tangalunga | T | FMNH | FMNH | FMNH | — | — | — | — | — | — |
| **Artiodactyla** | | | | | | | | | | |
| Cervus marianus | T | T | VISCA | VISCA | T | H | — | 1 | — | — |
| Sus barbatus | T | T | VISCA | T | T | H | H | UMMZ | — | 1 = reported to Heaney; no specimens |
| Total non-volant species | 32 | 13 | 18 | 11 | 10 | 16 | 8 | 12 | 6 | |
| Total indigenous species | 28 | 10 | 14 | 9 | 8 | 14 | 7 | 10 | 5 | |

*Introduced commensal species.
**Species endemic to faunal region.
H = Heaney & Rabor, 1982; L = Lawrence, 1939; S = Sanborn, 1953; T = Taylor, 1934.

## Table 3. List of mammal species known to occur on islands in the Luzon Faunal Region

| Island | Luzon | Catanduanes | Marinduque | Polillo | |
|---|---|---|---|---|---|
| Area (km²) | 108 171 | 1513 | 958 | 769 | |
| Elevation (m) | 2930 | 764 | 1182 | 219 | |
| Depth to Luzon (m) | — | 50 | 75 | 64 | |
| Distance to Luzon (km) | — | 8 | 17 | 18 | |
| Insectivora | | | | | |
|   *Crocidura grayi*** | T | — | — | — | |
|   *Suncus murinus** | T | — | T | — | |
| Primates | | | | | |
|   *Macaca fascicularis* | T | — | — | — | |
| Rodentia | | | | | |
|   *Abditomys latidens*** | 1 | — | — | — | 1 = Musser, 1982a |
|   *Apomys abrae*** | 1 | — | — | — | 1 = Musser, 1982b |
|   *Apomys datae*** | 1 | — | — | — | 1 = Musser, 1982b |
|   *Apomys microdon* | — | T | — | — | 1 = Musser, 1982b |
|   *Apomys musculus*** | 1 | — | — | — | 1 = Musser, 1982b |
|   *Apomys sacobianus*** | 1 | — | — | — | 1 = Musser, 1982b |
|   *Archboldomys luzonensis*** | 1 | — | — | — | 1 = Musser, 1982c |
|   *Batomys dentatus*** | T | — | — | — | |
|   *Batomys granti*** | T | — | — | — | |
|   *Bullimus bagobus* group | T | — | — | — | |
|   *Carpomys melanurus*** | T | — | — | — | |
|   *Carpomys phaeurus*** | T | — | — | — | |
|   *Celaenomys silaceus*** | T | — | — | — | |
|   *Chrotomys mindorensis* | 1 | — | — | — | 1 = Musser & Gordon, 1981 |
|   *Chrotomys whiteheadi*** | 1 | — | — | — | 1 = Musser & Gordon, 1981 |
|   *Crateromys schadenbergi*** | T | — | — | — | |
|   *Crunomys fallax*** | T | — | — | — | |
|   *Mus castaneus** | T | — | — | T | |
|   *Phloemys cumingi*** | T | — | T | — | |
|   *Phloemys pallidus*** | T | — | — | — | |
|   *Rattus argentiventer** | 1 | — | — | — | 1 = Barbehenn *et al.*, 1973 |
|   *Rattus everetti* group | T | — | — | — | |
|   *Rattus exulans** | T | T | — | — | |
|   *Rattus nitidus** | 1 | — | — | — | 1 = Musser, 1977a |
|   *Rattus norvegicus** | T | — | — | — | |
|   *Rattus rattus** | T | T | — | — | |
|   *Rhynchomys isarogensis*** | 1 | — | — | — | 1 = Musser & Freeman, 1981 |
|   *Rhynchomys soricoides*** | T | — | — | — | |
|   *Tryphomys adustus*** | 1 | — | — | — | 1 = Musser, 1981b |
| Carnivora | | | | | |
|   *Paradoxurus hermaphroditus* | T | — | T | — | |
|   *Viverra tangalunga* | T | — | — | T | |
| Artiodactyla | | | | | |
|   *Sus barbatus* | T | — | — | — | |
|   *Cervus mariannus* | T | — | — | — | |
| Total non-volant species | 35 | 3 | 3 | 2 | |
| Total indigenous species | 28 | 1 | 2 | 1 | |

  *Introduced commensal species.
  **Species endemic to faunal region.
  T = Taylor, 1934.

the present level (Bartlett & Borghoorn, 1973; Gascoyne, Benjamin & Schwartz, 1979; Bloom, 1983). It is possible to approximate the extent of late Pleistocene islands in SE Asia, and elsewhere in the world, by tracing the 120 m line around current islands. This method is likely to be generally accurate for the late

Table 4. List of mammal species known to occur on Mindoro Island

| | | |
|---|---|---|
| Area (km²) | 9735 | |
| Elevation (m) | 2585 | |
| Depth of Luzon (m) | 360 | |
| Distance to Luzon (km) | 18 | |
| Insectivora | | |
| *Crocidura halconus*** | | T |
| *Crocidura mindorus*** | | T |
| Primates | | |
| *Macaca fascicularis* | | T |
| Rodentia | | |
| *Anonomomys mindorensis*** | | Musser & Newcomb, 1983 |
| *Apomys musculus* | | Musser, 1982b |
| *Chrotomys mindorensis* | | Musser et al., 1981 |
| *Crateromys paulus***·*** | | Musser & Gordon, 1981 |
| *Rattus everetti* group | | T |
| *Rattus exulans** | | Musser, 1977a |
| *Rattus mindorensis*** | | Musser & Califia, 1982 |
| *Rattus norvegicus** | | T |
| *Rattus rattus** | | Musser, 1977a |
| Carnivora | | |
| *Paradoxurus hermaphroditus* | | T |
| *Viverra tangalunga* | | T |
| Artiodactyla | | |
| *Bubalus mindorensis*** | | T |
| *Sus barbatus* | | Groves, 1981 |
| *Cervus mariannus* | | Grubb & Groves, 1983 |
| Total non-volant species | 17 | |
| Total indigenous species | 14 | |

*Introduced commensal species.
**Species endemic to Mindoro Island.
***Restricted to islet of Ilin.
T = Taylor, 1934.

Pleistocene because 18 000 years allows time for relatively little geological change. Moreover, because uplifting has predominated in the critical areas in SE Asia, we can assume that this method provides the maximum extent of landbridges, and is thus a conservative estimate.

A recent review of vertebrate zoogeographic data (Heaney, 1985b) found strong support for the geologically based model of the Philippine late Pleistocene islands shown in Fig. 1. It appears that there was not a continuous landbridge to the Philippines from Asia during the late Pleistocene. Several channels over 200 m deep separate both the Sulu and Palawan chains from the main body of the Philippines, and much deeper water lies in all other directions.

During the late middle Pleistocene, eustatic sea level was 160–180 m lower than it is at present (Donn, Farrand & Ewing, 1962; Gascoyne et al., 1979). Much of the Philippines was tectonically active throughout the Pleistocene, and I therefore hesitate to estimate middle Pleistocene island connections from current topography. However, it should be noted that the Palawan region has been tectonically stable for a longer period than is typical for the region (see below) and shows evidence of a potentially unusual and interesting set of circumstances. Because the channel between Borneo and Palawan is 145 m deep, a landbridge may have existed between Borneo and Palawan during the

Table 5. List of the mammals of the Negros–Panay faunal region

| Island | Negros | Panay | Cebu |
|---|---|---|---|
| Area (km²) | 13 670 | 12 300 | 4421 |
| Elevation (m) | 2460 | 1765 | 1013 |
| Depth to Negros (m) | — | 15 | 90 |
| Distance to Negros (km) | — | 18 | 5 |
| Insectivora | | | |
|   *Crocidura negrinus*** | T | — | — |
|   *Suncus murinus** | UMMZ | T | AMNH |
| Primates | | | |
|   *Macaca fascicularis* | T | — | — |
| Rodentia | | | |
|   *Apomys littoralis* | $M_2$ | — | — |
|   *Mus castaneus** | T | T | AMNH |
|   *Rattus exulans** | $M_1$ | — | — |
|   *Rattus norvegicus** | $M_1$ | T | AMNH |
|   *Rattus rattus** | $M_1$ | T | AMNH |
| Carnivora | | | |
|   *Paradoxurus hermaphroditus* | T | T | — |
|   *Viverra tangalunga* | T | BMNH | — |
|   *Felis bengalensis* | T | T | T |
| Artiodactyla | | | |
|   *Sus barbatus* | T | T | T |
|   *Cervus alfredi* | T | T | T |
| Total non-volant species | 13 | 9 | 7 |
| Total indigenous species | 8 | 5 | 3 |

*Introduced commensal species.
**Species endemic to faunal region.
$M_1$ = Musser, 1977a; $M_2$ = Musser, 1982b; T = Taylor, 1934.

late middle Pleistocene (about 160 000 years ago), but not more recently. Thus, the Palawan region fauna seen today occurred on a single large island during the late Pleistocene (Fig. 1), and has been isolated from its source in Borneo since the middle Pleistocene. The shallow (140 m) San Bernardino Channel between southern Luzon and northern Samar might also have been dry during the late middle Pleistocene, allowing free exchange through much of the archipelago.

## Geology of the Philippines

The summary of the Philippine geology provided here is based on the following papers unless noted otherwise: Hamilton (1979), Holloway (1982), Ollier (1985), Vondra & Mathisen (1985). Locations of most features discussed below are shown in Fig. 2. My emphasis is on the formation of subaerial islands, rather than on the entire geological evolution of the archipelago.

The Philippine Islands were formed largely as a result of the collision of a major Pacific lithospheric plate with the South China Sea plate, an off-rider of the Asian land mass. The islands occur as a series of major arcs that are adjacent to active or inactive subduction zones, as shown in Fig. 2. Although a small amount of continental crust is included, it is likely that the islands have formed *de novo* as an oceanic group.

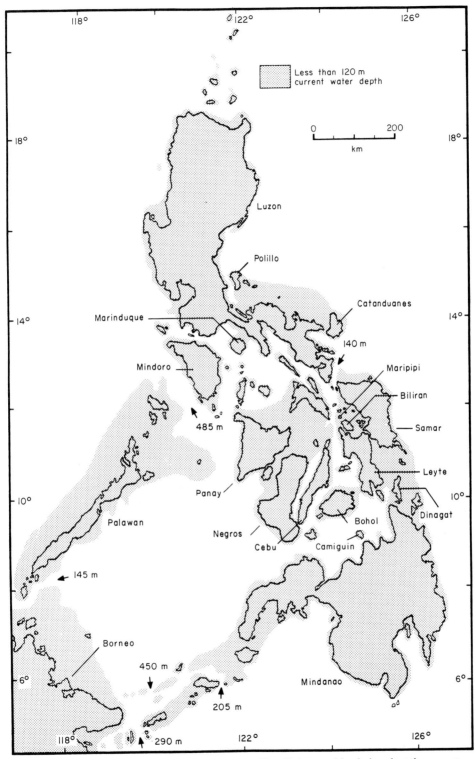

Figure 1. Map of the Philippines showing the extent of late Pleistocene islands, based on the current 120 m bathymetric line; from Heaney (1985a, b).

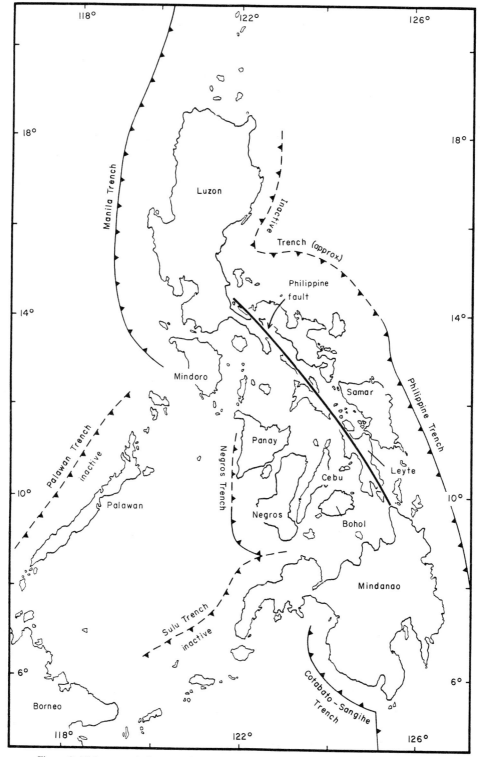

Figure 2. Major tectonic features of the Philippine Islands. Modified from Hamilton (1979).

The islands of the Palawan Arc are a composite of old continental crustal rocks (from the northern half of Palawan Island to southern Mindoro and northern Panay) and more recent fragments of oceanic crust. The continental rocks are Palaeozoic and Mesozoic in age and consist of some clastic sediments and limestone. Limestone sediments containing fossils of marine invertebrates on top of the continental rocks indicate that shallow marine conditions existed from the Jurassic to the Eocene. Recent data suggest a mid-Oligocene to early Miocene (32 to 17 Ma BP) rifting of this material away from the Asian continent (Taylor & Hayes, 1980; Holloway, 1982); no evidence yet suggests subaerial (emergent) islands before the Miocene. Sedimentary material of Pliocene and Quaternary origin on the edge of the Palawan trench suggests the presence of islands by the Pliocene. The subduction zone has been inactive since the Miocene.

Luzon, the largest and probably oldest island in the archipelago, originated as a series of small islands above water beginning in the late Eocene or early Oligocene near the Philippine Trench, and near the Manila Trench by the early Miocene. By the late Pliocene, the intervening basin had filled with enough sediment to project above water, resulting in a single large island (Vondra et al., 1982; Bachman, Lewis & Schweller, 1983).

Mindanao, Leyte and Samar are all associated with the Philippine Trench, the largest and most active subduction zone in the area. Southern Mindanao was also influenced by the Sangihe and Halmahera arcs; these become more prominent when they reach the islands of Celebes and Halmahera. Coal deposits present on the Zamboanga Peninsula indicate that subaerial conditions existed during the lower Miocene (Hamilton, 1979: 207). However, much of Mindanao consists of Pliocene to Recent volcanic deposits, and thus Mindanao has been a single large island since the late Pliocene at the earliest. Leyte consists primarily of Miocene limestone and volcanics of marine origin, but several Quaternary volcanoes are also present; subaerial conditions before the Pliocene seem unlikely. Samar contains more early Teriary volcanic deposits, but also much Miocene–Pliocene limestone.

The Miocene was marked by migration of the Pacific plate to the northwest over the floor of the Sulu Sea, forming the Sulu Arc. This subduction zone was active up until the Late Pleistocene, but is now dormant. Pliocene to Quaternary volcanic deposits on Jolo (Philippine Bureau of Mines, 1963) may mark the oldest subaerial deposition in the Sulus.

Miocene to Recent sedimentary deposits and inactive volcanoes on Mindoro (Philippine Bureau of Mines, 1963) suggest subaerial conditions on the island at least since the early Pliocene, and possibly earlier.

Negros and Panay lie on an active volcanic arc that is bounded on the west by the actively subducting Negros Trench. Although tectonic activity probably dates from the Miocene, limestone reefs of Miocene to Pleistocene age are common up to 200 m elevation on many parts of Negros; subaerial conditions probably did not exist until the late Pliocene. Most volcanic materials are of Quaternary age. On Panay, sedimentary material is mostly Quaternary in age; pre-Pliocene subaerial conditions are possible but seem unlikely. Cebu also contains old metamorphosed marine sediments and volcanics; its time of orgin as an island is uncertain.

Camiguin Island, north of central Mindanao, is composed entirely of

Quaternary volcanic material from a currently active volcano. Major eruptions have occurred within historic time.

In summary, although there is evidence that geological activity in the Philippines was initiated before the Palaeocene, most uplift has occurred since the beginning of the Miocene. Miocene activity resulted in the formation of at least some subaerial islands, and at least one large island, Luzon, had formed by the late Pliocene. Much of the present landform, however, was determined by Plio-Pleistocene tectonic and volcanic activity, and some areas remain active today.

Although it is desirable in a study such as this to include a discussion of the Pleistocene fauna, this topic is extremely poorly known at present. Only a few large mammals have been recorded, and all from fragmentary material from Luzon (Fox & Peralta, 1974; Groves, 1985).

### RESULTS

#### *Patterns of distribution*

##### *Sunda Shelf*

The islands on the continental shelf of SE Asia include Borneo, Java, Sumatra and a host of smaller islands. Most species of mammals in the region are widely distributed, demonstrating dispersal by mammals across the Sunda Shelf during the late Pleistocene (Heaney, 1984a). However, some endemics are present also. Borneo, for example, has about 29 endemics among its 124 indigenous species, and Sumatra and Java each have seven endemics out of 110 and 61 species, respectively (see Appendix; Medway, 1972, 1977; Heaney, 1985b). Most endemics are montane species. No endemics occur on islands smaller than Java that are within the 120 m bathymetric line, i.e. even on moderately large islands that were part of the late Pleistocene mainland. In contrast, many small islands beyond the 120 m limit support endemics (as discussed below).

##### *Philippines*

The terrestrial mammalian fauna of the Philippines has traditionally been divided into four major regions, based on richness, composition and degree of endemism (Steere, 1890; Heaney & Rabor, 1982): the Palawan, Mindanao, Luzon and Negros regions. Additionally, several large oceanic islands (e.g. Mindoro) often are mentioned as distinct. These parallel the faunal regions exhibited by birds (Dickerson, 1928), and reptiles and amphibians (Brown & Alcala, 1970), and correspond to the limits of late Pleistocene islands (Heaney, 1985b). The following brief descriptions of the faunal regions are intended to provide a general perspective. It should be noted that thorough faunal surveys and reports for all of the regions are badly needed, especially in the light of the extremely high current rates of deforestation.

##### *Palawan region*

The Palawan faunal region (Fig. 1) is noteworthy for its rich fauna (relative to island size), including many groups (carnivores, pangolins, porcupines and some insectivores) absent or poorly represented elsewhere in the Philippines (Table 1). Although many species are endemic, nearly all genera are found in northern Borneo (Fig. 3). Of 25 indigenous species, 11 (44%) are endemic to the region and the rest are shared with Borneo; 96% of the genera are shared with Borneo. Thus, the Palawan region is part of the Sunda zoogeographic province, not part of the Philippine faunal province.

The clear faunal relationship of Palawan to Borneo has long been attributed to the probable presence of a landbridge from Palawan to Borneo during the Pleistocene (Fig. 1; Everett, 1889). The channel between Borneo and Palawan is about 145 m deep; this is greater than the 120 m depth reached during the late Pleistocene, but less than the 160 m depth reached during the middle Pleistocene. The large number of endemic species but low number of endemic genera is consistent with the geological evidence of separation from Borneo for about 160 000 years (Heaney, 1985b).

*Mindanao faunal region*

A total of 33 indigenous species of non-volant mammals is known to occur in the Mindanao faunal region (Table 2). Four species are widespread within and outside the Philippines and three species are widespread within, but restricted to, the Philippines. The remaining 26 species (79%) are endemic. Of 21 genera of non-volant mammals, four (19%) are endemic to the faunal region, four (19%) are endemic to the Philippines, and the remaining 13 genera (62%) are moderately to extremely widespread in other parts of Australasia.

Twenty-five species of indigenous non-volant mammals have been recorded on Mindanao, nine of which (36%) are endemic (Table 2). Unexpectedly, the small island of Dinagat supports at least three endemic species of non-volant mammals, two of which (*Podogymnura* and *Batomys*) have their closest relatives on Mindanao and one of which (*Crateromys*) has relatives known only from Luzon and an islet near Mindoro. Other islands in the faunal region share nearly all of their species with Mindanao.

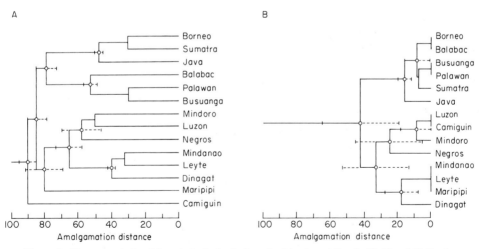

Figure 3. Cluster analysis of faunal similarity indices for 14 selected Sunda Shelf and Philippine islands. Data from Table 7. A, Jaccard's index; B, Simpson's index. Interrupted bars show standard errors for the node.

*Luzon region*

The current island of Luzon formed the core of a larger island during the late Pleistocene, one that included the current islands of Catanduanes, Marinduque and Polillo, as well as numerous smaller islands (Fig. 1). It has long been noted that the highlands of central Luzon support a rich fauna of endemic species; it is now becoming apparent that the highlands of the southern peninsula (south of Ragay Gulf) also support endemics. One new genus and one additional new species have been named on the basis of a single small collection from Mt Isarog (Musser & Freeman, 1981; Musser, 1982c).

The moderately large islands of Catanduanes, Marinduque and Polillo are included in this tabulation principally to demonstrate how little is known about them. Table 3 shows that each has had a maximum of three species of terrestrial mammals recorded; moreover, no museum specimens have been obtained from these islands since the 1930s.

Of the 29 indigenous species of non-volant mammals that occur in the Luzon region, 20 (69%) are endemic. Of the nine remaining, four (14%) otherwise occur only in the Philippines and five (18%) are widespread in Australasia. Of 21 genera that are indigenous, seven (33%) are endemic to the region; all seven are murid rodents. An additional five genera (24%) are restricted to the Philippines.

The boundary between the Luzon and Mindanao faunal regions is strikingly defined by the San Bernardino Channel, a narrow (15 km), shallow (140 m) strait whose zoogeographic importance is belied by its small size.

*Mindoro faunal region*

The deep water surrounding Mindoro (Fig. 1) makes it quite likely that this island retained a separate existence throughout the Pleistocene. Thirteen indigenous species of mammals are known from Mindoro (Table 4). An additional endemic, *Crateromys paulus*, is known from a single specimen from the tiny island of Ilin, adjacent to Mindoro's southwest coast; this species is the only one known from Ilin (Musser & Gordon, 1981). Among these 14 indigenous species, six (43%) are endemic. All eight remaining species are shared with Luzon, clearly demonstrating a faunal affinity between these islands. However, there is also a less apparent but important affinity to the south. According to Musser & Califia (1982), the endemic *Rattus mindorensis* is most closely related to *Rattus tiomanicus*, which is absent from Luzon but occurs on Palawan and Calawit (near Busuanga), and the endemic genus *Anonomomys* is most closely related to *Haeromys*, which occurs on Palawan and Busuanga but not Luzon (Musser & Newcomb, 1983: 559). This strongly implies colonization from two directions, with the two species mentioned arriving from Palawan (and ultimately Borneo), and at least four species arriving from Luzon or elsewhere in the main body of the Philippines.

*Negros–Panay faunal region*

This faunal region corresponds to one of the large late Pleistocene islands described above. Negros is one of the best known islands in the Philippines; other islands in the group are poorly known. The non-volant mammal fauna is limited to an endemic shrew, the long-tailed macaque, a murid rodent and the widespread carnivores and ungulates (Heaney, Heideman & Mudar, 1981; Musser, 1982b) (Table 5). The one native murid also occurs on Mindanao.

*Sulu Archipelago*

The Sulu Archipelago probably occurred as a series of islands during the late and middle Pleistocene, as it does today (Musser & Heaney, 1985: fig. 1). However, there were fewer and larger islands, and one island that extended from present-day Tawitawi to Jolo filled most of the gap between Borneo and Mindanao. The fauna of the archipelago consists of a widespread Sunda Shelf primate not found elsewhere in the Philippines (*Nycticebus coucang*), and several widespread large mammals, as well as an endemic shrew and an endemic murid (Musser & Heaney, 1985). Thus, two out of seven presumed native species (29%) are endemic.

By this tally, there are about 101 species of non-volant mammals in the Philippines, including eight introduced species (one insectivore and seven murids). About 79 (85%) non-volant species are endemic to the Philippines (Table 6).

In summary, each area bounded by the 120 m bathymetric line supports a mammalian fauna that is rich in endemics. In the Philippines, three faunally distinct groups of islands are formed by the contemporary islands that were part of the three late Pleistocene islands of Greater Luzon, Greater Mindanao and Greater Palawan. Each of these groups (and the Sunda Shelf group) is marked by a high level of within-group faunal similarity and each group supports a large number of endemics so that between-group similarity is low. The fauna of Greater Palawan is quite similar to Borneo at the generic level and has little in common with Luzon. This similarity with Borneo is indicative of a middle Pleistocene landbridge connection. Mindoro has elements of both the Luzon and Palawan faunas and thus appears to have received immigrants from both

Table 6. Summary of the non-volant mammal faunas of 12 selected Philippine islands

| | Area (km²) | Number of non-volant species | Number of indigenous species | Number of endemic species | Percentage of species endemic |
|---|---|---|---|---|---|
| Palawan | 11 785 | 27 | 23 | 3 | 13 |
| Busuanga | 938 | 18 | 15 | 0 | 0 |
| Culion | 400 | 11 | 9 | 0 | 0 |
| Balabac | 306 | 11 | 10 | 0 | 0 |
| Palawan region | — | 29 | 25 | 11 | 44 |
| Mindanao | 99 078 | 30 | 25 | 9 | 36 |
| Leyte | 7213 | 18 | 14 | 1 | 7 |
| Dinagat | 670 | 17 | 15 | 3 | 20 |
| Maripipi | 22 | 6 | 5 | 0 | 0 |
| Mindanao region | — | 38 | 33 | 26 | 79 |
| Luzon | 108 171 | 35 | 28 | 20 | 71 |
| Luzon region | — | 36 | 29 | 21 | 72 |
| Negros | 13 670 | 13 | 8 | 1 | 13 |
| Mindoro | 9735 | 17 | 14 | 6 | 43 |
| Camiguin | 265 | 5 | 2 | 0 | 0 |
| Sulu Archipelago | — | ? | 7 | 2 | 29 |
| Philippines (excluding Palawan) | | 101 | 93 | 79 | 85 |

directions. The isolated oceanic islands are generally depauperate, but usually support one or more species of the endemic Philippine genera.

## Quantitative regional similarities

In order to quantitatively evaluate the similarities of the fauna found on the Sunda Shelf and Philippine islands, I utilized two measures of similarity. The first was Jaccard's index (Udvardy, 1969: 273), which is defined as $(C/N_1 + N_2 - C) = R$, where $C$ = the number of taxa shared (in this case, genera), $N_1$ = the number of genera in the smaller fauna, $N_2$ = the number of genera in the larger fauna and $R$ = the index of faunal resemblance. This index is sensitive to species richness, underestimating the similarity of small to large islands. A second index was calculated to compensate for this, Simpson's index, defined as $(C/N_1) = R$. This index emphasizes the presence of the few genera that occur on small islands and thereby inflates the measure of similarity when the small islands have a few genera that are widespread. For both indices, a given index is most meaningful in the context of a single island compared to a series of others; i.e. the absolute value is of little utility without points of reference. The faunal similarity indices (Table 7) were then subjected to UPGMA cluster analysis (Fig. 3).

These analyses strongly support the existence of faunal regions defined by late Pleistocene islands. On the basis of similarity at the generic level, there are three groups of islands evident in both cluster analyses. The Sunda Shelf islands are very similar to each other, and are not consistently clustered separately from the Palawan group islands. The second group consists of Mindanao and the smaller islands derived from Greater Mindanao. The third cluster consists of Luzon and the isolated oceanic islands, which are alike in possessing a few very widespread species and at least some of endemic Philippine murid rodent genera. The Luzon and Mindanao clusters are themselves grouped together separate from the Sunda Shelf and Palawan islands.

It should be noted that the standard errors associated with several clustering nodes indicates that the ordering within the groups is not meaningful. For example, in Fig. 3B, the Greater Sunda islands and Palawan islands are intermixed in a way that is not statistically meaningful, as are islands in the islands in the Luzon/oceanic group. Future analyses using species, rather than genera, to form the similarity matrices would resolve many of these undefined clustering sequences.

## Influence of island size on faunal size and composition

### Species richness and island area

Among non-volant mammals on islands on the continental shelf of SE Asia, the number of species is highly correlated with island area (Heaney, 1984a), as is typically true of species–area curves (MacArthur, 1972; Williamson, 1981). Figure 4 shows that, in contrast, nearly all islands in the Philippines are depauperate and as a group have a lower correlation between species richness and area. However, islands that were part of a single late Pleistocene island typically have a high species–area correlation. Landbridge islands in the Palawan chain have fewer species than the Sunda Shelf reference group from

Table 7. Faunal similarity indices of genera of non-volant native mammals from selected SE Asian islands. Above the diagonal is Jaccard's index $(C/N_1 + N_2 - C)$; below the diagonal is Simpson's index $(C/N_1)$

| | Luzon | Mindoro | Palawan | Busuanga | Balabac | Mindanao | Leyte | Dinagat | Maripipi | Negros | Camiguin | Borneo | Sumatra | Java |
|---|---|---|---|---|---|---|---|---|---|---|---|---|---|---|
| Luzon | — | 0.50 | 0.17 | 0.17 | 0.15 | 0.37 | 0.42 | 0.29 | 0.01 | 0.33 | 0.10 | 0.08 | 0.08 | 0.09 |
| Mindoro | 0.85 | — | 0.21 | 0.22 | 0.21 | 0.31 | 0.35 | 0.32 | 0.20 | 0.50 | 0.15 | 0.10 | 0.09 | 0.11 |
| Palawan | 0.30 | 0.46 | — | 0.71 | 0.41 | 0.20 | 0.21 | 0.12 | 0.13 | 0.26 | 0.09 | 0.27 | 0.25 | 0.32 |
| Busuanga | 0.33 | 0.38 | 0.99 | — | 0.47 | 0.20 | 0.21 | 0.15 | 0.18 | 0.21 | 0.13 | 0.21 | 0.19 | 0.23 |
| Balabac | 0.44 | 0.40 | 0.90 | 0.80 | — | 0.15 | 0.33 | 0.18 | 0.15 | 0.29 | 0.09 | 0.14 | 0.14 | 0.18 |
| Mindanao | 0.55 | 0.62 | 0.33 | 0.40 | 0.40 | — | 0.67 | 0.61 | 0.24 | 0.32 | 0.09 | 0.15 | 0.13 | 0.14 |
| Leyte | 0.71 | 0.54 | 0.43 | 0.36 | 0.60 | 0.99 | — | 0.58 | 0.36 | 0.47 | 0.14 | 0.13 | 0.16 | 0.14 |
| Dinagat | 0.53 | 0.47 | 0.27 | 0.27 | 0.40 | 0.93 | 0.73 | — | 0.24 | 0.20 | 0.13 | 0.11 | 0.10 | 0.10 |
| Maripipi | 0.60 | 0.60 | 0.60 | 0.60 | 0.40 | 0.99 | 0.99 | 0.80 | — | 0.18 | 0.17 | 0.07 | 0.07 | 0.08 |
| Negros | 0.87 | 0.87 | 0.75 | 0.50 | 0.50 | 0.87 | 0.87 | 0.50 | 0.40 | — | 0.11 | 0.10 | 0.09 | 0.11 |
| Camiguin | 0.99 | 0.99 | 0.99 | 0.99 | 0.50 | 0.99 | 0.99 | 0.99 | 0.50 | 0.50 | — | 0.03 | 0.03 | 0.04 |
| Borneo | 0.35 | 0.62 | 0.95 | 0.99 | 0.99 | 0.57 | 0.71 | 0.60 | 0.99 | 0.87 | 0.99 | — | 0.69 | 0.51 |
| Sumatra | 0.35 | 0.54 | 0.91 | 0.93 | 0.99 | 0.52 | 0.64 | 0.53 | 0.99 | 0.87 | 0.99 | 0.82 | — | 0.54 |
| Java | 0.30 | 0.46 | 0.81 | 0.80 | 0.90 | 0.43 | 0.57 | 0.40 | 0.80 | 0.75 | 0.99 | 0.82 | 0.86 | — |

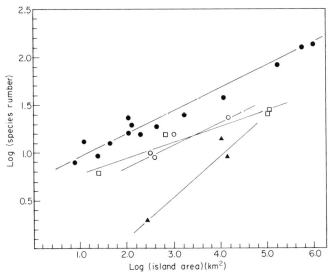

Figure 4. Relationship of log of island area and log of number of indigenous species of non-volant mammals on the Sunda Shelf in Malaysia and Indonesia (●); for Palawan chain islands (○); for Luzon and Mindanao group islands (□); and for oceanic islands in the Philippines (▲). Regression data in Table 8.

Malaysia and Indonesia, but only slightly so. The slope of the regression line (0.246) is almost identical to that of the shallow-water Sunda Shelf islands (0.230; Table 8). The large islands in the Luzon and Mindanao groups have smaller faunas than would islands of the same size on the Sunda Shelf, and also have fewer species than islands of their size in the Palawan group (28 species rather than 41 for Luzon, and 25 rather than 40 for Mindanao). However, small islands in the Mindanao region (e.g. Dinagat and Maripipi) have about the number of species expected for the Palawan group, but fewer than expected for the Sunda Shelf islands. Islands that comprised Greater Luzon and Mindanao appear to lie on a single regression line which is shallower in slope than the Palawan group line (0.167 versus 0.246). Inspection of Fig. 4 suggests that the difference in slope primarily reflects the depauperate faunas of Luzon and Mindanao, relative to the Palawan group.

Table 8. Regression coefficients for species–area curves. Commensal species were not included in analyses

| Region | $N$ | Correlation coefficient | Slope | Intercept |
|---|---|---|---|---|
| Malay Peninsula (mainland) | 6 | 0.85* | 0.09 | 1.67 |
| Sunda Shelf islands | 14 | 0.97** | 0.23 | 0.69 |
| Palawan chain | 4 | 0.95* | 0.25 | 0.38 |
| Mindanao and Luzon | 4 | 0.97* | 0.17 | 0.61 |
| Isolated oceanic group | 3 | 0.92 | 0.44 | −0.74 |
| Endemic species (all regions) | 14 | 0.75** | 0.30 | −0.63 |

*$P < 0.05$.
**$P < 0.01$.

The three isolated oceanic islands (Mindoro, Negros and Camiguin) lie below the other regression lines; the correlation coefficient for these islands (0.922) is high but not significant. Nevertheless, it is clear that isolated oceanic islands are the most impoverished in the Philippines. It is interesting to note that the relative degree of impoverishment (increasing from Mindoro to Negros to Camiguin) parallels the approximate geological age of these islands (Mio-Pliocene, Plio-Pleistocene, and Pleistocene–Recent, respectively). This correlation implies that colonization of these islands has been very slow. A substantial portion of Mindoro's fauna is endemic (43% of the 14 species), a lesser portion of the smaller fauna of Negros is endemic (12.5% of eight species) and neither of the two species indigenous to Camiguin is endemic. The trend in endemism correlates with the apparent age and the impoverishment of these islands. Thus, the size of mammalian faunas on isolated oceanic islands in the Philippines is correlated with the geological age of the islands. The older, less impoverished faunas contain proportionately and absolutely more endemic species than the newer, more impoverished faunas. The correlation between number of endemic species and area is discussed in the next section.

In summary, the mid-Pleistocene islands of the Palawan chain have fewer non-volant mammals than islands of comparable size on the shallow portion of the Sunda Shelf, but the slopes of the regression lines are equal. Luzon and Mindanao have fewer species than predicted from the Sunda Shelf or Palawan species–area regressions, but smaller islands in the Mindanao group have species numbers equivalent to those in the Palawan group. Isolated oceanic islands have impoverished faunas, with geological age of the island positively related to the degree of endemism and inversely related to the degree of impoverishment.

*Endemism and island area*

Island area and the number of endemic species within the study area are highly correlated (Table 9, Fig. 5). As noted earlier, endemic species are

Table 9. Island area and number of endemic species for islands in the study area that are known to support endemics

| Island name | Area | No. of endemics |
|---|---|---|
| Borneo | 743 244 | 29 |
| Sumatra | 473 607 | 7 |
| Malay Peninsula | 131 676 | 3 |
| Java | 125 628 | 7 |
| Luzon | 108 171 | 19 |
| Mindanao | 99 078 | 9 |
| Negros | 13 670 | 1 |
| Palawan | 11 785 | 11 |
| Mindoro | 9735 | 5 |
| Leyte | 7213 | 1 |
| Dinagat | 670 | 3 |
| Jolo | 345 | 1 |
| Tawitawi | 229 | 1 |
| Ilin | 47 | 1 |

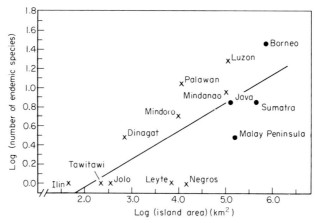

Figure 5. Relationship of island area and number of endemic non-volant mammals from islands known to support endemics. ●, Sunda Shelf island; ×, all Philippine islands.

restricted to islands over 125 000 km² on the continental shelf, but endemics occur on islands down to 47 km² off the edge of the shelf (see also Lawlor, 1983). Inspection of Fig. 5 indicates that: (1) island faunas on the continental shelf have a steeper slope to the endemic species–area curve than do the island faunas off the edge of the shelf; (2) the mid-Pleistocene island of Palawan has the highest relative level of endemism, but the geologically old oceanic island of Luzon is nearly as high, and (3) at least one geologically young oceanic island (Negros) has an unusually low level of endemism. More detailed and extensive analysis should be done to determine the quantitative effects of island age, degree of isolation and Pleistocene landbridge connections. These preliminary data indicate that increasing island age and lack of landbridges generally promote endemism, and the development of recent landbridges inhibits endemism, but old landbridge islands such as Palawan may have unusually high levels of endemism.

*Faunal composition*

Islands on the continental shelf show regular patterns in the composition of their mammal faunas (Heaney, 1984a; Fig. 6); for example, these islands always have about 10% of their fauna made up of primates, whether the island has 130 species or only eight. Rodents tend to be disproportionately well represented on small islands, and carnivores under-represented; the other groups show no significant trends.

The Philippine islands fit these patterns rather poorly (Fig. 6, Table 10). The faunas of the Palawan islands generally fall within the range of the shallow-water Sunda Shelf sample, except that they tend to have lower percentages of rodents and higher proportions of carnivores. Luzon has an exceptionally large rodent fauna, but small insectivore, carnivore and ungulate faunas. Mindanao has a typical proportion of rodents, insectivores and primates but few carnivores. Only the moderately small Dinagat has a fauna with the expected species richness and faunal composition. Maripipi has a smaller proportion of rodents and more primates than expected. Mindoro fits the composition pattern

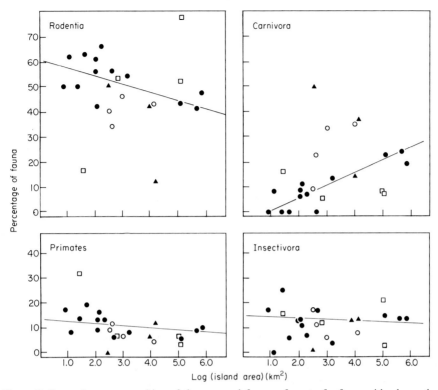

Figure 6. Proportionate composition of the mammal faunas of a set of reference islands on the Sunda Shelf and on selected Philippine islands (●Sunda Shelf shallow-water islands; ○, Palawan landbridge islands; □, Luzon and Mindanao groups; ▲, Philippine oceanic islands. Data on Sunda Shelf islands from Heaney (1984a). Data for Philippine islands from Table 10.

Table 10. Area and composition of the faunas (non-volant land mammals) of selected Philippine islands. For each group, the number of native species (and percentage of the fauna in parentheses) is given for each island

| Island | Type* | Log (area) (km²) | Total | Insectivores | Primates | Rodents | Carnivores | Ungulates | Dermoptera |
|---|---|---|---|---|---|---|---|---|---|
| Maripipi | P | 1.40 | 6 | 1 (16.7) | 2 (33.3) | 1 (16.7) | 1 (16.7) | 0 | 1 (16.7) |
| Camiguin | O | 2.42 | 2 | 0 | 0 | 1 (50.0) | 1 (50.0) | 0 | 0 |
| Balabac | L | 2.49 | 10 | 2 (20.0) | 1 (10.0) | 4 (40.0) | 1 (10.0) | 2 (20.0) | 0 |
| Culion | L | 2.60 | 9 | 1 (11.1) | 1 (11.1) | 3 (33.3) | 2 (22.2) | 2 (22.2) | 0 |
| Dinagat | P | 2.83 | 15 | 2 (13.3) | 1 (6.6) | 8 (53.3) | 1 (6.6) | 2 (13.3) | 1 (6.6) |
| Busuanga | L | 2.97 | 15 | 1 (6.6) | 1 (6.6) | 7 (46.7) | 5 (33.3) | 1 (6.6) | 0 |
| Mindoro | O | 3.99 | 14 | 2 (14.3) | 1 (7.1) | 6 (42.9) | 2 (14.3) | 3 (21.4) | 0 |
| Palawan† | L | 4.07 | 23 | 2 (8.7) | 1 (4.3) | 10 (43.7) | 8 (34.7) | 1 (4.3) | 0 |
| Negros | O | 4.14 | 8 | 1 (12.5) | 1 (12.5) | 1 (12.5) | 3 (37.5) | 2 (25.0) | 0 |
| Mindanao | P | 5.00 | 25 | 5 (20.0) | 2 (8.0) | 13 (52.0) | 2 (8.0) | 2 (8.0) | 1 (4.0) |
| Luzon | P | 5.03 | 28 | 1 (3.6) | 1 (3.6) | 22 (78.6) | 2 (7.1) | 2 (7.1) | 0 |

*L = Pleistocene landbridge island; P = Luzon and Mindanao groups; O = isolated oceanic island.
†The Palawan fauna also includes *Manis javanica*, order Pholidota.

better, differing from the Sunda Shelf pattern in having proportionately larger carnivore and ungulate faunas. Negros and Camiguin are atypical in nearly all respects; it should be recalled that these islands have markedly depauperate faunas.

I conclude that islands in the Philippines lack the consistency and predictability of community composition shown by the Sunda Shelf islands. Islands in the Palawan chain are most like those on the Sunda Shelf, differing most conspicuously in having more carnivores. Small islands in the Mindanao chain sometimes have faunas similar to those on Sunda Shelf islands (Dinagat), and sometimes not (Maripipi). Mindanao is moderately dissimilar, as is Mindoro. Luzon is strongly dissimilar, as are the isolated oceanic islands of Negros and Camiguin.

## Rates of colonization

The geological data cited above strongly indicate that all of the Philippine islands except Greater Palawan have had no landbridge connections to the Asian continent, i.e. they have arisen *de novo* from the ocean floor. The high proportion of rodents (especially murids) in the Philippines led Darlington (1957) to suggest that all of the non-volant mammals arrived there by rafting or swimming, except for a few that were introduced by humans. The large number of endemic species and genera suggests that at least some species originated as a result of speciation by colonizers, so that the number of colonizers need not have been great. Further, the degree of divergence of some groups (especially the murids and insectivores) indicates that colonization may have begun long ago. However, we need to know if clear evidence exists that overwater colonization does occur.

The obvious places to turn for such evidence are the isolated oceanic islands. These islands are largely volcanic in origin and are often surrounded by water over 300 m deep. If colonization over salt water does occur, there should be terrestrial mammals on these islands. This is clearly true: Negros has eight native species and Mindoro has 15 native species. A single native murid is known from Camiguin, as well as a small carnivore (Heaney, 1984b). All of these islands are also known to support bats and commensals. However, the oceanic islands are depauperate, and conspicuous, frequently taken species such as tree squirrels, flying lemurs and tree shrews have not been obtained and probably do not occur on any of the oceanic islands. The great majority of species on these oceanic islands are murids, indicating that they have better-than-average colonizing ability.

Thus, there is clear evidence of natural dispersal across salt-water channels. As discussed above, the degree of impoverishment of these islands is inversely correlated with geological age of a given island. This implies that colonization is very slow, with species accumulating over long periods of time. Mindoro, with 14 native species, has existed since Mio-Pliocene times, *c.* 8–10 Ma BP; Negros, with eight species, originated during Plio-Pleistocene times, *c.* 1–4 Ma BP; and Camiguin, with two native species, originated as a single volcano during the Pleistocene, less than 1 Ma BP. Minimum estimates for the ages of the islands as moderately large areas are not available, but are unlikely to be less than one-fourth of maximum age. Thus, successful colonization can be estimated as being on the order of magnitude of once per quarter-million to half-million years. All of these islands were separated during the late Pleistocene from larger, more speciose islands by no more than 15 km of sea water.

Given the low but real potential for colonization and the great geological age of Luzon, and possibly Mindanao, it is conceivable, and indeed likely, that the Philippine fauna (expect that of Palawan) is derived entirely from over-water immigrants.

*Human influence on mammalian dispersal*

The preceeding discussions have not dealt with an important variable in dispersal: transportation by humans, either accidental or purposeful. Musser (1977a) listed six species of commensal murid rodents, all of which he believed were introduced to the Philippines. To these may be added an insectivore, the house shrew (*Suncus murinus*), which has been transported into the Pacific as far as Guam (Heaney, unpubl. obs.). All of the species but one (*Rattus nitidus*) are widespread in SE Asia and much of Australasia, most occur in all faunal regions of the Philippines (Musser, 1977a) and most show no conspicuous variation within the Philippines (an exception is *Rattus exulans*).

Darlington (1957: 504) pointed out that the few non-endemic, non-commensal species on Luzon are among the very few non-volant species that occur on both sides of Wallace's Line further south. All of these species are economically important as food sources by humans: pigs, monkeys and civet cats. On this basis, Darlington suggested that they were introduced to Luzon. Groves (1983) has summarized evidence that pigs (*Sus*) were often transported from island to island in Australasia, with introductions dating as early as 4000 BP. He also showed evidence that *Macaca, Paradoxurus* and *Viverra* were transported widely (Groves, 1984). If these species have been introduced into the Philippines, then only three ungulates and one carnivore are indigenous to all of the Philippines, except for species on the Palawan chain. The one certainly indigenous ungulate, the endemic dwarf water buffalo, is confined to Mindoro; the other two indigenous species are deer of the genus *Cervus* (Grubb & Groves, 1983). The native carnivore, the tiger cat (*Felis bengalensis*), occurs only on Palawan, which was connected to Borneo, and on Cebu, Negros and Panay, which made up a single isolated island during the late Pleistocene.

When the potentially introduced species are subtracted from the lists of non-volant mammals on Philippine islands, the effect is staggering. Negros, a tropical island the size of the state of Connecticut, may have only five native non-volant mammals! Yet Negros lies only 30 km from Mindanao, which has at least 22 native species. If *Macaca, Paradoxurus, Viverra* and *Sus* are removed from the faunal similarity analyses discussed earlier, the result is to increase the distinctiveness of each of the Philippine faunal regions and to decrease their already low level of similarity to the Sunda Shelf islands. It also distinguishes the Philippine islands (excluding those of the Palawan chain) from islands on the Sunda Shelf in faunal composition (Fig. 6) by increasing the relative proportions of rodents and insectivores and greatly decreasing the proportion of carnivores, primates and ungulates. Removing these species from faunal lists would also serve to make the isolated oceanic islands even more impoverished and to lower the estimate of colonization rates still further.

*Origin of the Philippine fauna*

Having concluded that dispersal over salt water does occur, we might ask where the non-volant mammals originated. We may begin this by asking what the distribution of congeneric species of indigenous Philippine mammals is. This approach excludes nearly all of the murids, the largest portion of the Philippine fauna, because most are endemic; they are discussed below.

Table 11 contains a list of 14 genera that occur both in the Philippines and elsewhere. Two of the genera (*Crocidura* and *Rattus*) are widespread, and so provide little insight. One genus (*Crunomys*) occurs only in the Philippines and on Celebes and one (*Tarsius*) occurs in the Philippines, Sunda Shelf and the Celebes. The remaining nine Philippine genera have their closest relatives on the Sunda Shelf. These data indicate that the majority of mammalian genera entered the Philippines from the continental shelf of Asia, probably via Borneo.

It is worth noting that there is no evidence that mammals have entered the Philippines from the north, via Taiwan, as suggested by Misonne (1969). In fact, the only genera shared by Taiwan and Luzon are *Crocidura* and *Rattus*, which are extremely widespread, plus the potentially introduced genera discussed above.

Detailed analysis of relationships within and among genera of SE Asian mammals are now under way, so that a few examples can be cited for use in 'track analysis' (Nelson & Platnick, 1981) of dispersal. One such study involves pygmy squirrels, genera *Exilisciurus* and *Nannosciurus* (Heaney, 1985a). Moore (1959) suggested a complicated pattern of biogeographic distribution and relationship involving the pygmy squirrels and two genera of tree squirrels on the Sunda Shelf, Philippines and Celebes. A more comprehensive analysis demonstrated a simpler situation, in which pygmy squirrels originated on the Sunda Shelf and a single species dispersed into the Philippines from Borneo (Heaney, 1985a).

Table 11. List of selected indigenous non-volant mammal genera from the Philippines, with notation of their closest relative and the place of that relative's occurrence. Taxa from the Palawan group are excluded

| Philippine genus | Closest relative | Nearest occurrence of relative | Source |
|---|---|---|---|
| *Podogymnura* | *Echinosorex* | Borneo | Heaney & Morgan, 1982 |
| *Urogale* | *Tupaia* | Borneo | |
| *Crocidura* | *Crocidura* | Widespread | |
| *Tarsius* | *Tarsius* | Borneo & Celebes | |
| *Cynocephalus* | *Cynocephalus* | Borneo | |
| *Sundasciurus* | *Sundasciurus* | Borneo | Heaney, 1979 |
| *Exilisciurus* | *Exilisciurus* | Borneo | Heaney, 1985a |
| *Petinomys* | *Petinomys* | Borneo | |
| *Hylopetes* | *Hylopetes* | Borneo | |
| *Anonomomys* | *Haeromys* | Borneo/Palawan | Musser & Newcomb, 1983 |
| *Rattus* | *Rattus* | Widespread | |
| *Crunomys* | *Crunomys* | Celebes | Musser, 1982c |
| *Felis* | *Felis* | Borneo | |
| *Bubalus* | *Bubalus* | Borneo | Groves, 1969 |

As has often been noted, the family Muridae is represented in the Philippines by a large and diverse assemblage of species. Current studies (Musser, Heaney & Rabor, 1985; Musser & Heaney, unpubl. obs.) indicate that the 40 known species, representing 15 genera, are members of seven different clades that represent a maximum of seven and a minimum of five colonization events. Each clade is derived from a group of murids that is most diverse on the Sunda Shelf and appears to have originated in that region. It is not clear from the available data whether these clades entered the Philippines via the Palawan route or the Sulu route, but there is no evidence for their arrival from Celebes, New Guinea or Taiwan.

In summary, all of the available data indicate a Sunda Shelf origin for the Philippine fauna of non-volant mammals. Among the possible source areas for Philippine mammals, the Sunda Shelf is the closest; this reinforces the conclusion derived earlier regarding the rarity of successful colonization across broad salt-water channels. The species-richness and taxonomic divergence of Philippine clades varies greatly, suggesting that colonization has occurred over a long period of time.

### Extinction rates

During the middle and late Pleistocene periods of low sea level, large areas in SE Asia were joined to the Asian continent as a continuous land mass. The species–area relationship on this land area may be approximated by comparing forest reserves of differing sizes on the Malay Peninsula, which remains a part of the mainland today. Figure 7 shows that on the mainland the number of species declines slowly with area; a forest reserve of 10 km² has, on average, 51 of the 120 species (43%) that occur in peninsular Malaysia. In contrast, a late

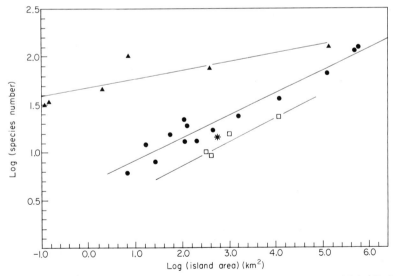

Figure 7. Comparison of species–area curves for mainland reference areas on the Malay Peninsula (▲), shallow-water Sunda Shelf islands (●) and Palawan chain islands (□). The asterisk represents Sipora Island, Mentawi Archipelago. Regression data in Table 8.

Pleistocene island of 10 km² typically has only four or five species, only 4% of the species on an area of the same size on the mainland. This reduction in species on the islands of the Sunda Shelf is due to extinction that has occurred since the islands became isolated from the mainland, an average of 12 000 years ago. For an 'average' island of 10 000 km², it is a reduction of 61%, from 104 species to 41; this is an average of 50%/10 000 years. In an earlier study, I used the time of isolation of landbridge islands (as determined by the depth of the surrounding water) to investigate rates of extinction (Heaney, 1984a). I concluded that extinction probably occurred rapidly after isolation (during the first few thousand years), occurring more slowly thereafter, but I was unable to measure extinction over longer periods of time.

A unique set of circumstances in SE Asia allows rough estimation of very long-term extinction rates. As discussed above, the islands in the Palawan chain have been separated from Borneo for about 160 000 years (Heaney, 1985b). The difference between the species–area curves for the Palawan group and the mainland is thus the result of about 160 000 years of extinction. The three lines in Fig. 7 are, in effect, a time series: mainland conditions, the result of 12 000 years of extinction, and the result of an additional 150 000 years of isolation.

Islands in the Palawan group have consistently fewer species than do islands in the Sunda Shelf group (Fig. 7). To continue the example given above, an island of the Palawan group of 10 000 km² typically has 23 species, or 22% of the 104 species on a comparable area on the mainland, and 56% of the 41 species on an island on the shallow Sunda Shelf. In other words, 78% of the fauna has become extinct in 160 000 years. However, as noted above, about 61% probably became extinct during the first 12 000 years and the rest (17%) during the next 150 000 years. For the period of 150 000 years following the initial flush of extinction this is a rate of 1.2 species/10 000 years (17/150 000), or 1.1%/10 000 years. Because the species–area lines are nearly parallel, the percentage of extinction on the middle Pleistocene islands in the Palawan chain appears to have been very nearly constant, regardless of island size; the number of species, however, varies with island area.

The estimates of extinction rates for an island of 10 000 km² are thus 50%/10 000 years for the period immediately following isolation, and 1.1%/10 000 years for the next 150 000 years. These estimates are shown in Fig. 8. The line is my estimation of the shape of the curve these points represent, with extinction initially high, but rapidly dropping off to a low but persistent level. The precise shape of the curve is unknown.

This method of estimating extinction assumes that colonization is absent. The estimate for colonization in the Philippines given above was a maximum of one event per quarter-million years. This implies that one or two species in the Palawan chain could be recent arrivals; if this is true, then the figures given here for extinction are slight underestimates.

A test of this interpretation of extinction rates is possible in SE Asia. Islands in the Mentawi Archipelago are separated from western Sumatra by water c. 150 m deep, and so should have been isolated from the mainland since the middle Pleistocene. This leads me to predict that the Mentawi islands will show faunal characteristics similar to the Palawan chain islands. This much is true: (1) the number of species on the one adequately surveyed island (Fig. 7, Table 12) falls in the range represented by the Palawan group; (2) it has a large

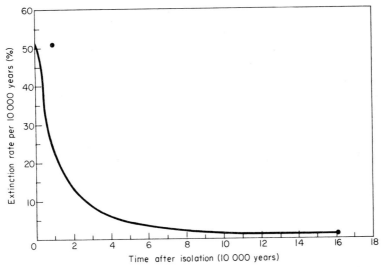

Figure 8. Extinction rate for non-volant mammal faunas in SE Asia. The two filled circles are data points discussed in the text; the curved line is an estimate of actual extinction rates for an island of 10 000 km² following isolation from the mainland.

proportion of endemics (*c.* 50%); and (3) the closest relatives of all (or nearly all) of its species are on the Sunda Shelf. The Mentawi archipelago is still poorly known but its importance for documenting the zoogeographic and evolutionary effects of isolation on landbridge faunas, and the need for full and careful surveys, should now be clear.

### Speciation in the Philippines

Once a species arrives in the Philippines, it finds itself in a highly fragmented archipelago. Species that occurred there during or before the late Pleistocene experienced dry land connections to many islands, but populations later became disjunct as sea level rose. We might then ask, have these vicariance processes induced speciation to occur in the Philippines? In this discussion, I exclude the islands of the Palawan group.

This question may be addressed initially by asking whether the endemic genera contain more species than the non-endemic genera. This approach assumes that endemic genera have been in the Philippines longer than the non-endemics and that the probability of speciation increases with time. The results clearly indicate the occurrence of speciation among the endemics: of 19 endemic genera, the mean number of species is 2.1 (s.D = 1.7) with a range of 1–8 species; 53% of the genera have two or more species. The 15 non-endemic genera have a mean of 1.6 species (s.D = 1.8), with a range of 1–8; but only two genera (13%) have more than one species. I suspect that the estimate of eight species in *Crocidura* is too high, based on my preliminary examination of specimens. If *Crocidura* is removed, the mean number of species in non-endemic genera falls to 1.1 (s.D = 0.5).

In a study of murid relationships mentioned earlier, Musser & Heaney (unpubl. obs.) have shown that the 40 known species and 15 genera of native

Table 12. Mammals known to occur on Sipora Island, Mentawi Archipelago (from Musser & Heaney, 1985; Musser & Newcomb, 1983; Honacki *et al.*, 1982)

| | |
|---|---|
| Area (km$^2$) | 594 |
| Elevation (m) | 302 |
| Depth to Sumatra (m) | 150 |
| Distance to Sumatra (km) | 110 |

Insectivora
  *Tupaia glis*
Primates
  *Presbytis potenziani***
  *Nasalis concolor***
  *Hylobates klossii***
Rodentia
  *Callosciurus melanogaster***
  *Lariscus insignis*
  *Sundasciurus lowii*
  *Petinomys hageni*
  *Hylopetes sipora***
  *Iomys horsfieldii*
  *Leopoldamys siporanus***
  *Maxomys pagensis***
  *Rattus lugens***
  *Rattus rattus**
Carnivora
  *Paradoxurus hermaphroditus*
  *Hemigalus derbyanus*
Artiodactyla
  *Cervus unicolor*

| | |
|---|---|
| Total non-volant species | 17 |
| Total indigenous species | 16 |

*Introduced commensal species.
**Species endemic to the Mentawi Archipelago.

murids in the Philippines (excluding the Palawan chain) represent between seven and five separate colonizations from the Sunda Shelf. Thus, each colonization resulted in an average of five or six species. However, most Philippine murids are members of a single clade that contains 26 species; the other clades contain only two to five species. Sixteen of the 28 species native to Luzon, or 57%, are members of the largest clade, showing the tremendous importance of indigenous speciation.

There is some evidence that speciation processes have resulted in increased species richness on the middle Pleistocene islands of the Palawan chain. There are two named species of squirrels (*Sundasciurus steeri* group) that are parapatric on Palawan Island. There are no specimens from the probable area of contact, but there is no evidence of intergradation and each population appears to be morphologically homogeneous (Heaney, 1979; unpubl. obs.). Whatever the method of differentiation (i.e. parapatric or allopatric), it appears that these populations now function as biological species. This has taken place in the *c.* 160 000 years since isolation of the Palawan chain from Borneo.

DISCUSSION

The mammalian fauna of the SE Asian islands has been affected in complex ways by the size, isolation and geographical history of the islands. The Philippine islands (excluding Palawan) are the most isolated of the islands considered here, having arisen *de novo* from the sea floor. The Palawan chain has been less isolated, having been joined to Borneo by a broad landbridge during the mid-Pleistocene. Non-volant mammals have entered the archipelago predominantly from Borneo, which is the nearest continental shelf land mass, by dispersal over narrow salt-water barriers. These barriers continue to be the major factors defining the distributions of species. Extinction on the Palawan chain was probably very high following its initial isolation from Borneo, but after about 160 000 years it retains a large and diverse fauna in which extinction is low and speciation does occur. Speciation elsewhere in the region has contributed substantially to the total faunal richness, with 55–70% of the fauna of Luzon having arisen in such a manner.

The results of this study indicate that the rate of colonization by non-volant mammals across landbridges is typically quite high. On the Sunda Shelf islands, levels of endemism are low and most endemics are limited to montane vegetation; nearly all lowland species are widespread. In the Philippines, small islands that were part of the late Pleistocene island of Greater Mindanao share the same species and populations of some species (e.g. pygmy squirrels; Heaney, 1985a) on different islands are nearly indistinguishable. On the other hand, narrow sea-water channels between islands have served as major, nearly insurmountable barriers to many non-volant mammals. Large but geologically young islands separated from rich faunal sources by 5–20 km of sea water have extremely depauperate faunas. For a large island such as Negros, with about five indigenous species, a rough estimate of one colonization event per 250 000 years is likely to be a *maximum* rate. Data from Mindoro and Camiguin support this estimate.

Because the fossil record from the Philippines is very poor it is not possible to measure directly the rate of extinction. However, a comparison of two sets of islands provides an estimate. The Palawan chain was isolated from Borneo about 160 000 years ago, whereas islands on the central Sunda Shelf were isolated only about 10 000 years ago. The fauna of the Palawan chain is about 50% smaller than the faunas on comparably sized islands that are on the shallow portion of the shelf, so that an estimate of 1–2% extinction/10 000 years is indicated.

Given the low colonization rate and non-trivial extinction rate, how is it that an isolated island such as Luzon has any non-volant mammals at all? The data cited above clearly demonstrate that speciation is the crucial variable. At least 55% of the non-volant mammals on Luzon have resulted from speciation within the archipelago, and an estimate of 70% may be more accurate.

*Goals and unanswered questions*

Earlier in this paper I posed four major questions. The first of these addressed the need for estimates of actual rates of colonization and extinction, and these have been calculated. The second question addressed the equality of these rates; given the estimate of one successful colonization per $c.$ 500 000 years and a rate of extinction on large, old landbridge islands of 1–2 species/10 000 years, but varying depending on the island's size, it seems unlikely that they are often equal. The third question addressed the role of speciation and its interaction with the prior variables. It is apparent that speciation within archipelagos is a major generative factor among SE Asian mammals; on Luzon, for example, speciation has exceeded colonization by a factor of about two to one. However, the matter of an interaction between speciation and colonization has not been addressed. Does speciation occur more rapidly in depauperate than in species-rich archipelagos? At what rate does speciation occur under these extreme conditions? How is speciation influenced by island size, habitat diversity and geological history (including sea level change)? Answers to these questions are not available.

The data discussed here demonstrate that colonization, extinction and speciation all play crucial roles in determining species richness patterns among insular mammal faunas in SE Asia. It is apparent that all three variables must be incorporated into any general model that attempts to explain the diversity of mammalian faunas on islands. Several authors (e.g. Wilson, 1969) have suggested that the combination of these three ecological and evolutionary processes could produce faunas that are in trivariate equilibrium, rather than the bivariate equilibrium of MacArthur & Wilson (1967). I view the development of such a model as an essential goal for biogeography if we are to have a predictive model that is applicable to more than a few systems characterized by highly vagile species and short time spans. Development of such a model requires an increased emphasis on obtaining data on long-term patterns of the three crucial variables and makes apparent the need for accurate, detailed analysis of phylogenetic relationships of species. Without these data, it will be impossible to measure or model actual rates of colonization or speciation. Such a model lies well outside the realm of the traditional equilibrium model, or more precisely, the equilibrium model would be a special case of this more general (hypothetical) model. Vicariance biogeography (e.g. Nelson & Platnick, 1981) provides the framework for quantification of speciation, and integration of the two models could be richly rewarding.

This study has provided an outline of the long-term dynamics of species richness of insular mammals. The estimates presented here, often the first of their kind, point the way for future research. The following topics, questions and empirical problems are ones that I believe are especially pertinent to further advancement of island biogeography. The comments are grouped under the general headings of extinction, colonization, speciation and endemism.

The estimate of long-term extinction rates given here is the first of which I am aware (but see Wilcox, 1978, for post-Pleistocene rate of extinction among lizards). More survey work is needed in mid-Pleistocene island chains to provide data for measurement of the influence of such factors as climatic regime and level of species richness on extinction rates. The ecological basis of extinction has been alluded to in this paper and elsewhere (e.g. Diamond, 1984; Patterson, 1984), but more detailed investigation of the mechanisms, especially those regarding the roles of body size, trophic level and population size, are badly needed (e.g. Heaney, 1978).

The estimates of colonization rate over evolutionary time provided here and by Morgan & Woods (1986) appear to be the first of their kind for mammals. Each is based on only a few islands, many of which are about the same distance to source areas. More oceanic islands must be surveyed to provide quantitative estimates of the influence of island size, geological age and distance on colonization rates. Wallacea appears to be the ideal place to conduct such research because of the unique configuration of islands. It is also essential that repeated surveys be done to provide data on turnover rates, which Morgan & Woods (1986) and I have had to disregard due to lack of data. The sole set of turnover data currently available for vertebrates on isolated islands comes from Krakatau Island, but these data do not include repeated thorough surveys of mammals (Simkin & Fiske, 1983).

The frequency of adaptive radiation in isolated archipelagos is axiomatic in Darwinian evolution (e.g. Carlquist, 1974; Patton, 1984), but it is rarely directly included in studies that utilize the equilibrium model (but see MacArthur & Wilson, 1967: 173). We need more phylogentic analyses to allow measurement of indigenous speciation rates in order to determine the effects of body size, trophic level and other variables on speciation rate. Data in this paper lead me to predict that speciation rate will be related to colonization rate in a complex fashion, with speciation rate initially increasing as colonization rate increases to some low level (providing the raw material for speciation), and decreasing thereafter as colonization rate increases. I know of no data that could be used to test this prediction, but its testing is fundamental to development of the trivariate equilibrium model discussed earlier.

Trends in endemism related to age, isolation and area of islands have been discussed here, but sample size was small and only rudimentary statistical analysis was attempted. A correlation between area and percentage endemism has been noted among birds (see MacArthur & Wilson, 1967: 174; Case & Cody, 1983: 334) but not previously noted among mammals. A quantitative analysis of a larger data set is needed.

Finally, I must add an explicit plea for research of the most fundamental sort. All of these studies are predicated on the availability of accurate taxonomic data, and yet the distributions and systematic relationships of many, if not most, insular mammals are poorly known, especially in the tropics. Theoretical advances in island biogeography are currently impeded by insufficient empirical data.

## Caveat: long-term insular stability and equilibrium

I must end with a caveat. The trivariate equilibrium model discussed here would have great theoretical and heuristic value, but I doubt that such equilibrium conditions often exist among insular mammal faunas. In the data presented above, I found evidence that the important processes in mammalian island biogeography often take place over thousands or millions of years. If these time spans are typically necessary for equilibrium to be achieved, then equilibrium will be rare, because major geological and climatic processes occur on the same time scale. Island arcs, for example, are intrinsically unstable, resulting from dynamic, ongoing tectonic processes, and habitat islands change in size and position as climate changes on a global scale. The appropriate model, then, becomes one of dynamic disequilibrium, in which geological and climatic processes are always a step ahead of the biotic systems, and faunas, in effect, chase their changing equilibrium point through time, always a step or two out of phase.

Nevertheless, the equilibrium model remains an invaluable point of departure for a study such as this. By raising questions about rates of colonization and extinction other questions are raised, and these new questions may point the way to a new holistic model of island biogeography.

## *Implications for conservation biology*

Modern conservation biology has two fundamental goals: (1) preservation of natural communities that are representative of the biotic regions of the world; and (2) prevention of extinction of species. Several conclusions drawn in this paper have direct implications for the conservation of non-volant mammals in SE Asia.

First, each area that is defined by historical events (e.g. Pleistocene islands) is likely to support endemic species. Even small islands often support endemics. Preserves should be situated to maximize protection of these centres of endemism.

Secondly, within a given biotic region (such as those defined by Pleistocene islands) most species of mammals will occur on the largest islands. Reserves might profitably be located on these high-diversity islands.

Thirdly, extinction is area dependent; thus, large parks will support more species than small parks (e.g. the SLOSS debate; see Newmark, 1986). Carnivores and large-bodied species are especially susceptible to area-dependent extinction, and they may often require special protection and management efforts.

Fourthly, most extinction in reserve areas will probably take place within several hundred years after isolation of the reserve from other suitable habitat. Given the evidence presented here for high colonization rates across suitable habitats and very low colonization rates across hostile habitats, the preservation of corridors between reserves appears to be an important management tool.

Fifthly, colonization and speciation by non-volant mammals usually occur on a time-scale that prevents them from being useful to conservation biologists.

## ACKNOWLEDGEMENTS

Assistance with field work in the Philippines was generously offered by the Philippine Bureau of Forest Development, Institute of Philippine Culture, Silliman University, and the Visayas State College of Agriculture, and has been gratefully accepted on many occasions. I also thank the following persons for encouragement and assistance with this project in its many phases: A. C. Alcala, W. E. Arce, R. Cadalena, P. C. Gonzales, P. D. Heideman, K. Hutterer, K. F. Koopman, G. G. Musser, P. Myers, D. S. Rabor, L. Raros, R. W. Thorington and R. M. Timm. Access to specimens or data under their care was granted by P. C. Gonzales, K. F. Koopman, G. G. Musser, D. Niles, D. S. Rabor, L. Raros, R. W. Thorington, R. M. Timm and W. C. Wozencraft. P. D. Heideman, S. M. G. Hoffman, G. G. Musser, P. Myers, B. D. Patterson and R. M. Timm critically reviewed earlier drafts of this manuscript. I am grateful to G. Lake and S. F. Campbell for typing innumerable drafts of the text and tables and for assistance with many other aspects as well. Field work was supported in part by the Rackham Foundation, University of Michigan.

## REFERENCES

BACHMAN, S. B., LEWIS, S. D. & SCHWELLER, W. J., 1983. Evolution of a forearc basin, Luzon Central Valley, Philippines. *Bulletin of the American Association of Petroleum Geologists, 67:* 1143–1162.

BARBEHENN, K., SUMANGIL, J. P. & LIBAY, J. L., 1973. Rodents of the Philippine croplands. *Philippine Agriculturalist, 56:* 217–242.

BARTLETT, A. S. & BARGHOORN, E. S., 1973. Phytogeographic history of the isthmus of Panama during the past 12 000 years (a history of vegetation, climate, and sea-level change) In A. Graham (Ed.), *Vegetation and Vegetational History of Northern Latin America.* Amsterdam: Elsevier.

BLOOM, A. L., 1983. Sea level and coastal morphology of the United States through the Late Wisconsin Glacial maximum. In S. C. Porter (Ed.), *Late-Quaternary Environments of the United States,* Vol. 1, *The Late Pleistocene:* 215–229. Minneapolis: Univerity of Minnesota Press.

BROWN, J. H., 1971. Mammals on mountaintops: nonequilibrium insular biogeography. *American Naturalist, 105:* 467–478.

BROWN, J. H., 1978. The theory of insular biogeography and the distribution of boreal birds and mammals. *Great Basin Naturalist Memoirs, 2:* 209–227.

BROWN, W. C. & ALCALA, A. C., 1970. The zoogeography of the herpetofauna of the Philippine Islands, a fringing archipelago. *Proceedings of the California Academy of Sciences, 38:* 105–130.

CARLQUIST, S., 1974. *Island Biology.* New York: Columbia University Press.

CASE, T. J. & CODY, M. L., 1983. *Island Biogeography in the Sea of Cortéz.* Berkeley: University of California Press.

CROWELL, K. L., 1986. A comparison of relict versus equilibrium models for insular mammals of the Gulf of Maine. *Biological Journal of the Linnean Society, 28:* 37–64.

DARLINGTON, P. J., 1957. *Zoogeography: the Geographical Distribution of Animals.* New York: J. Wiley.

DIAMOND, J. M., 1984. "Normal" extinction of isolated populations. In M. H. Nitecki (Ed.), *Extinctions:* 191–246. Chicago: University of Chicago Press.

DICKERSON, R. E., 1928. Distribution of life in the Philippines. *Monographs of the Bureau of Science, Manila, 2:* 1–322.

DIVIS, A. F., 1980. The petrology and tectonics of recent volcanism in the Central Philippine Islands. In D. E. Hayes (Ed.), *The Tectonic and Geological Evolution of Southeast Asian Seas and Islands. Geophysical Monographs of the American Geophysical Union, 23:* 127–144.

DONN, W. L., FARRAND, W. L. & EWING, M., 1962. Pleistocene ice volumes and sea level lowering. *Journal of Geology, 70:* 206–214.

EVERETT, A. H., 1889. Remarks on the zoo-geographical relationships of the island of Palawan and some adjacent islands. *Proceedings of the Zoological Society of London, 1889:* 220–228.

FOX, R. B. & PERALTA, J. T., 1974. Preliminary report on the paleolithic archeology of the Cagayan Valley, Philippines, and the Calawanian industry. *Proceedings of the First Regional Seminar on Southeast Asian Prehistory and Archeology:* 100–147. Manila: National Museum.

GASCOYNE, M., BENJAMIN, G. J. & SCHWARTZ, H. P., 1979. Sea-level lowering during the Illinoian glaciation: evidence from a Bahama "blue hole". *Science, 205:* 806–808.

GILBERT, F. S., 1980. The equilibrium theory of island biogeography: fact or fiction? *Journal of Biogeography, 7:* 209–235.

GROVES, C. P., 1969. Systematics of the anoa (Mammalia, Bovidae). *Beaufortia, 17:* 1–12.

GROVES, C. P., 1981. Ancestors for the pigs: taxonomy and phylogeny of the genus *Sus. Department of Prehistory, Research School of Pacific Studies, Australian National University Technical Bulletin, 3:* 1–96.

GROVES, C. P., 1983. Pigs east of Wallace's Line. *Journal de la Societe des Oceanistes, 39:* 105–119.

GROVES, C. P., 1984. Mammal faunas and the paleogeography of the Indo-Australian region. *Courier Forschungs Institut Senckenberg, 69:* 267–273.

GROVES, C. P., 1985. Plio-Pleistocene mammals in island Southeast Asia. *Modern Quaternary Studies in Southeast Asia, 9:* 43–54.

GRUBB, P. & GROVES, C. P., 1983. Notes on the taxonomy of the deer (Mammalia, Cervidae) of the Philippines. *Zoologischer Anzeiger, 210:* 119–144.

HAMILTON, W., 1979. Tectonics of the Indonesian region. *Geological Survey Professional Papers, 1078:* 1–345.

HANSKI, I., 1986. Population dynamics of shrews on small islands accord with the equilibrium model. *Biological Journal of the Linnean Society, 28:* 23–26.

HARRISON, J. L., 1969. The abundance and population density of mammals in Malayan lowland forests. *Malayan Nature Journal, 22:* 174–178.

HEANEY, L. R., 1978. Island area and body size of insular mammals: evidence from the tri-colored squirrel (*Callosciurus prevosti*) of Southeast Asia. *Evolution, 32:* 9–17.

HEANEY, L. R., 1979. A new species of tree squirrel (*Sundasciurus*) from Palawan Island, Philippines (Mammalia: Sciuridae). *Proceedings of the Biological Society of Washington, 92:* 280–286.

HEANEY, L. R., 1984a. Mammalian species richness on islands on the Sunda Shelf, Southeast Asia. *Oecologia, 61:* 11–17.

HEANEY, L. R., 1984b. Mammals from Camiguin Island, Philippines. *Proceedings of the Biological Society of Washington, 97:* 119–125.

HEANEY, L. R., 1985a. Systematics of Oriental pygmy squirrels of the genera *Exilisciurus* and *Nannosciurus* (Mammalia: Sciuridae). *Miscellaneous Papers of the Museum of Zoology, University of Michigan 170:* 1–58.

HEANEY, L. R., 1985b. Zoogeographic evidence for Middle and Late Pleistocene land bridges to the Philippine Islands. *Modern Quaternary Research in Southeast Asia, 9:* 127–144.

HEANEY, L. R., HEIDEMAN, P. D. & MUDAR, K. M., 1981. Ecological notes on the mammals of the Lake Balinsasayao region, Negros Oriental, Philippines. *Silliman Journal, 28:* 122–131.

HEANEY, L. R. & MORGAN, G. S., 1982. A new species of gymnure (*Podogymnura*) from Dinagat Island, Philippines (Mammalia: Erinaceidae). *Proceedings of the Biological Society of Washington, 95:* 13–26.

HEANEY, L. R. & RABOR, D. S., 1982. The mammals of Dinagat and Siargao Islands, Philippines. *Occasional Papers of the Museum of Zoology, University of Michigan, 699:* 1–30.

HOLLOWAY, N. H., 1982. North Palawan block, Philippines—its relation to Asian mainland and role in evolution of South China Sea. *Bulletin of the American Association of Petroleum Geologists, 66:* 1355–1383.

HONACKI, J. H., KINMAN, K. E. & KOEPPL, J. W., 1982. *Mammal Species of the World.* Lawrence: Association of Systematic Collections.

JENKINS, P. D., 1982. A discussion of Malayan and Indonesian shrews of the genus *Crocidura* (Insectivora: Soricidae). *Zoologische Mededelingen, Rijksmuseum van Natuurlijke Historie te Leiden, 56:* 267–279.

JOHNSON, D. H., 1946. A new Philippine rat allied to "*Bullimus*" *bagobus* Mearns. *Journal of the Washington Academy of Sciences, 36:* 317–320.

LACK, D., 1976. *Island Biology.* Berkeley: University of California Press.

LAWLOR, T. E., 1983. The mammals. In T. J. Case & M. L. Cody (Eds), *Island Biogeography in the Sea of Cortéz:* 265–289. Berkeley: University of California Press.

LAWRENCE, B. L., 1939. Collections from the Philippine Islands. Mammals. *Bulletin of the Museum of Comparative Zoology, Harvard University, 86:* 28–73.

LIM, B. L., MUUL, I. & CHAI, K. S., 1977. Zoonotic studies of small animals in the canopy transect at Bukit Lanjan Forest Reserve, Selangor, Malaysia. *Malayan Nature Journal, 31:* 127–140.

LOMOLINO, M. V., 1982. Species–area and species–distance relationships of terrestrial mammals in the Thousand Island region. *Oecologia, 54:* 72–75.

LOMOLINO, M. V., 1986. Mammalian community structure on islands: the importance of immigration, extinction and interactive effects. *Biological Journal of the Linnean Society, 28:* 1–21.

MACARTHUR, R. H. & WILSON, E. O., 1963. An equilibrium theory of insular zoogeography. *Evolution, 17:* 373–387.

MACARTHUR, R. H. & WILSON, E. O., 1967. *The Theory of Island Biogeography.* Princeton University Press, Monographs in Population Biology, *1.*

MACARTHUR, R. H., 1972. *Geographical Ecology: Patterns in the Distribution of Species.* New York: Harper and Row.

MEDWAY, L., 1972. The Quaternary mammals of Malesia; a review. In P. Ashton & M. Ashton (Eds), *The Quaternary Era in Malesia. Department of Geography, University of Hull, Miscellaneous Series, 13:* 1–122.

MEDWAY, L., 1977. The mammals of Borneo (2nd edition). *Monographs of the Malayan Branch Royal Asiatic Society, 7:* 1–172.

MISONNE, X., 1969. *Africa and Indo-Australian Muridae.* Bruxelles: Institut Royal des Sciences Naturelles de Belgique.

MOORE, J. C., 1959. Relationships among living squirrels of the Sciurinae. *Bulletin of the American Museum of Natural History, 118:* 153–206.

MORGAN, G. S. & WOODS, C. A., 1986. Extinction and the zoogeography of West Indian land mammals. *Biological Journal of the Linnean Society, 28:* 167–203.

MUSSER, G. G., 1977a. *Epimys benguetensis*, a composite, and one zoogeographic view of the rat and mouse faunas in the Philippines and Celebes. *American Museum Novitates, 2624:* 1–15.

MUSSER, G. G., 1977b. Results of the Archbold Expeditions. No. 100. Notes on the Philippine rat, *Limnomys*, and the identity of *Limnomys picinus*, a composite. *American Museum Novitates, 2636:* 1–14.

MUSSER, G. G., 1979. Results of the Archbold Expeditions. No. 102. The species of *Chiropodomys*, arboreal mice of Indochina and the Malay Archipelago. *Bulletin of the American Museum of Natural History, 162:* 377–445.

MUSSER, G. G., 1981a. Results of the Archbold Expeditions. No. 105. Notes on the systematics of Indo-Malayan murid rodents, and descriptions of new genera and species from Ceylon, Sulawesi, and the Philippines. *Bulletin of the American Museum of Natural History, 168:* 225–334.

MUSSER, G. G., 1981b. The giant rat of Flores and its relatives east of Borneo and Bali. *Bulletin of the American Museum of Natural History, 169:* 67–176.

MUSSER, G. G., 1982a. Results of the Archbold Expeditions. No. 107. A new genus of arboreal rat from Luzon Island in the Philippines. *American Museum Novitates, 2730:* 1–23.

MUSSER, G. G., 1982b. Results of the Archbold Expeditions. No. 108. The definition of *Apomys*, a native rat of the Philippine Islands. *American Museum Novitates, 2746:* 1–43.

MUSSER, G. G., 1982c. Results of the Archbold Expeditions. No. 110. *Crunomys* and the small-bodied shrew-rats native to the Philippine Islands and Sulawesi (Celebes). *Bulletin of the American Museum of Natural History, 174:* 1–95.

MUSSER, G. G. & CALIFIA, D., 1982. Results of the Archbold Expeditions. No. 106. Identities of rats from Pulau Maratua and other islands off East Borneo. *American Museum Novitates, 2726:* 1–30.

MUSSER, G. G. & FREEMAN, P. W., 1981. A new species of *Rhynchomys* (Muridae) from the Philippines. *Journal of Mammalogy, 62:* 154–159.

MUSSER, G. G. & GORDON, L. K., 1981. A new species of *Crateromys* (Muridae) from the Philippines. *Journal of Mammalogy, 62:* 513–525.

MUSSER, G. G., GORDON, L. K. & SOMMER, H., 1981. Species limits in the Philippine murid, *Chrotomys. Journal of Mammalogy, 63:* 514–521.

MUSSER, G. G. & HEANEY, L. R., 1985. Philippine *Rattus;* a new species from the Sulu Archipelago. *American Museum Novitates, 2818:* 1–32.

MUSSER, G. G., HEANEY, L. R. & RABOR, D. S., 1985. Philippine rats: description of a new species of *Crateromys* from Dinagat Island. *American Museum Novitates, 2821:* 1–25.

MUSSER, G. G. & NEWCOMB, C., 1983. Malaysian murids and the giant rat of Sumatra. *Bulletin of the American Museum of Natural History, 174:* 327–598.

NELSON, G. & PLATNICK, N., 1981. *Systematics and Biogeography: Cladistics and Vicariance.* New York: Columbia University Press.

NEWMARK, W. D., 1986. Species–area relationship and its determinants for mammals in western North American national parks. *Biological Journal of the Linnean Society, 28:* 83–98.

OLLIER, C. D., 1985. The geological background to prehistory in island Southeast Asia. *Modern Quaternary Studies in Southeast Asia, 9:* 25–42.

PATTERSON, B. D., 1980. Montane mammalian biogeography in New Mexico. *Southwestern Naturalist, 25:* 33–40.

PATTERSON, B. D., 1984. Mammalian extinction and biogeography in the Southern Rocky Mountains. In M. H. Nitecki (Ed.), *Extinction:* 247–293. Chicago: University of Chicago Press.

PATTON, J. L., 1984. Genetical processes in the Galapagos. *Biological Journal of the Linnean Society, 21:* 97–113.

PPHILIPPINE BUREAU OF MINES, 1963. *Geological Map of the Philippines.* Manila: Bureau of Mines.

SANBORN, C. C., 1952. Philippine Zoological Expedition 1946–1947. Mammals. *Fieldiana: Zoology, 33:* 89–158.

SANBORN, C. C., 1953. Mammals from Mindanao, Philippine Islands collected by the Danish Philippine Expedition, 1951–1952. *Videnskabelige Meddelelser fra Dansk Naturhistorisk Forening, 115:* 283–288.

SIMKIN, T. & FISKE, R. S., 1983. *Krakatau 1883: the Volcanic Eruption and its Effects.* Washington, D.C.: Smithsonian Institution Press.

STEERE, J. B., 1890. *A list of the birds and mammals collected by the Steere Expedition to the Philippines, with localities and with brief preliminary descriptions of supposed new species.* Ann Arbor.

TAYLOR, E. H., 1934. Philippine land mammals. *Monographs of the Bureau of Science (Manila), 30:* 1–548.

TAYLOR, B. & HAYES, D. E., 1980. The tectonic evolution of the South China Basin. In D. E. Hayes (Ed.), *The tectonic and geological evolution of Southeast Asian Seas and islands. Geophysical Monographs of the American Geophysical Union, 23:* 89–104.

UDVARDY, M. D. F., 1969. *Dynamic Zoogeography, with Special Reference to Land Animals.* New York: Van Nostrand Reinhold Co.

VONDRA, C. F. & MATHISEN, M. E., 1985. Plio-Pleistocene stratigraphy and paleoenvironments, Cagayan basin, northern Luzon, Philippines. *Modern Quaternary Studies in Southeast Asia, 9:* 145–157.

VONDRA, C. F., MATHISEN, M. E., BURGGRAF Jr, D. R. & KVALE, E. P., 1982. Plio-Pleistocene geology of northern Luzon, Philippines. In G. Rapp & C. F. Vondra (Eds), *Hominid Sites: Their Geological Settings:* 255–309. Boulder: Westview Press.

WILCOX, B. A., 1978. Supersaturated island faunas: a species–age relationship for lizards on post-Pleistocene land-bridge islands. *Science, 199:* 996–998.

WILSON, E. O., 1969. The species equilibrium. In G. M. Woodwell (Ed.), *Diversity and stability in ecological systems. Brookhaven Symposia in Biology, 22:* 38–47.

WILLIAMSON, M., 1981. *Island Populations.* Oxford: Oxford University Press.

Appendix. Lists of the non-volant mammals of Java and Sumatra. A single asterisk denotes introduced species and two asterisks denotes endemic species

---

### JAVA

Insectivora
*Hylomys suillus, Crocidura attenuata, Crocidura fuliginosa, Crocidura maxi, Crocidura monticola, Suncus murinus\*, Tupaia glis, Tupaia javanica*

Dermoptera
*Cynocephalus variegatus*

Primates
*Nycticebus coucang, Macaca fascicularis, Presbytis aygula, Presbytis cristatus, Hylobates moloch*

Pholidota
*Manis javanica*

Lagomorpha
*Lepus nigricollis\**

Rodentia
*Callosciurus nigrovittatus, Callosciurus notatus, Lariscus insignis, Nannosciurus melanotis, Ratufa bicolor, Hylopetes lepidus, Iomys horsfieldii, Petaurista elegans, Petaurista petaurista, Petinomys bartelsi\*\*, Petinomys sagitta, Bandicota bengalensis\*, Bandicota indica\*, Chiropodomys gliroides, Kadarsanomys sodyi\*\*, Leopoldomys sabanus, Maxomys surifer, Maxomys bartelsii\*\*, Mus castaneus\*, Mus caroli\*, Mus cervicolor\*, Mus vulcani\*\*, Niviventer bukit, Niviventer cremoriventer, Niviventer lepturus\*\*, Pithecheir melanurus\*\*, Rattus argentiventer\*, Rattus exulans\*, Rattus norvegicus\*, Rattus rattus\*, Rattus tiomanicus, Sundamys maxi\*\*, Hystrix javanica*

Carnivora
*Cuon alpinus, Aonyx cinerea, Martes flavigula, Melogale orientalis, Mustela lutreolina, Mydaus javanensis, Arctictis binturong, Arctogalidia trivirgata, Herpestes javanicus, Paradoxurus hermaphroditus, Prionodon linsang, Viverricula indica, Felis bengalensis, Felis viverrina, Panthera pardus, Panthera tigris*

Perissodactyla
*Rhinoceros sondaicus*

Artiodactyla
*Sus verrucosus, Sus scrofa, Tragulus javanicus, Cervus timorensis, Muntiacus muntjak, Bos javanicus, Bubalus babalis\**

| | |
|---|---|
| Total non-volant species | 73 |
| Total introduced species | 12 |
| Total native species | 61 |
| Number of endemic species | 7 |

---

### SUMATRA

Insectivora
*Echinosorex gymnurus, Hylomys suillus, Chimarrogale platycephala, Crocidura attenuata, Crocidura fuliginosa, Suncus murinus\*, Ptilocercus lowii, Tupaia glis, Tupaia javanica, Tupaia minor, Tupaia tana*

Dermoptera
*Cynocephalus variegatus*

Primates
*Nycticebus coucang, Tarsius bancanus, Macaca fascicularis, Macaca nemestrina, Presbytis cristatus, Presbytis melalophos, Presbytis thomasi\*\*, Hylobates agilis, Hylobates lar, Symphalangus syndactylus, Pongo pygmaeus*

Pholidota
*Manis javanica*

Lagomorpha
*Nesolagus netscheri\*\**

Rodentia
*Callosciurus albescens\*\*, Callosciurus nigrovittatus, Callosciurus notatus, Callosciurus prevosti, Lariscus insignis, Lariscus niobe* (Musser, ms.), *Nannosciurus melanotis, Ratufa affinis, Ratufa bicolor, Rhinosciurus laticaudatus, Sundasciurus hippurus, Sundasciurus lowii, Sundasciurus tenuis, Aeromys tephromelas, Hylopetes lepidus, Iomys horsfieldi, Petinomys genibarbis, Petinomys hageni, Petinomys setosus, Petaurista elegans, Petaurista petaurista, Pteromyscus pulverulentus, Rhizomys sumatrensis, Bandicota bengalensis\*, Berylmys bowersi, Chiropodomys gliroides, Lenothrix canus, Leopoldamys edwardsi, Leopoldamys sabanus, Maxomys hylomyoides\*\*, Maxomys inflatus\*\*, Maxomys rajah, Maxomys surifer, Maxomys whiteheadi, Mus caroli\*, Mus castaneus\*, Mus cervicolor\*, Mus crociduroides\*\*, Niviventer bukit, Niviventer*

*cremoriventer, Niviventer rapit, Rattus annandalei, Rattus argentiventer\*, Rattus baluensis, Rattus exulans\*, Rattus hoogerwerfi\*\*, Rattus norvegicus\*, Rattus rattus\*, Rattus tiomanicus, Sundamys infraluteus, Sundamys muelleri, Hystrix brachyura, Hystrix sumatrae\*\*, Trichys fasciculata*

Carnivora

*Cuon alpinus, Helarctos malayanus, Aonyx cinerea, Arctonyx collaris, Lutra lutra, Lutra perspicillata, Lutra sumatrana, Martes flavigula, Mustela lutreolina, Mustela nudipes, Mydaus javanensis, Arctictis binturong, Arctogalidia trivirgata, Cynogale bennettii, Hemigalus derbyanus, Herpestes brachyurus, Herpestes semitorquatus, Paguma larvata, Paradoxurus hermaphroditus, Prionodon linsang, Viverra tangalunga, Viverricula indica, Felis bengalensis, Felis marmorata, Felis planiceps, Felis temminckii, Felis viverrina, Neofelis nebulosa, Panthera tigris*

Proboscidea

*Elephas maximus*

Perissodactyla

*Dicerorhinus sumatrensis, Rhinoceros sondaicus, Tapirus indicus*

Artiodactyla

*Sus barbatus, Sus scrofa, Tragulus javanicus, Tragulus napu, Cervus unicolor, Muntiacus muntjak, Capricornis sumatraensis*

| | |
|---|---|
| Total non-volant species | 119 |
| Total introduced species | 9 |
| Total native species | 110 |
| Number of endemic species | 7 |

*Biological Journal of the Linnean Society* (1986), *28:* 167–203. With 4 figures

# Extinction and the zoogeography of West Indian land mammals

GARY S. MORGAN AND CHARLES A. WOODS

*Florida State Museum, University of Florida, Gainesville, Florida 32611, U.S.A.*

*Accepted for publication 14 February 1986*

The timing and causes of extinctions of West Indian land mammals during three time intervals covering the last 20 000 years (late Pleistocene and early Holocene, Amerindian, and post-Columbian) are discussed in detail. Late Pleistocene extinctions are attributed to climatic change and the post-glacial rise in sea level, whereas most late Holocene extinctions are probably human caused, resulting from predation, habitat destruction and introduction of exotic species. Extinctions have dramatically altered the composition of the non-volant mammal fauna, but have had a lesser impact on bats. Of the 76 recognized species of living and extinct non-volant mammals in the West Indies, 67 species (88%) have gone extinct since the late Pleistocene, whereas only eight of the 59 species of bats (14%) have disappeared during this same time interval. A larger percentage of Antillean bat species (24%) have suffered localized extinction on certain islands, particularly obligate cave-dwelling forms. These local extinctions occurred primarily on small islands, and probably resulted from changes in cave microclimates and flooding of low-lying caves by rising sea levels.

The majority of West Indian bats and all of the edentates, primates and rodents are Neotropical in origin. The South American fossil record indicates that most West Indian terrestrial mammals did not evolve until the early Miocene or thereafter. The Caribbean islands had assumed essentially their modern position and configuration by the Miocene, thus leaving overwater dispersal as the primary mechanism by which these endemic South American mammal groups reached the islands. The primitive insectivores, *Solenodon* and *Nesophontes*, are derived from Early Tertiary forms in North America that may have reached the islands through vicariance by way of a proto-Antillean archipelago. Many of the bats are either conspecific or congeneric with mainland taxa, suggesting that most species reached the islands by overwater dispersal during the Late Cenozoic, primarily from Central and South America.

Two hypothetical immigration rates are calculated for West Indian land mammals, one assuming the earliest colonization in the late Eocene and the other based on an early Miocene origin. The known Late Quaternary and living Antillean land mammal fauna was derived from approximately 50 separate colonization events (13 for non-volant mammals and 37 for bats) giving immigration rates of one species per 800 000 years since the late Eocene, or one species per 400 000 years since the early Miocene. Immigration rates for bats are approximately three times greater than those for non-volant mammals throughout the Tertiary and eight times greater in the Pleistocene, presumably reflecting their greater dispersal abilities. These immigration rates should be considered rough values, owing to deficiencies in the fossil record, especially the absence of pre-Pleistocene fossils. Extinction rates calculated for the last 20 000 years demonstrate that an average of one species of mammal went extinct every 267 years during that time period. Since the arrival of man in the West Indies some 4500 years ago, 37 species of non-volant mammals have disappeared giving the rapid extinction rate of one species every 122 years. Island area–species diversity curves are plotted for both the current and late Pleistocene mammal faunas. All Caribbean islands with a reasonably complete fossil record have more species in the late Pleistocene and Holocene than in the living fauna. The living non-volant mammals of the West Indies do not constitute a natural fauna, but are an impoverished subset of species that managed to escape the extinctions that decimated the remainder of the fauna. Historical or theoretical biogeographic analyses of Antillean mammals that fail to incorporate extinct forms will be unlikely to elicit any meaningful patterns.

167

KEY WORDS:—West Indies – mammals – fossils – Late Quaternary – island biogeography – extinction – colonization.

CONTENTS

INTRODUCTION

The recent and fossil mammals of the West Indies have been the subject of intensive study since early in this century, and now represent one of the best known mammalian faunas of the world's major island groups. A taxonomic review of the living and extinct mammalian fauna, including species lists for all major islands, has recently been published (Varona, 1974), as has a more current list of the bats (Baker & Genoways, 1978). As a natural outgrowth of faunal and taxonomic studies, many authors have contemplated the origin and affinities of the West Indian mammals (Matthew, 1918; Simpson, 1956; Hershkovitz, 1958; Savage, 1974; Baker & Genoways, 1978). Most zoogeographers agree that the Antillean mammal fauna was derived primarily from Central and South America, since only a small percentage of the taxa are related to North American groups. Recent studies on the plate tectonic history of the circum-Caribbean region have led to a divergence of opinion between biogeographers who advocate a vicariance model for the origin of the West Indian biota (e.g. Rosen, 1975) and those who favour overwater dispersal (e.g. Pregill, 1981a). Although it is not the primary objective of this paper, we will briefly discuss these two biogeographic models as they pertain to the West Indian mammalian fauna.

It has long been recognized that massive extinctions in the late Pleistocene and Holocene drastically altered the West Indian vertebrate fauna, especially the non-volant mammals. In North and South America the extinction of a significant portion of the large mammals, the 'Pleistocene megafauna', occurred at approximately 10 000 years BP, coinciding with the arrival of humans in the New World and terminal Pleistocene climatic changes. Although many species of mammals also disappeared from the islands of the West Indies at this time, a second and probably more extensive wave of extinctions took place in the middle to late Holocene (between 4500 years BP and the present), after the arrival of man. Many hypotheses have been proposed to explain the extinction of the Pleistocene megafauna; however, the theories generally fall into two major categories: (1) climatic change at the end of the Pleistocene; and (2) prehistoric overkill or human-caused extinction. Pregill & Olson (1981) attributed many late Pleistocene extinctions of vertebrates in the West Indies, especially birds and reptiles, to climatic change and the post-glacial sea level rise. Steadman, Pregill & Olson (1984a) and Olson (1982) suggested that many Holocene extinctions in the Antilles were human-caused, as a result of direct exploitation, habitat destruction or introduction of exotic species such as *Rattus* and *Herpestes*. Only recently have the extinctions of Antillean vertebrates been analysed in a zoogeographic context (e.g. Pregill & Olson, 1981). In this paper we will discuss the timing and causes of extinctions of West Indian mammals and the ways in which these extinctions have affected interpretations of the mammalian biogeography.

## METHODS

Several terms used throughout the paper are clarified here to eliminate any confusion regarding their meaning. 'West Indies' is used in a zoogeographic sense following the classification of Hershkovitz (1958), in which the West Indies is considered a subregion of the Neotropical Region. The West Indies include the Greater Antilles (Cuba, Jamaica, Hispaniola and Puerto Rico), Bahamas, Cayman Islands, Swan Islands, Virgin Islands and Lesser Antilles south to St. Vincent and Barbados. Figure 1 identifies all islands mentioned in the text. Grenada and the Grenadines, Trinidad, Tobago, Margarita and the Netherlands Antilles (Aruba, Bonaire and Curacao) have no Antillean endemic species of mammals, and are thus excluded from our concept of the West Indies. These islands are regarded as a northern extension of the Brazilian Subregion of the Neotropics. The primary zoogeographic subdivision within the West Indian mammal fauna is between the bats and the non-volant mammals. These two fundamental groupings of Antillean mammals will be compared and contrasted throughout the paper. The term 'land mammals' refers to the entire mammalian fauna of the islands exclusive of marine mammals.

All mammals introduced into the West Indies during historical (i.e. post-Columbian) times are omitted from our analysis. Several other species appear to have been introduced by Amerindian peoples, but their zoogeographic status is open to question. Based on their absence from Pleistocene fossil sites and occurrence only in an archaeological or historical context, all species of *Didelphis*, *Dasyprocta* and *Procyon* are regarded as human introductions. The supposedly endemic Cuban canids, *Cubacyon transversidens* Arredondo & Varona (1974) and *Paracyon* (= *Indocyon*) *caribensis* (Arredondo, 1981), are almost certainly synonyms of *Canis familiaris*, and were also introduced by Amerindian peoples. It is not our intention to revise taxonomic nomenclature in this paper, but we have found it necessary to make several judgements concerning the validity of certain genera and species so as to clarify their standing in a zoogeographic context. The genera and species of West Indian non-volant mammals we regard as valid are listed in the Appendix. For the bats we follow the checklist of Antillean Chiroptera provided by Baker & Genoways (1978: table 1). Undescribed taxa are included only when calculating the overall faunal diversity of an island or the diversity of a particular taxonomic group.

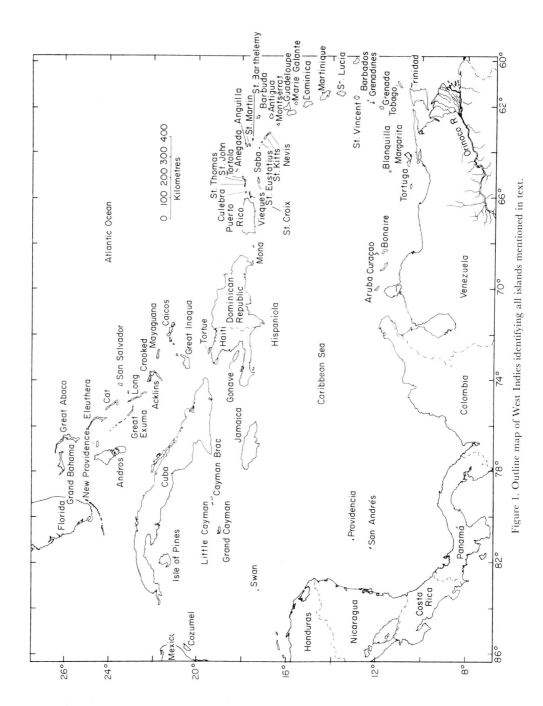

Figure 1. Outline map of West Indies identifying all islands mentioned in text.

Several new distributional records based on fossils in the Florida State Museum vertebrate palaeontology collection are identified by (FSM) following the species name. Because we are concentrating on extinct taxa, most of our data are derived from palaeontological and archaeological sites, and cover the islands for which the fossil record is most complete, i.e. Cuba, Hispaniola (including the countries of Haiti and the Dominican Republic), Jamaica, Puerto Rico, Bahamas (New Providence, Andros and Little Exuma), Cayman Islands (Grand Cayman and Cayman Brac) and several islands in the Lesser Antilles, including Anguilla, Antigua, Barbados, Barbuda, Montserrat and St. Kitts.

## ORIGINS OF THE WEST INDIAN MAMMAL FAUNA

Before the 1960s almost all geologists and biogeographers operated under the concept of stable continents and islands. As a consequence, overwater dispersal was the only credible biogeographic hypothesis that could explain the presence of land mammals on oceanic islands such as the West Indies (Matthew, 1918; Darlington, 1938; Simpson, 1956). Simpson was so sure of a dispersal origin for the Antillean mammal fauna that he stated (1956: 14), "On the basis of present evidence, the over-water dispersal theory is so much the more probable that the land bridge theory is not worthy of further serious consideration". However, the confirmation of continental drift (more accurately known as plate tectonics) over the last two decades has generated many new hypotheses on the origin of island floras and faunas. Almost all recent commentaries on Caribbean biogeography have addressed plate tectonics and its bearing on the geological and biogeographic history of the islands (Hedges, 1982; Buskirk, 1985). Rosen (1975) proposed a vicariance model whereby the West Indian fauna and flora were derived from an ancestral mainland biota that occupied a proto-Antillean archipelago situated between North and South America during the Late Mesozoic and Early Cenozoic. According to this theory, the proto-Antilles began moving eastward along two major faults in the Late Mesozoic, and the Caribbean Plate was subsequently decoupled from the Pacific Plate by the late Eocene. The West Indian islands had arrived in the vicinity of their present locations by about the mid-Cenozoic, carrying with them an ancestral North and South American fauna and flora. MacFadden (1980) proposed a vicariant origin for the West Indian insectivores by way of this supposed proto-Antillean archipelago. Other authors have argued that either the geological evidence for a proto-Antillean archipelago is not convincing or that a pre-late Eocene origin for the majority of the terrestrial vertebrate fauna is much too early (Baker & Genoways, 1978; Pregill, 1981a). These authors maintain that overwater dispersal is still the most reasonable hypothesis for the origin of the West Indian land vertebrate fauna.

The biogeography of the West Indian fauna and flora is obviously dependent in large part upon the geological history of the islands. Although the plate tectonic evolution of the circum-Caribbean region is currently undergoing extensive study, the geological history of the region is so complex and ideas about the origin of the islands are changing so rapidly that no two models are likely to agree completely (for review of recent literature see Hedges, 1982; Buskirk, 1985; Donnelley, 1985; Smith, 1985). Any biogeographic analysis based solely on one geological model is likely to be seriously flawed, and indeed many recent papers on Caribbean tectonics have been subject to considerable misinterpretation by biogeographers. We do not intend to propose yet another theory of West Indian biogeography based on a geological model that may be disproved or modified at any time. Instead, we briefly review the available evidence on the relationships and time of origin of the various taxa of Antillean land mammals.

Although depauperate at higher taxonomic levels, the West Indian mammalian fauna has a complicated zoogeographic history involving a myriad of origins both in space and time. Only three orders of land mammals are represented in the modern fauna: Insectivora, Chiroptera and Rodentia. Edentata and Primates are added when the palaeontological record is considered. Marsupialia, Lagomorpha, Carnivora and the various ungulate orders are notably absent from the native fauna. Simpson (1956) proposed that most Greater Antillean non-volant mammals were descended from South American forms that reached the islands during the Miocene and Pliocene. The exceptions noted by Simpson were the primitive insectivores *Solenodon* and *Nesophontes* of obvious North American affinities and the cricetid rodent *Oryzomys*, which he considered a Pleistocene immigrant from Central America. Hershkovitz (1958) also recognized that most extant Antillean mammals were related to taxa from Central and South America and classified the West Indies as a subregion of the Neotropics. Baker & Genoways (1978) advocated a Neotropical origin for the majority of the Antillean bat fauna.

*Solenodon* and *Nesophontes* are descended from archaic North American insectivores that may have reached the Greater Antilles in the Early Tertiary, either through vicariance by way of a proto-Antillean archipelago (MacFadden, 1980), or by dispersal from nuclear Central America. Most authors (McDowell, 1958; MacFadden, 1980; Lillegraven, McKenna & Krishtalka, 1981) consider the Antillean insectivores to be a monophyletic group derived from Eocene or Oligocene members of the Geolabididae or Apternodontidae. Although we agree that *Solenodon* and *Nesophontes* probably form a monophyletic group (the "solenodontoids" of MacFadden, 1980), their radically divergent dental morphologies seem to preclude placement of these two genera in the same family, at least in the present state of knowledge of insectivore relationships. For this reason, the families Solenodontidae and Nesophontidae are used throughout this paper (see Appendix).

Megalonychid ground sloths, ceboid monkeys and hystricognath rodents first appear in the fossil record in the Oligocene (Deseadan) of southern South America. The Deseadan has traditionally been regarded as early to middle Oligocene in age (Marshall, Hoffstetter & Pascual, 1983), but recent work on the Deseadan Salla Beds in Bolivia (MacFadden *et al.*, 1985) strongly suggests that the latter part of this land mammal age may be as young as early Miocene (about 25 to 20 Ma BP). By the Miocene the supposed proto-Antilles no longer occupied the region between North and South America, and the Greater Antilles had assumed essentially their modern configuration (Donnelley, 1985). Hence dispersal, and not vicariance, more appropriately explains the arrival of these South American groups in the West Indies.

According to de Paula Couto (1967), the Antillean megalonychids are most closely related to forms from the early Miocene (Santacrucian) of South America, and probably arrived in the West Indies during the Miocene or early

Pliocene. Although the relationships of these small ground sloths are not fully understood, they appear to be a monophyletic group (Webb & Perrigo, 1985) that underwent a significant adaptive radiation after reaching the Greater Antilles, especially on Cuba and Hispaniola. As currently understood, the three Greater Antillean primate genera (one each from Cuba, Jamaica and Hispaniola) are unrelated and were derived from three separate colonizations. These three taxa have not been adequately compared to South American fossil ceboids; however, they are certainly derived from forms more advanced than *Branisella*, the only known Deseadan primate, and must stem from Miocene or younger stock.

The West Indies have been colonized by three separate groups of hystricognath rodents, the Echimyidae, Capromyidae and Heptaxodontidae. The Capromyidae and Heptaxodontidae are endemic to the West Indies, whereas the Antillean echimyids are a monophyletic assemblage of four genera belonging to the otherwise mainland Neotropical subfamily Heteropsomyinae. Although several authors have postulated that the Antilles may have served as a route of invasion for hystricognath rodents into South America in the Eocene or Oligocene (Woods & Howland, 1979; Patterson & Wood, 1982; Woods, 1982), a recent analysis of a variety of morphological and biochemical characters indicates that the Capromyidae and Antillean Echimyidae were derived from South American post-Oligocene echimyids (Woods & Hermanson, 1985). The phylogenetic relationships of the Heptaxodontidae are unclear (Patterson & Wood, 1982), but appropriate ancestors or sister groups for this family are unknown before the early Miocene. The fossil record of hystricognath rodents in South America suggests that the progenitors of the endemic Antillean groups reached the islands in the early Miocene or thereafter.

The several endemic genera of Lesser Antillean oryzomyine rodents must have reached the islands by overwater dispersal from northern South America some time after the early Pliocene (Montehermosan), as cricetid rodents are unknown in South America before that time. The Jamaican *Oryzomys* is closely related to, if not conspecific with, *O. palustris* from the southeastern United States and Central America, and probably arrived in Jamaica by overwater dispersal during the Pleistocene.

The bats are the most diverse group of mammals in the West Indies and their zoogeographic and evolutionary history is complex. Unfortunately, the pre-Pleistocene fossil record of bats in Central and South America is exceedingly poor. Only two species have been described, the phyllostomine *Notonycteris magdalenensis* from the middle Miocene (Friasian) of Colombia (Savage, 1951) and the molossid *Mormopterus faustoi* de Paula Couto from the Oligocene of Brazil (Legendre, 1985). The zoogeographic relationships of West Indian bats must be deduced entirely from comparisons with the extant mainland chiropteran fauna. The antiquity of the various Antillean bat groups is speculative and based primarily on morphological distinctiveness. The majority of West Indian bats have Neotropical affinities, while only a few species are of North American (Nearctic) origin (Baker & Genoways, 1978). Most are either conspecific or congeneric with mainland taxa and probably arrived in the West Indies in the Late Tertiary and Quaternary by overwater dispersal. The highly derived endemic phyllostomid subfamily Brachyphyllinae, as well as the four endemic stenodermatine genera, may represent groups of bats that reached the

West Indies in the Early or Middle Tertiary. The Neotropical bat families Mormoopidae and Natalidae attain their greatest diversity in the West Indies, including a number of endemic species, probably reflecting a long independent evolution in these islands.

CHRONOLOGY

To preserve space we have omitted the error factors and laboratory numbers associated with each radiocarbon ($^{14}$C) date cited in this paper. The original publications should be consulted for these data. The problems associated with radiocarbon dates on land snail shell carbonate are summarized by Goodfriend & Stipp (1983). Anomalies may occur when dating land snails as a result of ingestion of 'old' or 'dead' carbon by the living animal, thus giving erroneously old dates in some instances. The maximum dating error of 3000 years using land snail shells (Goodfriend & Stipp, 1983) presents a major problem for Holocene dates obtained from land snails, but its significance is diminished in late Pleistocene sites. There are also problems associated with radiocarbon dates obtained from bones (see discussion in Taylor, 1980), as bone collagen often provides age determinations that are too young. Therefore, bone dates should be considered minimum ages and snail shell dates maximum ages.

Until recently, palaeontologists have made little effort to develop a rigorous chronology for vertebrate fossil sites in the West Indies. Almost no reliable radiocarbon dates were published for West Indian fossil vertebrate sites prior to the 1970s. The age of most sites has been determined primarily through relative-dating methods, such as the association with *Rattus* or archaeological material, or lack of such associations (the latter usually taken to indicate a late Pleistocene age). Pregill (1981b) made the first serious attempt to obtain a radiocarbon chronology for a series of fossil sites on one island. He published six dates based on land snail shells and one date on tooth enamel from four cave deposits in Puerto Rico, ranging in age from 43 000 to 13 080 years BP. Steadman *et al.* (1984a) published four dates on charcoal from a Holocene fissure deposit on Antigua, ranging in age from 4300 to 2500 years BP. Steadman & Morgan (1985) obtained three dates on shells of a single species of arboreal snail from a late Pleistocene fissure deposit on Cayman Brac, ranging in age from 13 850 to 11 180 years BP, and Morgan (in press) obtained dates of 860 and 375 years BP on peat from a mangrove swamp deposit containing extinct vertebrates on Grand Cayman. Woods (in press) presented a large series of radiocarbon dates from six cave deposits in Hispaniola, ranging in age from late Pleistocene to late Holocene (21 170–3715 years BP). These dates were obtained from bone collagen derived from limb bones of extinct hystricognath rodents. Despite the problems associated with bone-based dates, they become credible when repeatedly corroborated by other samples, or as in the Hispaniolan fossil deposits, when they yield results consistent with the associated fauna and stratigraphic context. These dates strongly indicate the survival of much of the now extinct endemic terrestrial mammalian fauna well after the arrival of man on Hispaniola.

Due to the paucity of radiocarbon dates available from West Indian fossil and archaeological sites, the chronology of major extinction events presented here is not as rigorous as we would prefer and is probably not without errors resulting from stratigraphic mixing of faunas. Since radiocarbon dates are not available for most published West Indian fossil sites, the age of undated deposits has been determined by faunal associations or the evidence of human occupation. Three time periods are recognized in the Late Quaternary of the West Indies. As discussed by Olson (1978), each of these periods is characterized by major extinctions of vertebrates.

*Post-Columbian (500 years BP to the present)*: The best evidence for the age of post-Columbian deposits is the presence of the introduced murid rodent, *Rattus rattus*. *Rattus* was inadvertently introduced into the West Indies by Europeans shortly after the discovery of the islands in 1492, and it is abundant and ubiquitous in fossil and archaeological sites deposited after that time. Other evidence of a post-Columbian age includes the presence of domestic animals, glass and metal artefacts.

*Amerindian (4500–500 years BP)*: Humans did not arrive in the West Indies until well after the end of the Pleistocene. The earliest secure date for human presence in the Caribbean is 4500 years BP (Rouse & Allaire, 1978), although these authors speculated that this date may eventually be pushed back to 7000 years BP. Much information on the distribution and occurrence of non-volant mammals in the West Indies, especially in the Lesser Antilles, is derived from bones identified from Amerindian kitchen middens (Olson, 1982; Wing & Reitz, 1982). Many species of extinct West Indian mammals, especially rodents, are common in archaeological sites and must have constituted a significant portion of the Indian diet in some cases. Amerindian sites are identified by the presence of cook fires, potshards, shell and stone artefacts, human bones, and some introduced species such as the agouti, *Dasyprocta*.

*Late Pleistocene and early Holocene (c. 40 000–4500 years BP)*: The age of late Pleistocene sites in the West Indies has generally been inferred from negative evidence such as the absence of introduced mammals or lack of evidence of human occupation, rather than from actual radiocarbon dates. We have also determined the age of late Pleistocene and early Holocene fossil sites (i.e. pre-human sites) from faunal associations when radiocarbon dates are not available. We suspect that many West Indian fossil sites, although lacking evidence of human occupation and thus previously regarded as late Pleistocene, are actually Holocene in age. When larger series of radiocarbon dates become available, a further refinement of this chronology would be in order, thereby allowing a distinction between species that disappeared at the end of the Pleistocene and those that survived into the early Holocene.

## EXTINCTIONS

The living non-volant mammalian fauna of the West Indies is remarkably depauperate. Puerto Rico has no surviving non-volant mammals, while Jamaica has a single species of the capromyid rodent *Geocapromys*. One species each of the capromyid rodent *Plagiodontia* and the solenodontid insectivore *Solenodon* survive on Hispaniola. Cuba supports the largest extant mammalian fauna of the Greater Antilles, including a species of *Solenodon* that is almost extinct, and from four to nine species of the capromyid rodent *Capromys*. Kratochvíl, Rodrigues & Baruš (1978) and Varona (1979) recognize nine living species of *Capromys* in Cuba, four of which have been described in the last 15 years from small offshore islands. We recognize only four valid Recent species of *Capromys* and tentatively regard the rest as subspecies of previously named forms. The only extant non-volant mammal occurring outside the Greater Antilles is an endemic species of *Geocapromys* found on tiny East Plana Cay in the southern Bahamas. No native non-volant mammals survive in the Lesser Antilles.

The important role played by extinction in the West Indies is clearly demonstrated by the number of recent species of mammals that have disappeared in the last 100 years. Thomas (1898) described two new Antillean rice rats, *Oryzomys antillarum* from Jamaica, based on three skins and skulls, and *O. victus* from St. Vincent in the Lesser Antilles, represented by a single specimen. Neither species has been collected or seen since it was described, and both are presumed extinct. The Jamaican *Oryzomys* is common in late Pleistocene and Holocene fossil deposits and Amerindian archaeological sites throughout the island, and its extinction is almost certainly related to the introduction of *Rattus* and *Herpestes*. Recent species of giant rice rats, *Megalomys*, were known to have inhabited Martinique (*M. desmaresti*) and St. Lucia (*M. luciae*) until the early part of this century, but both are certainly now extinct. Bones of *Megalomys* and other oryzomyine rodents are common in Amerindian kitchen middens throughout the Lesser Antilles, providing convincing evidence that these muskrat-sized rodents were exploited extensively for food. The most recent extinction is that of the Swan Island hutia, *Geocapromys thoracatus*, which survived on Little Swan Island until the 1950s. This species was exterminated in a period of no more than 30 years through the combination of a severe hurricane and the introduction of cats and goats (Clough, 1976; Morgan, 1985). Although not a land mammal, the Caribbean monk seal, *Monachus tropicalis*, is another well-documented example of an apparent recent extinction in the West Indies (Kenyon, 1977).

In Hispaniola three species of the small shrew-like insectivore *Nesophontes*, as well as the capromyid rodent *Isolobodon portoricensis* and the echimyid rodent *Brotomys voratus*, appear to have survived into this century although they are not known from skins (Miller, 1929a, b). There are also historical accounts in the early Spanish chronicles of several apparently extinct rodents (Miller, 1929b). A survey of Hispaniola during 1985 confirmed that *Nesophontes*, *Isolobodon*, *Brotomys* and even an additional larger species of *Plagiodontia* were present well into this century, but have become extinct within the last 30 years, probably as a result of deforestation and the associated increase in rats, dogs, cats, and mongoose (Woods, Ottenwalder & Oliver, in press).

Three general theories have been proposed to explain the late Pleistocene and Holocene extinctions of vertebrates in the West Indies: (1) climatic change and post-glacial sea level rise at the end of the Pleistocene; (2) human-caused extinction through direct exploitation for food or habitat destruction; and (3) competition with or predation by the introduced Old World murid rodent, *Rattus*, and other introduced mammals in post-Columbian times. Although many species of land mammals appear to have gone extinct in the West Indies at the end of the Pleistocene, we suspect that a number of these species actually survived into the Holocene, but have not been recovered from Amerindian and post-Columbian sites. Only with the development of a rigorous chronology generated by an augmented set of radiocarbon-dated sites, such as that already available for North America (Meltzer & Mead, 1983), will it be possible to

Table 1. Numbers of living and extinct species of West Indian land mammals

| Order | Total number of species | Living species | Extinct species | Percentage extinction |
|---|---|---|---|---|
| Insectivora | 12 | 2 | 10 | 83 |
| Chiroptera | 59 | 51 | 8 | 14 |
| Edentata | 16 | 0 | 16 | 100 |
| Primates | 3 | 0 | 3 | 100 |
| Rodentia | 45 | 7 | 38 | 84 |
| Total | 135 | 60 | 75 | 56 |

establish when most West Indian mammals disappeared. The history of extinctions in each of the five mammal orders inhabiting the West Indies is reviewed below (see Table 1). The geographic distribution and time period of last recorded occurrence (if extinct) for each species of Antillean non-volant mammal is summarized in the Appendix.

## Insectivora

The only living members of the Insectivora in the West Indies are two species of the primitive lipotyphlan *Solenodon*, one each from Cuba and Hispaniola. Two extinct species of *Solenodon* and at least eight species of the extinct genus *Nesophontes* are known from Holocene and late Pleistocene deposits. Morgan, Ray & Arredondo (1980) reported the femur of a giant extinct species of *Solenodon* from a late Pleistocene fossil deposit in Cuba. Three of the four described species of *Nesophontes* from Cuba (several are certainly synonyms) have been found in Amerindian sites (Arredondo, 1970), one of which, *N. micrus*, has also been reported from a barn owl, *Tyto alba*, deposit in association with *Rattus* (Acevedo González, Arredondo & González Gotera, 1972). A second extinct species of *Solenodon*, *S. marcanoi* (originally placed in the monotypic genus *Antillogale*) was described from a late Pleistocene cave deposit in the Dominican Republic (Patterson, 1962). *Solenodon marcanoi* has recently been found in association with *Rattus* in fossil deposits in the montane plateaus of southwestern Haiti (Woods, in press). Three species of *Nesophontes* are known from Holocene and late Pleistocene deposits throughout Hispaniola. Miller (1929b) found remains of all three Hispaniolan species of *Nesophontes* in association with *Rattus* from a barn owl deposit in the rainforest region of the Dominican Republic. He concluded that the remains were so fresh they could not have been more than a few years old. The largest species in the genus, *N. edithae*, is the only insectivore known from Puerto Rico. Although all published records of *N. edithae* are from late Pleistocene deposits, we have examined specimens of this species from an Amerindian site on Vieques, a small island located off the southeastern coast of Puerto Rico. An undescribed species of *Nesophontes* from the Cayman Islands (Morgan, in press) has been found in post-Columbian surficial cave deposits in association with *Rattus*.

All species of *Nesophontes* appear to have survived the late Pleistocene extinction event, and at least five species are known to have existed into post-Columbian times. Several species apparently did not go extinct until the early part of this century. A recent investigation of the extant mammals of Hispaniola

(Woods, 1986; Woods *et al.*, in press) surveyed remote areas on the southwestern peninsula of Haiti where remains of *Nesophontes* are abundant in post-Columbian barn owl deposits. Trapping in these areas of near-pristine pine and evergreen broad-leaved forests revealed high densities of *Rattus norvegicus* and *R. rattus*, but no *Nesophontes*. Predation by or competition with *Rattus* undoubtedly resulted in the extinction of these small shrew-like insectivores throughout the Greater Antilles.

## Edentata

The megalonychid ground sloths are perhaps the most interesting members of the extinct West Indian land mammal fauna. This group achieved a far greater diversity of genera and species in the late Pleistocene and Holocene of the Greater Antilles, in particular Cuba and Hispaniola, than in all of North and South America combined. The Antillean megalonychids appear to represent the ecological counterparts of several other groups of medium- to large-sized herbivorous vertebrates that evolved on islands lacking ungulates, such as the giant lemurs of Madagascar, the diprotodont marsupials of Australia and the moas of New Zealand. Although the West Indian ground sloths have twice been reviewed (Matthew & de Paula Couto, 1959; de Paula Couto, 1967), their taxonomy and relationships are currently in a state of flux because of recent discoveries in Hispaniola and descriptions of a number of new taxa from Cuba.

The single species of ground sloth from Puerto Rico, *Acratocnus odontrigonus*, has not been reported from Amerindian or post-Columbian sites and presumably became extinct at the end of the Pleistocene. The youngest radiocarbon date associated with a sloth in Puerto Rico is 13 180 years BP (Pregill, 1981b). The great majority of Cuban ground sloth fossils are also from late Pleistocene deposits (Matthew & de Paula Couto, 1959; de Paula Couto, 1967). We have been unable to find any positive evidence for the association of ground sloths with man in Cuba, or any radiocarbon dates that would definitely establish their presence there in the Holocene. Hispaniola, however, produces convincing evidence for the survival of ground sloths into the Amerindian period. In two caves at St. Michel, Haiti, Miller (1929a) found ground sloth bones in close association with human bones and pottery. The species name given by Miller (1929a) to the small ground sloth from these caves, *Acratocnus* (= *Synocnus*) *comes*, "alludes to the circumstance that the type specimen was found so closely associated with fragments of pottery as to lend strong support to the belief that the animal existed in Haiti as a contemporary of man". Woods (in press) obtained several late Holocene radiocarbon dates associated with ground sloth fossils from caves and sink holes in the high plateaus of southwestern Haiti. Although none of these sites contained a direct association with man they date as recently as 3715 years BP, thus providing strong circumstantial evidence that humans and ground sloths were contemporaries in Hispaniola.

## Primates

Three species of extinct primates have been described from the Greater Antilles. Williams & Koopman (1952) and all subsequent authors placed the

Cuban primate, *Montaneia anthropomorpha* Ameghino, in synonymy with the mainland species, *Ateles fuscipes*, and regarded it as introduced by Amerindians. Arredondo & Varona (1983) re-examined the type and argued that it represents an endemic Cuban species of *Ateles*. Pending further study we tentatively follow Arredondo & Varona (1983) in considering the Cuban primate as an Antillean endemic. The type and only known specimen of *A. anthropomorphus* was collected from an Amerindian burial cave. Although the type mandible of *Xenothrix mcgregori* from Jamaica was found in a cave containing an Amerindian kitchen midden, Anthony's field notes (quoted in Williams & Koopman, 1952) clearly stated that this specimen was collected 10 in to 1 ft below any human material. Ford & Morgan (in press) reported a primate femur from a second cave in Jamaica. Land snails associated with this femur have been radiocarbon dated at approximately 36000 years BP. Miller (1929b) reported the distal end of a primate tibia from an Amerindian kitchen midden in the Dominican Republic, which he tentatively referred to *Cercopithecus*, an Old World anthropoid. Ford (in press) has re-examined this tibia and concluded that it is definitely a New World ceboid apparently related to the callitrichids. Rímoli (1977) described a new species of primate, *Saimiri bernensis*, from an Amerindian site in a cave in the Dominican Republic associated with a $^{14}$C date on charcoal of 3850 years BP. MacPhee & Woods (1982) reported a primate mandible from a cave in southwestern Haiti associated with a $^{14}$C date on bone of 9550 years BP.

### Rodentia

The rodents are the most diverse group of non-volant mammals in the West Indies, and have a complex history of extinctions. At least four species of Cuban rodents are known from archaeological sites: these include the echimyids, *Boromys offella* and *B. torrei*, and the capromyids, *Geocapromys columbianus* and *G. pleistocenicus* (Arredondo, 1970). With the exception of *G. pleistocenicus*, all of these rodents apparently survived into post-Columbian times as well (Acevedo Gonzales *et al.*, 1972; Guarch Delmonte, 1984). The remaining five species of Cuban rodents apparently went extinct before the arrival of humans on the island. Among the four species of rodents known from Jamaica only *Geocapromys brownii* still survives. *Oryzomys antillarum* disappeared within the last 100 years, presumably from competition with introduced rats and mongoose. In a recent taxonomic review of the large extinct heptaxodontid rodents from Jamaica, MacPhee (1984) recognized only a large and a medium-sized species of *Clidomys*. He considered the three monotypic genera of Jamaican heptaxodontids described by Anthony (1920), *Alterodon*, *Speoxenus* and *Spirodontomys*, to be synonyms of one of the two species of *Clidomys*. MacPhee (1984) obtained a radiocarbon date of 33250 years BP from turtle shell fragments associated with *Clidomys* in an indurated breccia deposit in Jamaica. Fossils of *Clidomys* have been found only in late Pleistocene cave breccias and thus may represent one of the few Antillean mammals that went extinct prior to the end of the Pleistocene. Five extinct species of rodents have been recorded from Puerto Rico. The capromyid, *Isolobodon portoricensis*, occurs only in Amerindian kitchen middens in Puerto Rico, and was apparently introduced by man from Hispaniola where it is found in late Pleistocene fossil sites. The large echimyid, *Heteropsomys insulans*, occurs in both palaeontological and Amerindian sites (Olson, 1982), whereas

*H. antillensis*, the heptaxodontid *Elasmodontomys obliquus*, and the echimyid *Proechimys corozalus* are found only in fossil deposits. *Geocapromys ingrahami* survives at the present time only on East Plana Cay in the southeast Bahamas; however, it occurs in fossil deposits on New Providence, Little Exuma and Andros, and in archaeological sites on most of the larger Bahama Islands (Koopman, Hecht & Ledecky-Janecek, 1957; Olson & Pregill, 1982). Extinct species of *Capromys* and *Geocapromys* are known from Holocene and late Pleistocene fossil deposits in the Cayman Islands (Morgan, in press). A radiocarbon date of 375 years BP associated with capromyid bones on Grand Cayman and unfossilized remains of both species associated with *Rattus* in surficial cave deposits on Grand Cayman and Cayman Brac indicate that both species survived into post-Columbian times.

Hispaniola has the most diverse rodent assemblage of any Antillean island, spanning three families (Capromyidae, Echimyidae and Heptaxodontidae), six genera (*Plagiodontia, Isolobodon, Hexolobodon*, a new undescribed genus of capromyid, *Brotomys* and *Quemisia*) and at least 13 species. With the exception of *Plagiodontia aedium* all of these species are now extinct. Most of the species existed into the Amerindian period and at least four are found in post-Columbian deposits. Two extinct species of *Plagiodontia*, *P. araeum* (placed in the genus *Hyperplagiodontia* by Rímoli, 1976) and *P. velozi*, occur together in Amerindian deposits, and the latter species survived into post-Columbian times (Woods, in press). *Isolobodon portoricensis* is common in Amerindian kitchen midden deposits throughout Hispaniola, as well as on Puerto Rico, Vieques, St. Croix, St. Thomas, Mona, La Gonave and La Tortue. According to Miller (1929b), this species and *Brotomys voratus* survived into the post-Columbian era where they have been found in barn owl deposits in association with *Rattus*. Remains of both species are common in midden deposits in early Spanish sites in northern Haiti. Reliable reports indicate that *I. portoricensis* survived into this century on La Tortue off the north coast of Haiti (Woods *et al.*, in press). The species *I. montanus* (formerly placed in the monotypic genus *Aphaetreus*) and *Hexolobodon phenax* were common throughout mountainous regions of Hispaniola into Amerindian times (Woods, in press). Both species of *Isolobodon* are present in Hispaniolan deposits dated at older than 15 000 years BP, confirming that this genus is endemic to Hispaniola. The large heptaxodontid rodent, *Quemisia gravis*, has been reported from at least one archaeological site in northern Haiti (Miller, 1929a). A new extinct genus of capromyid recently discovered in southwestern Haiti has been identified from a fossil deposit dated at less than 4000 years BP. This new genus occurs in the site with three species of *Plagiodontia*, both species of *Isolobodon*, *Hexolobodon phenax* and *Brotomys voratus*, as well as the three species of *Nesophontes*, two species of *Solenodon*, at least two species of ground sloth and one primate. Although this fossil deposit contains no associated archaeological material, its age suggests that all of these species survived into the Amerindian period in remote regions of Hispaniola.

No native non-volant mammals currently inhabit the Lesser Antilles; however, a recently extinct species of *Oryzomys* is known from St. Vincent, and species of *Megalomys* occurred on Martinique and St. Lucia until early in this century. Palaeontological and archaeological remains of oryzomyine rodents have been recorded from nine additional Lesser Antillean islands (see Fig. 2). Oryzomyine rodents were exploited extensively for food by Amerindian peoples

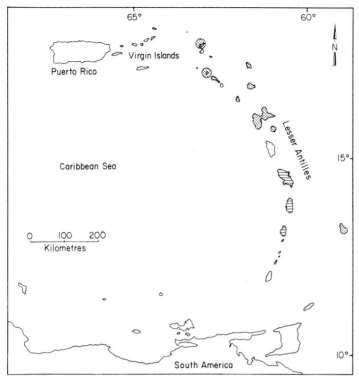

Figure 2. Occurrence of extinct taxa of oryzomyine rodents in Lesser Antilles. Stippled islands represent species known only from palaeontological or archaeological sites, while islands with horizontal bars represent recently extinct species. See Fig. 1 for names of individual islands.

in the Lesser Antilles, and are often the most abundant terrestrial vertebrates in archaeological sites on these islands (Wing, Hoffman & Ray, 1968; Wing & Reitz, 1982). Steadman *et al.* (1984a) suggested that some species of rice rats in the Lesser Antilles may not have gone extinct until after the introduction of *Rattus* in post-Columbian times. Hopwood (1926) described the rice rat, *Megalomys audreyae*, from a fossil deposit on Barbuda. Ray (1964) reported an undescribed species of *Oryzomys* from a fossil deposit on Barbados. A large undescribed genus of oryzomyine has been recorded from two localities in Antigua, an Amerindian site ranging in age from 1450 to 800 years BP (Wing *et al.*, 1968) and a late Holocene fossil deposit radiocarbon dated at 4300–2500 years BP (Steadman *et al.*, 1984a). Wing *et al.* (1968) noted the occurrence of this same species in Amerindian middens in Guadeloupe and Montserrat, and a fossil deposit on Barbuda, and Watters *et al.* (1984) reported it from prehistoric archaeological sites on Barbuda and Marie Galante, a small island south of Guadeloupe. Smaller species of undescribed oryzomyines are known from archaeological and/or palaeontological sites on Montserrat, St. Kitts and Anguilla (Wing, 1973; Steadman *et al.*, 1984b). Previously unreported remains of a small oryzomyine have recently been identified from an Amerindian site on St. Eustatius (FSM zooarchaeology collection). The giant extinct heptaxodontid, *Amblyrhiza inundata*, occurs only in indurated breccia deposits on the tiny islands of Anguilla and St. Martin in the northernmost Lesser Antilles.

Like the large Jamaican heptaxodontids, it appears that *Amblyrhiza* went extinct before the end of the Pleistocene.

## *Chiroptera*

The Chiroptera is the most diverse order of mammals in the living West Indian fauna, including six of the nine families found in the New World: Noctilionidae, Mormoopidae, Phyllostomidae, Natalidae, Vespertilionidae and Molossidae. The Antillean bat fauna numbers 59 species, composed of 51 living species, five extinct species and three species extinct in the West Indies but still found in Central and South America. The bats have suffered fewer extinctions than other Antillean mammal groups, as only 14% of the known species no longer occur in the West Indies. Four of the five extinct Caribbean bats are recorded only from Cuba: *Mormoops magna*, *Pteronotus pristinus*, *Artibeus anthonyi* and *Phyllops vetus*. The two extinct mormoopids (Silva Taboada, 1974) and *Artibeus anthonyi* (Woloszyn & Silva Taboada, 1977) were described from undated, but presumed late Pleistocene cave deposits. Only *Phyllops vetus* is known from the Holocene, as it has been reported from a supposedly post-Columbian cave deposit on the Isla de Pinos (Silva Taboada & Woloszyn, 1975). The fifth extinct species of bat, *Phyllonycteris major*, was originally described from late Pleistocene cave deposits in Puerto Rico (Anthony, 1917) and has recently been reported from a late Holocene fissure deposit on Antigua (Steadman *et al.*, 1984a).

Three species of bats recorded from West Indian fossil sites are absent in the modern fauna, but still live on the mainland from Mexico southward. *Mormoops megalophylla* has been identified from the late Pleistocene of Cuba (Silva Taboada, 1974), the Dominican Republic (FSM) and New Providence, Bahamas (FSM). *Tonatia bidens* occurs in a single late Pleistocene cave deposit in Jamaica (Koopman & Williams, 1951). The vampire bat, *Desmodus rotundus*, is known from two fossil deposits in Cuba, one of late Pleistocene age (Koopman, 1958) and one of supposed Holocene age (Woloszyn & Mayo, 1974). The reasons for the disappearance of *Mormoops megalophylla* and *Tonatia bidens* are unknown; however, *M. megalophylla* also occurs in the late Pleistocene of Florida (Ray, Olsen & Gut, 1963) where it is now extinct. Koopman (1958) suggested that vampire bats in Cuba may have fed on the blood of ground sloths and that the extinction of ground sloths ultimately led to the disappearance of *Desmodus*. In addition to species of bats that disappeared from the West Indies altogether, some bats went extinct only on certain islands but still survive on others. These local extinctions are also a common phenomenon among West Indian birds and reptiles and appear to have resulted from climatic changes and the rise in sea level at the end of the Pleistocene (Pregill & Olson, 1981). The localized extinctions of bats in the West Indies will be discussed in detail in the following section.

### CHIROPTERAN RANGE REDUCTIONS AND THEIR ENVIRONMENTAL SIGNIFICANCE

Certain species of bats, in particular mormoopids, brachyphylline phyllostomids, and natalids, provide the best examples among West Indian mammals of range reductions since the end of the Pleistocene. Today these

groups of bats roost almost exclusively in caves in the West Indies. Most
Antillean bats that have undergone localized extinctions are not only obligate
cave dwellers, but also prefer specialized cave environments. Silva Taboada &
Pine (1969) distinguished two general types of microenvironments in West
Indian caves. The first is a variable microenvironment that is strongly
influenced by external factors. Caves with this microenvironment are generally
small or have many openings, are often dimly lit and have variable temperature
and humidity. The caves found on most small islands in the West Indies are
characterized by a variable microclimate. The second type of microenvironment
is more stable and is usually found in the deep recesses of large caves. This stable
microenvironment is characterized by complete darkness and high temperature
and humidity. According to Silva Taboada & Pine (1969), the bats in Cuba
that favour the hot, climatically stable portions of caves include all species of
mormoopids (*Mormoops blainvillii* and three species of *Pteronotus*) and the three
genera of brachyphyllines (*Brachyphylla*, *Phyllonycteris* and *Erophylla*), whereas
*Monophyllus redmani* and the species of *Natalus* are restricted to more temperate,
but stable portions of caves. These are precisely the groups of bats that have
suffered the most extensive localized extinctions in the West Indies. There are
two likely explanations for this pattern: (1) cave environments on some islands
have been altered since the end of the Pleistocene, presumably reflecting overall
climatic changes; (2) there has been a change in the size and distribution of
caves, primarily on small islands, resulting from the post-glacial rise in sea level
and subsequent flooding of low-lying areas.

There have been a number of extinctions among the species of *Phyllonycteris*,
the Antillean bats most highly adapted for the hot, stable cave environment
(Silva Taboada & Pine, 1969). The large extinct species, *P. major*, is known
from Puerto Rico (Choate & Birney, 1968) and Antigua (Steadman *et al.*,
1984a). Fossils of the Cuban species, *P. poeyi*, from outside its modern range
have been identified from Cayman Brac (Morgan, in press) and New
Providence, Bahamas (FSM). Extinct populations of *Brachyphylla nana* are
known from Jamaica (Koopman & Williams, 1951), Cayman Brac (Morgan, in
press), New Providence (Olson & Pregill, 1982) and Andros, Bahamas (FSM).
No extinctions have been recorded within the genus *Erophylla*, the species of
which inhabit a broader range of cave microenvironments than do other
brachyphyllines. Among the Natalidae, the large species *Natalus major* is extinct
on Cuba (Silva Taboada, 1979), Andros (FSM) and New Providence (FSM),
and the endemic Bahamian species *N. tumidifrons* is known from fossil deposits on
several islands in the Bahamas where it no longer occurs (Koopman *et al.*, 1957;
FSM).

The Mormoopidae have suffered more local extinctions than any other group
of West Indian bats. Distributional data in Smith (1972) suggest that the
occurrence of mormoopids is limited by the availability of caves. For example,
mormoopids are rare throughout much of lowland tropical South America
where caves are uncommon, and are found primarily in the arid coastal regions
of northern Colombia and Venezuela, and western Ecuador and Peru. Their
preference for hot, stable cave environments and an apparent affinity for dry
habitats may explain the wider distribution of mormoopids in the late
Pleistocene of the West Indies. Silva Taboada (1974) described an extinct
species of *Pteronotus*, a large extinct species of *Mormoops* and the first West Indian

specimens of *M. megalophylla* from late Pleistocene cave deposits in Cuba. Late Pleistocene fossils of *M. megalophylla* are also known from the Dominican Republic (FSM), New Providence (FSM) and Tobago (Eshelman & Morgan, 1985). Extinct populations of *M. blainvillii* are known from Little Exuma (Koopman *et al.*, 1957) and New Providence (Olson & Pregill, 1982) in the Bahamas and Antigua (Steadman *et al.*, 1984a) and Barbuda (FSM) in the northern Lesser Antilles. Fossils of *Pteronotus parnellii* from outside the modern range of the species (see Fig. 3) have been recorded from Isla de Pinos off the coast of Cuba (Silva Taboada, 1979), Grand Cayman (Morgan, in press), New Providence (Olson & Pregill, 1982), La Gonave off the coast of Haiti (Koopman, 1955), Antigua (Steadman *et al.*, 1984a) and Tobago (Eshelman & Morgan, 1985). Neither *M. blainvillii* nor *P. parnellii* currently occur on any Antillean island east of Puerto Rico.

Except for Cuba, which lost three of the seven species of mormoopids found in late Pleistocene deposits there, almost all other localized extinctions of mormoopids in the West Indies took place on small islands. Many of these small islands do not possess the extensive cave systems and hot, stable cave microenvironments that mormoopids prefer. However, during the late Pleistocene periods of low sea level, many of these islands, such as Antigua and Barbuda and the islands on the Great Bahama Bank, would have been considerably larger in size and approximately 100 m higher in elevation relative to the sea level at that time. These two facts, coupled with the limestone composition of most of these islands, would almost certainly have allowed the

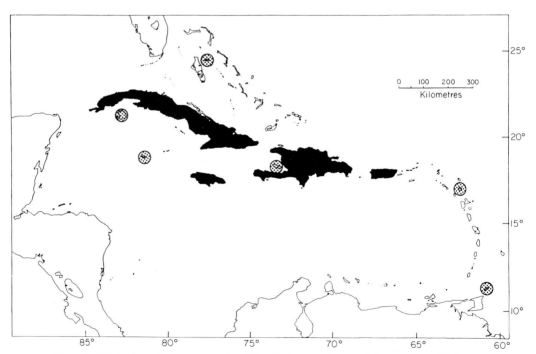

Figure 3. Distribution of recent and extinct West Indian populations of *Pteronotus parnellii*. Recent distribution indicated by filled areas (also includes parts of Central and South America), extinct populations indicated by stippling. See Fig. 1 for names of individual islands.

development of more extensive cave systems. With the post-glacial rise in sea level many of these caves would have become flooded, with the subsequent extirpation of species inhabiting them.

Mormoopid and brachyphylline bats also seem to have been vulnerable to human-caused environmental degradation in the West Indies. Steadman *et al.* (1984a) identified *Mormoops blainvillii*, *Pteronotus parnellii* and *Phyllonycteris major* from a late Holocene fissure deposit on Antigua that clearly post-dates any late Pleistocene climatic changes. They hypothesized that habitat destruction by Amerindian peoples during the last 3000 years led to the disappearance of these three species on Antigua. Woods (1986) recorded similar post-Pleistocene chiropteran extinctions from a mountainous region in southwestern Haiti. Bat remains collected from surficial cave deposits in the Massif de la Selle confirm that eight species were present within the past few thousand years, whereas recent field work (Woods, 1986) indicates that only four species of bats currently inhabit this region. The bats lost from la Selle include three forms restricted to hot, climatically stable portions of caves, *Phyllonycteris obtusa*, *Brachyphylla pumila* and *Erophylla bombifrons*. It is not clear whether the primary reason for the disappearance of these species relates to deforestation or to the exposure of cave entrances to increased sunlight and activity, but their loss is certainly associated with extensive habitat alteration.

There are other examples of localized extinctions of bats in the West Indian fossil record, but the preceding data should suffice to establish that many species have undergone considerable contraction of their ranges. Other species of bats have undoubtedly expanded their ranges since the end of the Pleistocene, although this is difficult to demonstrate as the absence of a fossil record of a species from a particular island cannot be taken as proof that it did not occur there. Williams (1952) hypothesized that *Artibeus jamaicensis* arrived in Jamaica very recently as it is abundant in younger surficial cave deposits but absent from older, presumably late Pleistocene, strata. Morgan (in press) also noted the absence of *A. jamaicensis* in late Pleistocene and early Holocene fossil deposits in the Cayman Islands, even though it is one of the most common living species in the Caymans and is abundant in modern barn owl deposits on Grand Cayman and Cayman Brac.

Pregill & Olson (1981) reviewed the zoogeography of West Indian vertebrates in relation to extinctions and range reductions resulting from climatic changes and sea level rise since the end of the Pleistocene. They concluded that during the last glaciation the climate throughout the West Indies was drier than at present, as was probably true for most lowland tropical regions of the New World (Van der Hammen, 1974). Consequently, grassland and savanna habitats and species preferring these drier habitats were probably more widely distributed in the West Indies during the late Pleistocene. Many shallow carbonate banks, particularly in the Bahamas and between Jamaica and Central America, were islands in the late Pleistocene. Furthermore, many smaller islands now located on shallow carbonate banks would have been combined to form much larger islands, such as the islands on the Great and Little Bahama Banks, the Puerto Rican Bank and in the northern Lesser Antilles. Large areas of low-lying land exposed during the late Pleistocene were flooded when sea levels returned to near their present level after 13 000 years BP. The most convincing examples of extinctions resulting from climatic change and the subsequent expansion of more mesic habitats are xerophilic species of birds and reptiles that now have restricted or spotty distributions, but were more widespread in the late Pleistocene (Pregill & Olson, 1981), such as the burrowing owl (*Athene cunicularia*), thick-knee (*Burhinus bistriatus*) and several species of rock iguanas (*Cyclura*).

### EXTINCTION AND THE ZOOGEOGRAPHY OF MAMMALS IN THE LESSER ANTILLES

The difference between the pre-human and modern mammal faunas of the Lesser Antilles is striking. A zoogeographer analysing living species would find only bats in the Lesser Antilles, and might arrive at the logical, but erroneous conclusion that the deep water gaps separating these oceanic islands from one another and from the South American mainland prevented the northward dispersal of all non-volant mammals. A zoogeographer taking into account recently extinct forms would find, in addition to bats, only three species of oryzomyine rodents, one each on the large southern islands of Martinique, St. Lucia and St. Vincent. The historical zoogeographer, with the added benefit of data from numerous fossil and archaeological sites, sees a completely different picture of rodent diversity, evolution and zoogeography in the Lesser Antilles. Moreover, the fossil bats modify previous ideas on zoogeographic boundaries between the Greater and Lesser Antilles.

The extinct oryzomyine rodents in the Lesser Antilles are found primarily in Amerindian archaeological sites that are no more than several thousand years old. Most, if not all, of these species would probably survive today if not for direct exploitation by man, habitat destruction and competition with or predation by introduced Old World rats (*Rattus*). Rather than being totally absent or represented by waifs on only three islands, the oryzomyine rodents underwent an adaptive radiation in the Lesser Antilles that produced at least three genera and eight species and encompassed almost every island (Fig. 2, see earlier discussion on extinct rodents for distribution of individual oryzomyine species). Evidence from archaeological sites on Montserrat (Steadman *et al.*, 1984b) and palaeontological sites on Barbuda (Hopwood, 1926; FSM) demonstrates that at least two species of oryzomyines were sympatric on some islands. As more palaeontological sites are discovered in the Lesser Antilles, additional new species of endemic rice rats will undoubtedly be found. The giant extinct heptaxodontid rodent *Amblyrhiza inundata* from Anguilla and St. Martin in the northernmost Lesser Antilles belongs to a family otherwise endemic to the Greater Antilles.

The present chiropteran fauna of the West Indies is composed of 34 species restricted to the Greater Antilles, 12 species restricted to the Lesser Antilles, and five species that occur in both regions (Baker & Genoways, 1978). Fossil bats from Puerto Rico and from Antigua and Barbuda, two small islands located 400 km east of Puerto Rico in the northern Lesser Antilles, provide convincing evidence that faunal boundaries in this region have not remained stable over the last 10 000 years. The presence of a Lesser Antillean bat *Monophyllus plethodon* in the late Pleistocene of Puerto Rico (Choate & Birney, 1968), and the occurrence of the Greater Antillean species *Mormoops blainvillii*, *Pteronotus parnellii*, *Phyllonycteris major* and *Macrotus waterhousii* in fossil deposits on Antigua and Barbuda (Steadman *et al.*, 1984; FSM) blur the sharp distinction that exists between the modern bat faunas of the Greater and Lesser Antilles. For example, the current mammalian fauna of Antigua consists of seven species of bats, four species that are widespread throughout the West Indies and are of little zoogeographic significance (*Noctilio leporinus*, *Artibeus jamaicensis*, *Tadarida brasiliensis* and *Molossus molossus*), and three species that are essentially Lesser Antillean endemics (*Monophyllus plethodon*, *Brachyphylla cavernarum* and *Natalus stramineus*). Holocene fossils from Antigua (Steadman *et al.*, 1984a) add three species of bats, two of which are now restricted to the Greater Antilles (*M. blainvillii* and *P. parnellii*) and one of which is an extinct species belonging to a genus otherwise endemic to the Greater Antilles (*Phyllonycteris major*). These three species of bats inhabited Antigua until at least 2500 years BP, and would probably still survive there if not for human-caused habitat destruction (Steadman *et al.*, 1984a). Disregarding human-caused extinctions, the bat fauna of Antigua would have consisted of three species with Greater Antillean affinities, three species with Lesser Antillean affinities and four widespread forms. The occurrence of *Macrotus waterhousii* in fossil deposits in Puerto Rico (Choate & Birney, 1968) and Barbuda (FSM), both of which are east of the species' modern range, further emphasizes the wider distribution of certain Greater Antillean bats in the late Pleistocene and Holocene.

These data suggest that the distinct zoogeographic boundary between the modern bat faunas of the Greater and Lesser Antilles has been enhanced by Late Quaternary extinctions. The northern Lesser Antilles and perhaps the Virgin Islands as well could probably be more accurately characterized as a transition zone between these two faunas. Although some mixing of Greater and Lesser Antillean mammals did occur in the late Pleistocene and Holocene, especially among bats, there is nonetheless an undeniable distinction between these two faunas. The extensive Late Quaternary fossil record of the Greater Antilles clearly establishes that mammals with Lesser Antillean affinities do not occur west of Puerto Rico. Only through the discovery of pre-Amerindian fossil deposits on Lesser Antillean islands which have no fossil record (which includes most of the islands) will the complete extent of the invasion of Greater Antillean species be documented.

## SOME IMPLICATIONS FOR ISLAND BIOGEOGRAPHIC THEORY

In the two decades since the publication of MacArthur & Wilson's (1967) treatise on theoretical island biogeography, there have been numerous attempts by ecologists to explain the zoogeography of bird and lizard faunas on Caribbean islands using various ecological models (Williams, 1969; Ricklefs & Cox, 1972; Lack, 1976; Terborgh, Faaborg & Brockman, 1978). Physical and ecological parameters of the islands, including area, elevation, water depths and distance from closest presumed source of colonization, and habitat diversity, have been analysed to determine their effect on the composition of the faunas. As pointed out by Pregill & Olson (1981), most of these ecological studies failed to incorporate pertinent palaeontological, archaeological and geological data (with the notable exception of Williams, 1969), even though they attempted to explain biogeographic concepts like colonization and extinction that have a strong historical component. The empirical data necessary to actually calculate rates of colonization and extinction, and to test theoretical concepts such as faunal equilibrium and the species–area effect, are available through analysis of the West Indian fossil record.

We use palaeontological and archaeological data to calculate rates of colonization and extinction for Antillean mammals and to analyse the effects of various historical factors, particularly extinction and changes in island size, on the relationship between island area and species diversity. We stress that these results are preliminary and subject to modification based on future fossil discoveries and taxonomic changes.

### Rates of colonization and extinction

Our data base for the calculation of colonization rates is derived from various sources, including the phylogenetic relationships of the various West Indian mammal groups, the Tertiary fossil history of their closest relatives in South or North America and the geologic history of the islands. Regardless of how the Antillean fauna and flora originally reached the islands, most authors would agree that from about the late Eocene onward the West Indies were oceanic islands (MacFadden, 1981; Buskirk, 1985). The late Eocene would also be an appropriate time period for the derivation of the most ancient Antillean mammal group, the solenodontoid insectivores. For these two reasons the late Eocene (approximately 40 million years BP) will be considered the earliest time the West Indies could have been colonized by the terrestrial mammal groups subsequently represented in the Late Quaternary and current fauna. For the remaining groups of mammals that reached the West Indies, early Miocene (approximately 20 million years BP) or younger ages would be reasonable postulated arrival dates based on the South American fossil record of their closest sister taxa (see earlier discussion). It is conceivable that either the West Indies were unsuitable for habitation by most land mammals before the early Miocene or that an earlier archaic mammalian fauna inhabited the islands but, except for the insectivores, disappeared before the known fossil record of Antillean vertebrates. Because of the uncertainties resulting from the absence of a pre-Pleistocene fossil record of land mammals in the West Indies, two separate immigration rates for land mammals are calculated using the late Eocene and the early Miocene as the earliest times of colonization.

The number of presumed colonization events necessary to account for the known Antillean mammal fauna has been determined from the number of monophyletic groups present (Table 2). Our calculations involve only the colonization of the West Indies from South and North America. Inter-island colonizations within the Caribbean were also important, but are not discussed in detail here. The West Indian non-volant mammal fauna could have been derived from as few as 13 separate immigration events (Table 2) over the last 40 million years (the late Eocene scenario), giving a rate of approximately one colonization every 3.1 million years. The same 13 colonizations occurring over 20 million years (the early Miocene scenario) yields a rate of one colonization every 1.5 million years. Whichever of these two hypothetical immigration rates is closer to the actual rate, it seems clear that throughout the Tertiary colonizations of the West Indies by non-volant mammals must have been extremely uncommon. The derivation of this fauna appears to be one of rare immigration events followed by extensive adaptive radiations of a few groups

## Table 2. Number of colonization events by West Indian land mammals

| Taxonomic group | Number of species in West Indies | Number of colonizations (= Number of monophyletic groups) |
|---|---|---|
| *Non-volant mammals* | | |
| Insectivora (incl. Solenodontidae and Nesophontidae) | 12 | 1 |
| Edentata | | |
| Megalonychidae (incl. all Antillean taxa) | 16 | 1 |
| Primates | | |
| Cebidae | | |
| *Ateles* | 1 | 1 |
| 'Saimiri' | 1 | 1 |
| *Xenothrix* | 1 | 1 |
| Rodentia | | |
| Capromyidae | 26 | 1 |
| Echimyidae (incl. all Antillean taxa) | 7 | 1 |
| Heptaxodontidae | 4 | 1 |
| Cricetidae | | |
| *Oryzomys* | 3 | 2 |
| *Megalomys* | 3 | 1 |
| large undesc. oryzomyine | 1 | 1 |
| small undesc. oryzomyine | 1 | 1 |
| Total | 76 | 13 |
| *Bats* | | |
| Chiroptera | | |
| Noctilionidae | | |
| *Noctilio* | 1 | 1 |
| Mormoopidae | | |
| *Mormoops* | 3 | 2 |
| *Pteronotus* | 5 | 3 |
| Phyllostomidae | | |
| *Macrotus* | 1 | 1 |
| *Tonatia* | 1 | 1 |
| *Glossophaga* | 2 | 2 |
| *Monophyllus* | 2 | 1 |
| *Sturnira* | 2 | 1 |
| *Chiroderma* | 1 | 1 |
| *Artibeus* | 3 | 3 |
| *Ardops, Ariteus, Phyllops* and *Stenoderma* | 6 | 1 |
| Brachyphyllinae (*Brachyphylla, Erophylla* and *Phyllonycteris*) | 9 | 1 |
| *Desmodus* | 1 | 1 |
| Natalidae | | |
| *Natalus* | 5 | 3 |
| Vespertilionidae | | |
| *Myotis* | 2 | 1 |
| *Eptesicus* | 3 | 2 |
| *Lasiurus* | 2 | 2 |
| *Nycticeius* | 1 | 1 |
| *Antrozous* | 1 | 1 |
| Molossidae | | |
| *Tadarida* | 3 | 3 |
| *Mormopterus* | 1 | 1 |
| *Eumops* | 3 | 3 |
| *Molossus* | 1 | 1 |
| Total | 59 | 37 |

within the West Indies, in particular insectivores, ground sloths and rodents. The relationships of the various mammal groups suggest that these adaptive radiations involved a number of interisland colonizations as well.

The living and extinct chiropteran fauna of the West Indies can be derived from approximately 37 independent colonizations (Table 2). Immigration rates of bats for the same two time periods discussed above are as follows: one colonization every 1.1 million years since the late Eocene and one colonization every 550 000 years since the early Miocene. These rates are both roughly three times as fast as those for non-volant mammals, presumably reflecting the considerably greater dispersal abilities of bats. Even the highest immigration rate for Caribbean bats has only one new species arriving in the islands every 500 000 years. This supports Koopman's (1970) contention that bats do not have unlimited capabilities of dispersing across wide expanses of open ocean, and in fact have immigrated to the West Indies only rarely throughout the Tertiary.

It is unlikely that many living species of mammals evolved before the beginning of the Pleistocene (about 2 Ma BP). Therefore, the large number of West Indian bats that are conspecific with mainland species (23 species comprising 39% of the total chiropteran fauna) argues for a considerably higher rate of immigration during the last 2 Ma. This assumes that each of these 23 species originated on the mainland and dispersed to the West Indies, which is a reasonable hypothesis considering there is little evidence that the West Indies have been a source area for the Neotropical or Nearctic bat faunas. The immigration rate for bats since the beginning of the Pleistocene would have been one species every 87 000 years. The most obvious explanation for this apparently rapid increase in the immigration rate of bats relates to glacio-eustatic fluctuations in sea level during the Pleistocene. Large areas of the Nicaraguan Plateau, Campeche Bank and northern edge of the South American continental shelf would have been above water during low sea level stands. This extension of continental land areas would have lessened the distance between some West Indian islands and the mainland, greatly facilitating overwater dispersal of bats, especially to Cuba, Jamaica and the southern Lesser Antilles. This suggests a similar hypothesis for the apparent peak of West Indian landfalls by non-volant mammals in the Miocene, as several unusually low sea level stands during that epoch are recorded by Vail, Mitchum & Thompson (1977).

The available data do not support a comparable increase in the colonization rate of non-volant mammals during the Pleistocene. The deep water barriers that have isolated the West Indies since the Early Tertiary apparently limited overwater dispersal of terrestrial mammals, despite the narrower water gaps present at certain times during the Pleistocene. Among the 76 species of native Antillean non-volant mammals, only the Jamaican *Oryzomys* may be conspecific with a mainland species. Species of *Oryzomys* from St. Vincent and Barbados represent the only other Antillean terrestrial mammals that are even congeneric with mainland forms ('*Proechimys*' *corozalus* is almost certainly not closely related to mainland *Proechimys*, and the Cuban and Hispaniolan primates need further study to establish their generic status). The remainder of the Lesser Antillean oryzomyines belong to endemic West Indian genera that probably evolved before the Pleistocene. The colonization of the West Indies by three species of *Oryzomys* during the Pleistocene yields an immigration rate of one species every

670 000 years. Although this is about twice the rate for non-volant mammals over the last 20 Ma, the closer proximity to the Recent would argue for a greater likelihood of survival and preservation of Pleistocene immigrants. The rate of immigration for bats during the Pleistocene is almost eight times greater than that for non-volant mammals. The combined colonization rates for all land mammals in the West Indies (based on 50 separate colonizations, i.e. 13 for non-volant mammals and 37 for bats) are one species per 800 000 years since the late Eocene or one species per 400 000 years since the early Miocene.

There are several possible inconsistencies with our calculations of colonization rates. The most obvious problem is one of missing data. As a result of the absence of a pre-late Pleistocene fossil record of land mammals in the West Indies, our analysis is based solely on the Late Quaternary and living fauna. There are undoubtedly many species of mammals that inhabited the West Indies but went extinct before the late Pleistocene. Moreover, new species of mammals continue to be discovered in Late Quaternary deposits. Although it is impossible to estimate the number of mammals that colonized the West Indies and then disappeared without leaving a fossil record, these hypothetical species would argue for an increased number of immigrations and hence a faster colonization rate than those calculated from the Late Quaternary fauna alone. Changes in the taxonomy of Antillean mammals may also affect the calculation of colonization rates. The number of monophyletic groups of mammals, and hence the number of presumed colonizations, have been determined from the most current data available on their phylogenetic relationships. However, future studies of these relationships could alter our results somewhat.

To calculate extinction rates of mammals in the West Indies during the Late Quaternary, we have selected 20 000 years BP as the most recent date when all members of the late Pleistocene fauna still survived. Several species may have gone extinct before 20 000 years BP, such as the heptaxodontids *Clidomys* and *Amblyrhiza*, but these are more than offset by species known to have survived well into the Holocene. The rate of extinction of non-volant mammals accelerated rapidly after the arrival of man in the West Indies 4500 years ago. To demonstrate this we have determined two separate extinction rates for West Indian non-volant mammals. One is an average rate of extinction for all species over the last 20 000 years, whereas the second rate includes only those species known to have disappeared during the Amerindian and post-Columbian periods (4500 years BP to present). Of the 76 species of Antillean terrestrial mammals we regard as valid, 67 species have gone extinct during the last 20 000 years, giving an extinction rate of one species every 299 years. At least 37 of these species disappeared in the last 4500 years, yielding the extremely high extinction rate of one species every 122 years. Between 40 000 and 10 000 years BP the Caribbean islands appear to have experienced very few immigrations or extinctions of non-volant mammals and hence little or no faunal turnover. The anomalously high extinction rates in the latest Pleistocene and Holocene drastically altered this apparent faunal equilibrium. The net result is an extremely depauperate modern fauna that has not yet been replenished either through immigration or autochthonous speciation.

The extinction rate for bats since the late Pleistocene has not been nearly so high as that recorded for the non-volant mammals. With the possible exception of *Phyllops vetus* and *Desmodus rotundus*, all other extinct or extirpated Caribbean bats are known only from late Pleistocene deposits. Therefore, we have determined the rate of extinction of bats only for the last 20 000 years. Eight species of bats went extinct in the West Indies during the Late Quaternary, giving an extinction rate of one species every 2500 years. A total of 75 species of land mammals have disappeared from the West Indies during the last 20 000 years, giving a combined rate of one extinction every 267 years.

## Species–area relationships

Figure 4 is a log–log species–area plot of the recent and fossil mammalian faunas from the West Indian islands listed in Table 3. For those islands with a reasonably complete fossil record, two figures are included on the graph. The letters represent the number of living species, while the circled letters represent the total number of species recorded in fossil deposits and/or archaeological sites. The recent and fossil values for each island represent the total land mammal fauna, including both bats and non-volant mammals. We have included data on

Table 3. Land areas and number of species of living and fossil land mammals for West Indian islands used in constructing species–area plot

| Island | Area* (km²) | Species of living mammals† | | | Species of fossil mammals† | | |
|---|---|---|---|---|---|---|---|
| | | Total | NV | B | Total | NV | B |
| Cuba | 114524 | 31 | 5 | 26 | 55 | 26 | 29 |
| Hispaniola | 76190 | 20 | 2 | 18 | 44 | 25 | 19 |
| Jamaica | 11425 | 22 | 1 | 21 | 24 | 5 | 19 |
| Puerto Rico | 8897 | 13 | 0 | 13 | 18 | 6 | 12 |
| Trinidad‡ | 4828 | 94 | 30 | 64 | +§ | | |
| Andros | 4144 | 5 | 0 | 5 | 14 | 1 | 13 |
| Guadeloupe | 1779 | 10 | 0 | 10 | + | | |
| Martinique | 1101 | 9 | 0¶ | 9 | + | | |
| Dominica | 751 | 12 | 0 | 12 | + | | |
| St. Lucia | 616 | 8 | 0¶ | 8 | + | | |
| Barbados | 430 | 6 | 0 | 6 | + | | |
| St. Vincent | 389 | 9 | 0¶ | 9 | + | | |
| Tobago‡ | 300 | 36 | 16 | 20 | + | | |
| Antigua | 280 | 7 | 0 | 7 | 11 | 1 | 10 |
| New Providence | 250 | 5 | 0 | 5 | 15 | 1 | 14 |
| Cayman Islands | 216 | 8 | 0 | 8 | 13 | 3 | 10 |
| Barbuda | 161 | 6 | 0 | 6 | 10 | 2 | 8 |
| Montserrat | 102 | 8 | 0 | 8 | 10 | 2 | 8 |
| Anguilla | 91 | 5 | 0 | 5 | 7 | 2 | 5 |

*Land areas were taken from: *The Times Atlas of the World*, Comprehensive Edition, 1980. New York: John Bartholomew and Son Limited.

†Total number of species for both living and fossil faunas are subdivided into number of non-volant mammals (NV) and bats (B).

‡The land areas and living mammalian faunas of Trinidad and Tobago are included in this table only because they appear on the species–area plot. However, these figures were not used in calculating the 'recent' curve, as both Trinidad and Tobago are South American landbridge islands and not part of the West Indian faunal region.

§Fossil vertebrates are either unknown from islands marked (+) or are too incomplete to accurately represent the extinct fauna.

¶Species of oryzomyine rodents are known from Martinique (*Megalomys desmaresti*), St. Lucia (*M. luciae*), and St. Vincent (*Oryzomys victus*); however, these three species are excluded from our analysis as they are recently extinct and thus not technically part of the living fauna.

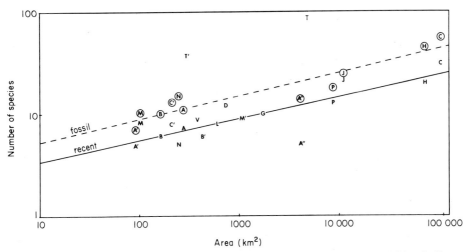

Figure 4. Species–area plot of recent and fossil mammalian faunas from selected West Indian islands. Exact land areas and numbers of recent and fossil species for all islands in this figure can be found in Table 3. Islands on plot and their abbreviations are as follows: Antigua (A), Anguilla (A′), Andros (A″), Barbuda (B), Barbados (B′), Cuba (C), Cayman Islands (C′), Dominica (D), Guadeloupe (G), Hispaniola (H), Jamaica (J), Montserrat (M), Martinique (M′), New Providence (N), Puerto Rico (P), St. Lucia (L), St. Vincent (V), Trinidad (T), and Tobago (T′).

extant species for all of the larger Lesser Antillean islands, although most lack fossil deposits. The continuous line is a species–area curve calculated from the number of living species in the modern fauna of each island, whereas the dashed line is the species–area curve based on the species known from late Pleistocene and Holocene fossil deposits and archaeological sites.

If only recent species are considered, there is a rather strong correlation ($r = 0.83$) between island size and mammalian species diversity. The slope or $z$ value of the 'recent' species–area curve is 0.21, which compares favourably with $z$ values for various animal groups from both the West Indies and other island archipelagos (MacArthur & Wilson, 1967). Thus, 69% of the variance ($R^2$) in mammalian species diversity on Antillean islands can be explained by area alone. The remaining 31% of the variance must be dependent upon other variables such as habitat diversity and distance from source areas. Among the Greater Antilles, Cuba and Jamaica have larger living mammal faunas than are predicted from the species–area curve, while the more remote islands of Hispaniola and Puerto Rico fall somewhat below their expected values. The Recent faunas of all Antillean islands are composed predominantly of bats (85%), and thus the islands closest to the Neotropical mainland (e.g. Cuba, Jamaica and Grenada) would more likely be colonized, especially during periods of low sea level.

Many of the large Lesser Antillean islands are close to the 'recent' species–area curve, but fall well below the 'fossil' curve. There are two possible explanations for the apparently impoverished Lesser Antillean mammal fauna: (1) since most of these islands lack fossil deposits, the actual number of species recorded from them is probably too low; (2) the great distance from the nearest source area and deep water gaps have limited overwater dispersal. The actual situation probably is a combination of these two factors. Although islands such as Dominica, Guadeloupe and Martinique are relatively large and supported extensive rainforests before the arrival of man, it is nonetheless unlikely that more than several additional species will be found on the islands when fossil deposits are eventually discovered (anywhere from five to ten more species are required for these three islands to fit the predicted 'fossil' curve). An analysis based solely on living mammals reaches the seemingly erroneous conclusion that the large Lesser Antillean islands closely fit the theoretical species–area curve, whereas our fossil data suggest these islands possess a more depauperate mammalian fauna than would be predicted from their land area alone. The landbridge islands of Trinidad and Tobago are included on the species–area plot for illustrative purposes only. The species diversity and land area values for these two islands were not used in calculating the 'recent' curve, as neither island possesses Antillean endemic species of mammals. A direct land connection of both Trinidad and Tobago to South America during the late Pleistocene low sea level stand (Eshelman & Morgan, 1985), coupled with their current proximity to that continent, have had a dramatic effect on their mammalian faunas, which are composed of about five times as many species as West Indian islands of similar size.

The mammalian species diversity of the current Antillean fauna is unnaturally low due to extensive extinctions, particularly of non-volant mammals. All West Indian islands with a reasonably good fossil record supported more species of mammals in the late Pleistocene and early Holocene than in the living fauna (Table 3). Furthermore, the number of fossil species must be considered minimum values owing to deficiencies in the fossil record. The late Pleistocene and Holocene bat fauna has about the same number of species as the living fauna, but the diversity of non-volant mammals has been dramatically reduced. Most Caribbean islands lack living non-volant mammals altogether, although practically every island supported one or more species prior to man's arrival. Of the curves shown in Fig. 4, the 'fossil' curve more closely approximates the true native land mammal fauna of the West Indies. The correlation between island size and mammalian species diversity ($r = 0.93$) is stronger for the fossil curve than the recent curve, accounting for 86% of the variance, while the $z$ value of 0.22 is very similar. The 'recent' curve is based on an incomplete data set, and thus represents the island faunas as being more depauperate than they actually were under natural conditions.

The species–area curve generated from the fossil data has several inherent problems. Besides the Greater Antilles and their satellites, fossil sites are well-sampled on only four other islands in the western Caribbean: Grand Cayman and Cayman Brac (Morgan, in press), New Providence (Olson & Pregill, 1982), and Andros (FSM, unpubl. obs.). Palaeontological sites are known from only a few Lesser Antillean islands (Antigua, Barbuda, Anguilla, St. Martin and Barbados), and these data are by no means complete. Our treatment of the fossil data does not take into account the vast increase in land area of some islands during the late Pleistocene low sea level stand. We have used the modern land areas for all islands to avoid the complex interpretations of how sea level fluctuations might have altered species–area values. For the islands on the Great Bahama Bank and Puerto Rican Bank the increase in land area would have been substantial, while for other islands (e.g. Hispaniola and Jamaica) such increases would have been minor. The small island of New Providence in the Bahamas appears to fall well above the predicted curve based on the fossil data, while in actuality at the time the fossils were deposited New Providence and Andros, along with many other islands in the Bahamas, were united into a huge island nearly the size of Hispaniola. The fossil points for New Providence and Andros should actually be moved far to the right on Fig. 4, where they fall well below the predicted value. The 'fossil' curve is strongly affected by the large number of extinct non-volant mammals from Cuba and Hispaniola, the two largest Caribbean islands. Both islands experienced significant adaptive radiations of rodents, ground sloths and insectivores, thereby greatly augmenting their species diversity compared to all other Antillean islands. Among non-volant mammals, Puerto Rico has a single species each of insectivore and ground sloth and only four species of rodents, while Jamaica totally lacks insectivores and sloths and has but one primate and four species of rodents. The living mammalian fauna of Jamaica, which consists of one species of rodent and 21 bats, falls well above the 'recent' curve. The close proximity of Jamaica to Central America would account for the relatively high diversity of bats in both its present and fossil faunas, whereas the absence of many non-volant mammal groups is an enigma relating to complex geological and zoogeographic factors. Puerto Rico has a depauperate living mammal fauna, consisting of 13 species of bats. The fossil mammalian fauna of Puerto Rico is impoverished as well and falls below the 'fossil' curve, a point further magnified when the island's larger area during the last glacial interval is considered. Perhaps Jamaica and Puerto Rico are below some critical size that would allow for the extensive adaptive radiations of mammals that occurred on Cuba and Hispaniola.

## CONCLUSIONS

Aside from bats, the living endemic land mammals of the West Indies are a depauperate remnant of the unique and diverse fauna that inhabited these islands in the late Pleistocene and early Holocene before the arrival of man about 4500 years ago. The few surviving non-volant mammals do not constitute a natural fauna, but instead represent those species that managed to escape extinction by virtue of their morphology and ecology, or by characteristics of the islands on which they are found, such as geological history, land-use patterns or absence of introduced species. Through an in-depth analysis of the West Indian fossil record we have shown that almost 90% of the 76 known species of Antillean non-volant mammals went extinct in the last 20 000 years (Table 1, Appendix). Furthermore, although only 14% of the 59 species of West Indian bats disappeared during this same time interval, 24% of the living species have undergone localized extinction on certain islands, thereby altering their apparent distributions. It has been hypothesized that the expansion of mesic habitats in the latest Pleistocene and Holocene at the expense of more arid grasslands and savannas, coupled with the post-glacial reduction in land area or fragmentation of many Caribbean islands, led to the extinction or reduction in range of many species of West Indian land vertebrates (Pregill & Olson, 1981). Cave-dwelling bats were particularly susceptible to local extinction, probably as a result of changing cave microclimates and flooding of low-lying caves. However, many extinct species of Antillean non-volant mammals are found in archaeological sites or Holocene fossil deposits that clearly post-date any Pleistocene changes in climate or sea level. Evidence presented here and by other authors (Olson, 1982; Steadman *et al.*, 1984a; Woods *et al.*, in press) suggests that predation and habitat alteration by Amerindian peoples and the introduction of exotic species in post-Columbian times, in particular *Rattus rattus*, *R. norvegicus*, *Herpestes auropunctatus* and feral dogs and cats, are the primary causes for the decimation of most of the remaining post-Pleistocene non-volant mammalian fauna.

Although land mammals have almost certainly inhabited the Caribbean islands since at least the early Miocene and perhaps dating back to the Eocene, the absence of a pre-late Pleistocene fossil record negates the possibility of determining actual immigration rates. As a consequence, the immigration rates calculated for West Indian land mammals (one species per 800 000 years since the late Eocene or one species per 400 000 years since the early Miocene) are based solely on the number of colonization events necessary to account for the Late Quaternary fauna. Species of mammals that successfully colonized the West Indies, but which disappeared before about 100 000 years ago, obviously cannot be included in our calculations. Colonization rates for bats have been approximately three times greater than those for non-volant mammals since the early Miocene, but eight times greater during the Pleistocene. These higher immigration rates reflect the better, but not limitless, dispersal capabilities of bats and also the higher incidence of dispersal during periods of lower sea level in the Pleistocene. Extinction rates have been calculated only for the late Pleistocene and Holocene, the time period for which the Antillean fossil record is superb. Since these rates are based on recorded extinctions, they are inherently more accurate than the admittedly hypothetical colonization rates. The postulated extinction rates of one species disappearing every 267 years during the last 20 000 years and one species every 129 years since the arrival of man are incredibly high, but must still be regarded as minimum figures owing to deficiencies in the fossil record. Species diversity–island area calculations for both the current and fossil mammalian faunas of the West Indies indicate that the current fauna does not accurately reflect the species diversity in the late Pleistocene and early Holocene. The pre-Amerindian mammalian fauna is a much more accurate indicator of the number of species each island supported under natural conditions than is the current fauna. Obvious deficiencies in the Late Quaternary fossil record, in particular the location of the great majority of sites in caves and the absence of fossils from many of the Lesser Antilles, caution that the number of species listed for each island should be considered minimum values.

A large number of palaeontological and archaeological sites have been excavated throughout the West Indies, especially in the Greater Antilles, but only a small handful have been subjected to thorough radiocarbon analysis. Only through the careful stratigraphic excavation of sites and subsequent radiocarbon dating will it be possible to establish a chronology of extinction for the many species of terrestrial vertebrates that have disappeared from the islands. The radiocarbon dates currently available establish minimum or maximum ages for the presence of certain taxa on certain islands, but are insufficient to determine when the various species actually disappeared. The rarity of wood in most West Indian fossil deposits emphasizes the need for obtaining accurate dates directly from fossil bones, especially those of extinct taxa. A new highly precise radiocarbon dating technique using a tandem accelerator mass spectrometer (TAMS) promises to be particularly applicable for dating small samples of bone (Gillespie, 1984). A more robust chronology of West Indian fossil sites should make it possible to differentiate human-caused extinctions in the Holocene from those caused by climatic changes and rising sea levels in the latest Pleistocene. On other islands that have been studied in detail, the palaeontological and archaeological record has clearly demonstrated a direct correlation between major vertebrate extinctions and human colonization (e.g. Hawaiian Islands—Olson & James, 1982; Madagascar—Dewar, 1984; New Zealand—Cassels, 1984).

The most significant gaps in our knowledge of the palaeontology of West Indian land mammals are the complete lack of a pre-late Pleistocene fossil record and the scarcity of fossil sites in the Lesser Antilles. Terrestrial, fluvial and deltaic deposits of Tertiary age are found throughout the Greater Antilles and with persistent field efforts should eventually yield remains of land mammals. Several terrestrial vertebrates have been described from late Oligocene or early Miocene amber in the Dominican Republic, including an iguanid lizard, *Anolis dominicanus* (Rieppel, 1980), a gekkonid lizard, *Sphaerodactylus dommeli* (Schlee, 1984), and a hylid frog (Schlee, 1984). A bird feather and what may be a strand of mammal hair are also known from Dominican amber but are as yet unpublished. Over the last five years, D. W. Steadman, G. K. Pregill and S. L. Olson have been exploring small islands in the northern Lesser Antilles in search of fossil deposits. Their efforts have uncovered several important new sites (e.g. Steadman *et al.*, 1984a) and promise to add further information on the composition and subsequent extinction of the Lesser Antillean mammal fauna. Fossil deposits are completely unknown on the larger volcanic islands in the Lesser Antilles (Dominica, Guadeloupe, Martinique, etc.), although archaeological sites are known from several of the islands. Late Pleistocene fossils from these islands should shed light on several important zoogeographic questions, such as the extent of the oryzomyine radiation and the relative importance of the South American and the Greater Antillean components of the mammalian fauna.

It has been argued by several workers (e.g. Hershkovitz, 1958) that zoogeographic analyses of recent mammals should be restricted to the Recent geological epoch (i.e. the Holocene) and should not include species known only from the Pleistocene. According to Hershkovitz (1958: 604), ". . . what the fauna of the Greater Antilles *was* at one time, even in some not too remote Recent period, is not germane to the zoogeographic classification of the present fauna of the islands". Our data confirm that many, if not most, extinct Antillean mammals survived into the Holocene and would probably be alive today if not for depredation and habitat destruction by humans. We would maintain that few reliable zoogeographic inferences could be made about the West Indian land mammal fauna without consideration of recently extinct forms.

### ACKNOWLEDGEMENTS

We are grateful to the editors of this volume, L. R. Heaney and B. D. Patterson, for inviting us to participate in the symposium on the Island

Biogeography of Mammals at the Fourth International Theriological Congress in Edmonton, Alberta. The published version of this paper has given us the opportunity to present some of our new data and ideas and to summarize much of the available information on Late Quaternary mammalian extinctions in the West Indies. It is our hope that this paper will generate further research on the timing and causes of these extinctions and, perhaps more importantly, will spur conservation efforts already in progress to save the few surviving non-volant mammals in the Caribbean islands. We thank L. R. Heaney, B. D. Patterson, A. E. Pratt and S. D. Webb for reviewing an earlier draft of this manuscript. Their comments have greatly improved the quality of the paper. R. C. Hulbert Jr provided advice on the calculation and interpretation of the species–area plot. E. M. Paige drew Fig. 1. We owe a special debt of gratitude to L. R. Heaney, whose intense interest in the island biogeography of mammals, untiring enthusiasm and patience have brought the present volume to fruition. G.S.M. was able to attend the Fourth I.T.C. thanks to the generous financial assistance of B. J. MacFadden and S. D. Webb. C.A.W. would like to thank the National Science Foundation and the Agency for International Development for their financial support. Both authors appreciate the support provided by the Natural Sciences Department of the Florida State Museum. This is University of Florida Contribution to Vertebrate Paleontology Number 247.

REFERENCES

ACEVEDO GONZÁLEZ, M., ARREDONDO, O. & GONZÁLEZ GOTERA, N., 1972. *La Cueva del Túnel*. La Habana, Cuba: Instituto Cubana del Libro.
ANTHONY, H. E., 1917. Two new fossil bats from Porto Rico. *Bulletin of the American Museum of Natural History, 37*: 565–568.
ANTHONY, H. E., 1920. New mammals from Jamaica. *Bulletin of the American Museum of Natural History, 42*: 469–476.
ARREDONDO, O., 1970. Dos nuevos especies subfósiles de mamíferos (Insectivora: Nesophontidae) del Holoceno Precolombino de Cuba. *Memoria de la Sociedad de Ciencias Naturales La Salle, 30* (86): 122–152.
ARREDONDO, O., 1981. Nuevos género y especie de mamífero (Carnivora: Canidae) del Holoceno de Cuba. *Instituto de Zoología, Academia de Ciencias de Cuba, Poeyana, 218*: 1–28.
ARREDONDO, O. & VARONA, L. S., 1974. Nuevos género y especie de mamífero (Carnivora: Canidae) del Cuaternario de Cuba. *Instituto de Zoología, Academia de Ciencias de Cuba, Poeyana, 131*: 1–12.
ARREDONDO, O. & VARONA, L. S., 1983. Sobre la validez de *Montaneia anthropomorpha* Ameghino, 1910 (Primates: Cebidae). *Instituto de Zoología, Academia de Ciencias de Cuba, Poeyana, 255*: 1–21.
BAKER, R. J. & GENOWAYS, H. H., 1978. Zoogeography of Antillean bats, In F. B. Gill (Ed.), *Zoogeography in the Caribbean. Proceedings of the Philadelphia Academy of Sciences, Special Publication, 13*: 53–97.
BUSKIRK, R. E., 1985. Zoogeographic patterns and tectonic history of Jamaica and the northern Caribbean. *Journal of Biogeography, 12*: 445–461.
CASSELS, R., 1984. The role of prehistoric man in the faunal extinctions of New Zealand and other Pacific islands. In P. S. Martin & R. G. Klein (Eds), *Quaternary Extinctions: a Prehistoric Revolution*: 741–767. Tucson: University of Arizona Press.
CHOATE, J. R. & BIRNEY, E. C., 1968. Sub-recent Insectivora and Chiroptera from Puerto Rico, with the description of a new bat of the genus *Stenoderma. Journal of Mammalogy, 49*: 400–412.
CLOUGH, G. C., 1976. Current status of two endangered Caribbean rodents. *Biological Conservation, 10*: 43–47.
DARLINGTON Jr, P. J., 1938. The origin of the fauna of the Greater Antilles, with discussion of dispersal of animals over water and through the air. *Quarterly Review of Biology, 13*: 274–300.
DEWAR, R. E., 1984. Extinctions in Madagascar: the loss of the subfossil fauna. In P. S. Martin & R. G. Klein (Eds), *Quaternary Extinctions: a Prehistoric Revolution*: 574–593. Tucson: University of Arizona Press.
DONNELLY, T. W., 1985. Mesozoic and Cenozoic plate evolution of the Caribbean region. In F. G. Stehli & S. D. Webb (Eds), *The Great American Biotic Interchange*: 89–121. New York: Plenum Press.
ESHELMAN, R. E. & MORGAN, G. S., 1985. Tobagan Recent mammals, fossil vertebrates, and their zoogeographical implications. *National Geographic Society, Research Reports, 21*: 137–143.

FORD, S. M., in press. A subfossil platyrrhine tibia (Primates: Callitrichidae) from Hispaniola: a possible further example of island gigantism. *American Journal of Physical Anthropology*.

FORD, S. M. & MORGAN, G. S., in press. A new ceboid fossil femur from Jamaica. *Journal of Vertebrate Paleontology*.

GILLESPIE, R., 1984. Radiocarbon user's handbook. *Oxford University Committee for Archaeology Monograph, 3*: 1–36.

GOODFRIEND, G. A. & STIPP, J. J., 1983. Limestone and the problem of radiocarbon dating of land-snail shell carbonate. *Geology, 11*: 575–577.

GUARCH DELMONTE, J. M., 1984. Evidencias de la existencia postcolombina de *Geocapromys* y *Heteropsomys* (Mammalia: Rodentia) en Cuba. *Instituto de Zoología, Academia de Ciencias de Cuba, Miscelanea Zoologica, 18*: 1.

HEDGES, S. B., 1982. Caribbean biogeography: implications of recent plate tectonic studies. *Systematic Zoology, 31*: 518–522.

HERSHKOVITZ, P., 1958. A geographical classification of Neotropical mammals. *Fieldiana: Zoology, 36* (6): 581–620.

HOPWOOD, A. T., 1926. A fossil rice-rat from the Pleistocene of Barbuda. *Annals and Magazine of Natural History, Series 9, 17*: 328–330.

KENYON, K. W., 1977. Caribbean monk seal extinct. *Journal of Mammalogy, 58*: 97–98.

KOOPMAN, K. F., 1955. A new subspecies of *Chilonycteris* from the West Indies, and a discussion of the mammals of La Gonave. *Journal of Mammalogy, 36*: 109–113.

KOOPMAN, K. F., 1958. A fossil vampire bat from Cuba. *Museum of Comparative Zoology, Breviora, 90*: 1–5.

KOOPMAN, K. F., 1970. Zoogeography of bats. In B. H. Slaughter & D. W. Walton (Eds), *About Bats*: 29–50. Dallas: Southern Methodist University Press.

KOOPMAN, K. F., HECHT, M. K. & LEDECKY-JANECEK, E., 1957. Notes on the mammals of the Bahamas, with special reference to bats. *Journal of Mammalogy, 38*: 164–174.

KOOPMAN, K. F. & WILLIAMS, E. E., 1951. Fossil Chiroptera collected by H. E. Anthony in Jamaica, 1919–1920. *American Museum Novitates, 1519*: 1–29.

KRATOCHVÍL, J., RODRIGUES, L., & BARUŠ, V., 1978. Capromyidae (Rodentia) of Cuba 1. *Acta Scientiarum Naturalium Brno, 12* (11): 1–60.

LACK, D., 1976. *Island Biology Illustrated by the Land Birds of Jamaica*. Oxford: Blackwell Scientific Publications.

LEGENDRE, S., 1985. Molossidés (Mammalia: Chiroptera) Cénozoïques de l'Ancien et du Nouveau Monde; statut systématique; intégration phylogénique des données. *Neues Jahrbuch fuer Geologie und Palaeontologie, Abhandlungen, 170*(2): 205–227.

LILLEGRAVEN, J. A., McKENNA, M. C. & KRISHTALKA, L., 1981. Evolutionary relationships of middle Eocene and younger species of *Centetodon* (Mammalia: Insectivora: Geolabididae), with a description of the dentition of *Ankylodon* (Adapisoricidae). *University of Wyoming Publication, 45*: 1–115.

MACARTHUR, R. H. & WILSON, E. O., 1967. *The Theory of Island Biogeography*. Princeton: Princeton University Press.

McDOWELL Jr, S. B., 1958. The Greater Antillean insectivores. *Bulletin of the American Museum of Natural History, 115*: 113–214.

MACFADDEN, B. J., 1980. Rafting mammals or drifting islands?: biogeography of the Greater Antillean insectivores *Nesophontes* and *Solenodon*. *Journal of Biogeography, 7*: 11–22.

MACFADDEN, B. J., 1981. Comments on Pregill's appraisal of historical biogeography of Caribbean vertebrates: vicariance, dispersal, or both? *Systematic Zoology, 30*: 370–372.

MACFADDEN, B. J., CAMPBELL Jr, K. E., CIFELLI, R. L., SILES, O., JOHNSON, N. M., NAESSER, C. W. & ZEITLER, P. K., 1985. Magnetic polarity stratigraphy and mammalian fauna of the Deseadan (late Oligocene–early Miocene) Salla Beds of northern Bolivia. *Journal of Geology, 93*: 223–250.

MACPHEE, R. D. E., 1984. Quaternary mammal localities and heptaxodontid rodents of Jamaica. *American Museum Novitates, 2803*: 1–34.

MACPHEE, R. D. E. & WOODS, C. A., 1982. A new fossil cebine from Hispaniola. *American Journal of Physical Anthropology, 58*: 419–436.

MARSHALL, L. G., HOFFSTETTER, R. & PASCUAL, R., 1983. Mammals and stratigraphy: Geochronology of the continental mammal-bearing Tertiary of South America. *Palaeovertebrata, Memoire Extraordinaire*: 1–93.

MATTHEW, W. D., 1918. Affinities and origin of the Antillean mammals. *Bulletin of the Geological Society of America, 29*: 657–666.

MATTHEW, W. D. & PAULA COUTO, C. DE, 1959. The Cuban edentates. *Bulletin of the American Museum of Natural History, 117*: 1–56.

MELTZER, D. J. & MEAD, J. I., 1983. The timing of late Pleistocene extinctions in North America. *Quaternary Research, 19*: 130–135.

MILLER Jr, G. S., 1929a. A second collection of mammals from caves near St. Michel, Haiti. *Smithsonian Miscellaneous Collections, 81*(9): 1–30.

MILLER Jr, G. S., 1929b. Mammals eaten by Indians, owls, and Spaniards in the coast region of the Dominican Republic. *Smithsonian Miscellaneous Collections, 82*(5): 1–16.

MORGAN, G. S., 1985. Taxonomic status and relationships of the Swan Island Hutia, *Geocapromys thoracatus*

(Mammalia: Rodentia: Capromyidae), and the zoogeography of the Swan Islands vertebrate fauna. *Proceedings of the Biological Society of Washington, 98:* 29–46.

MORGAN, G. S., in press. Late Pleistocene and Holocene fossil vertebrates from the Cayman Islands, West Indies. *Bulletin of the Florida State Museum, Biological Sciences.*

MORGAN, G. S., RAY, C. E. & ARREDONDO, O., 1980. A giant extinct insectivore from Cuba (Mammalia: Insectivora: Solenodontidae). *Proceedings of the Biological Society of Washington, 93:* 597–608.

OLSON, S. L., 1978. A paleontological perspective of West Indian birds and mammals. In F. B. Gill (Ed.), *Zoogeography in the Caribbean. Academy of Natural Sciences of Philadelphia, Special Publication, 13:* 99–117.

OLSON, S. L., 1982. Biological archeology in the West Indies. *Florida Anthropologist, 35:* 162–168.

OLSON, S. L. & JAMES, H. F., 1982. Fossil birds from the Hawaiian Islands: evidence for wholesale extinction by man before Western contact. *Science, 217:* 633–635.

OLSON, S. L. & PREGILL, G. K., 1982. Introduction to the paleontology of Bahaman vertebrates. In S. L. Olson (Ed.), *Fossil Vertebrates from the Bahamas. Smithsonian Contributions to Paleobiology, 48:* 1–7.

PATTERSON, B., 1962. An extinct solenodontid insectivore from Hispaniola. *Museum of Comparative Zoology, Breviora, 165:* 1–11.

PATTERSON, B. & WOOD, A. E., 1982. Rodents from the Deseadan Oligocene of Bolivia and relationships of the Caviomorpha. *Bulletin of the Museum of Comparative Zoology, 149:* 371–543.

PAULA COUTO, C. DE, 1967. Pleistocene edentates of the West Indies. *American Museum Novitates, 2304:* 1–55.

PREGILL, G. K., 1981a. An appraisal of the vicariance hypothesis of Caribbean biogeography and its application to West Indian terrestrial vertebrates. *Systematic Zoology, 30:* 147–155.

PREGILL, G. K., 1981b. Late Pleistocene herpetofaunas from Puerto Rico. *University of Kansas Museum of Natural History, Miscellaneous Publications, 71:* 1–72.

PREGILL, G. K. & OLSON, S. L., 1981. Zoogeography of West Indian vertebrates in relation to Pleistocene climatic cycles. *Annual Review of Ecology and Systematics, 12:* 75–98.

RAY, C. E., 1964. A small assemblage of vertebrate fossils from Spring Bay, Barbados. *Journal of the Barbados Museum and Historical Society, 31:* 11–22.

RAY, C. E., OLSON, S. J. & GUT, H. J., 1963. Three mammals new to the Pleistocene fauna of Florida, and a reconsideration of five earlier records. *Journal of Mammalogy, 44:* 373–395.

RICKLEFS, R. & COX, G. W., 1972. Taxon cycles in the West Indian avifauna. *American Naturalist, 106:* 195–219.

RIEPPEL, O., 1980. Green anole in Dominican amber. *Nature, 286:* 486–487.

RÍMOLI, R. O., 1976. Roedores fósiles de la Hispaniola. *Universidad Central del Este (San Pedro de Macorís, Republica Dominicana), Serie Científica, 3:* 1–93.

RÍMOLI, R. O., 1977. Una nueva especie de monos (Cebidae: Saimirinae: *Saimiri*) de la Hispaniola. *Universidad Autonomia de Santo Domingo, Cuadernos del CENDIA, 242:* 1–14.

ROSEN, D. E., 1975. A vicariance model of Caribbean biogeography. *Systematic Zoology, 24:* 431–461.

ROUSE, I. & ALLAIRE, L., 1978. Caribbean. In R. E. Taylor & C. W. Meighan (Eds), *Chronologies in New World Archaeology:* 431–481. New York: Academic Press.

SAVAGE, D. E., 1951. A Miocene phyllostomatid bat from Colombia, South America. *University of California Publications in the Geological Sciences, 28:* 357–366.

SAVAGE, J. M., 1974. The isthmian link and the evolution of Neotropical mammals. *Natural History Museum of Los Angeles County, Contributions in Science, 260:* 1–51.

SCHLEE, D., 1984. Besonderheiten des Dominikanischen Bernsteins. *Bernstein-Neuigkeiten, Stuttgarter Beitrage zur Naturkunde, Serie C, Nr. 18.*

SILVA TABOADA, G., 1974. Fossil Chiroptera from cave deposits in Central Cuba, with description of two new species (Genera *Pteronotus* and *Mormoops*) and the first West Indian record of *Mormoops megalophylla. Acta Zoologica Cracoviensia, 19* (3): 33–73.

SILVA TABOADA, G., 1979. *Los Muciélagos de Cuba.* La Habana, Cuba: Editorial Academia.

SILVA TABOADA, G. & PINE, R. H., 1969. Morphological and behavioral evidence for the relationship between the bat genus *Brachyphylla* and the Phyllonyctcrinac. *Biotropica, 1:* 10–19.

SILVA TABOADA, G. & WOLOSZYN, B. W., 1975. *Phyllops vetus* (Mammalia: Chiroptera) en Isla de Pinos. *Instituto de Zoología, Academia de Ciencias de Cuba, Miscellanea Zoologica, 1:* 3.

SIMPSON, G. G., 1956. Zoogeography of West Indian land mammals. *American Museum Novitates, 1759:* 1–28.

SMITH, D. L., 1985. Caribbean plate relative motions. In F. G. Stehli & S. D. Webb (Eds), *The Great American Biotic Interchange:* 17–48. New York: Plenum Press.

SMITH, J. D., 1972. Systematics of the chiropteran family Mormoopidae. *University of Kansas Museum of Natural History, Miscellaneous Publications, 56:* 1–132.

STEADMAN, D. W. & MORGAN, G. S., 1985. A new species of Bullfinch (Aves: Emberizinae) from a Late Quaternary cave deposit on Cayman Brac, West Indies. *Proceedings of the Biological Society of Washington, 98:* 544–553.

STEADMAN, D. W., PREGILL, G. K. & OLSON, S. L., 1984a. Fossil vertebrates from Antigua, Lesser Antilles: evidence for late Holocene human-caused extinctions in the West Indies. *Proceedings of the National Academy of Sciences of the U.S.A., 81:* 4448–4451.

STEADMAN, D. W., WATTERS, D. R., REITZ, E. J. & PREGILL, G. K., 1984b. Vertebrates from archaeological sites on Montserrat, West Indies. *Carnegie Museum of Natural History, Annals, 53:* 1–29.

TAYLOR, R. E., 1980. Radiocarbon dating of Pleistocene bone: toward criteria for the selection of samples. *Radiocarbon, 22:* 969–979.

TERBORGH, J., FAABORG, J. & BROCKMAN, H. J., 1978. Island colonization by Lesser Antillean birds. *Auk, 95:* 59–72.

THOMAS, O., 1898. On indigenous Muridae in the West Indies, with the description of a new Mexican *Oryzomys. Annals and Magazine of Natural History, Series 7, 1:* 176–180.

VAIL, P. R., MITCHUM Jr, R. M. & THOMPSON, S., 1977. Seismic stratigraphy and global changes of sea levels, part 4: Global cycles of relative changes of sea level. *American Association of Petroleum Geologists, Memoir 26:* 83–97.

VAN DER HAMMEN, T., 1974. The Pleistocene changes of vegetation and climate in tropical South America. *Journal of Biogeography, 1:* 3–26.

VARONA, L. S., 1974. *Catálogo de los Mamíferos Vivientes y Extinguidos de las Antillas.* La Habana, Cuba: Academia de Ciencias de Cuba.

VARONA, L. S., 1979. Subgénero y especie nuevos de *Capromys* (Rodentia: Capromyidae) para Cuba. *Instituto de Zoología, Academia de Ciencias de Cuba, Poeyana, 194:* 1–33.

VARONA, L. S. & ARREDONDO, O., 1979. Nuevos taxones fósiles de Capromyidae (Rodentia: Caviomorpha). *Instituto de Zoología, Academia de Ciencias de Cuba, Poeyana, 195:* 1–51.

WATTERS, D. R., REITZ, E. J., STEADMAN, D. W. & PREGILL, G. K., 1984. Vertebrates from archaeological sites on Barbuda, West Indies. *Carnegie Museum of Natural History, Annals, 53* (13): 383–412.

WEBB, S. D. & PERRIGO, S., 1985. New megalonychid sloths from El Salvador. In G. G, Montgomery (Ed.), *The Evolution and Ecology of Armadillos, Sloths, and Vermilinguas:* 113–120. Washington: Smithsonian Institution Press.

WILLIAMS, E. E., 1952. Additional notes on fossil and subfossil bats from Jamaica. *Journal of Mammalogy, 33:* 171–179.

WILLIAMS, E. E., 1969. The ecology of colonization as seen in the zoogeography of anoline lizards on small islands. *Quarterly Review of Biology, 44:* 345–389.

WILLIAMS, E. E. & KOOPMAN, K. F., 1952. West Indian fossil monkeys. *American Museum Novitates, 1546:* 1–16.

WING, E. S. 1973. Notes on faunal remains excavated from St. Kitts, West Indies. *Caribbean Journal of Science, 13:* 253–255.

WING, E. S., HOFFMAN Jr, C. A. & RAY, C. E., 1968. Vertebrate remains from Indian sites on Antigua, West Indies. *Caribbean Journal of Science, 8:* 129–139.

WING, E. S. & REITZ, E. J., 1982. Prehistoric fishing economies of the Caribbean. *New World Archaeology, 5:* 13–32.

WOLOSZYN, B. W. & MAYO, N. A., 1974. Postglacial remains of a vampire bat (Chiroptera: *Desmodus*) from Cuba. *Acta Zoologica Cracoviensia, 19* (13): 253–265.

WOLOSZYN, B. W. & SILVA TABOADA, G., 1977. Nueva especie fósil de *Artibeus* (Mammalia: Chiroptera) de Cuba, y tipificación preliminar de los depósitos fosilíferos cubanos contentivos de mamíferos terrestres. *Instituto de Zoología, Academia de Ciencias de Cuba, Poeyana, 161:* 1–17.

WOODS, C. A., 1982. The history and classification of South American hystricognath rodents: reflections on the far away and long ago. In M. A. Mares & H. H. Genoways (Eds), *Mammalian Biology in South America, Pymatuning Laboratory of Ecology, University of Pittsburgh, Special Publication 6:* 377–392.

WOODS, C. A., 1986. *The mammals of the National Parks of Haiti.* Haiti: U.S. Agency for International Development.

WOODS, C. A., in press. A new capromyid rodent from Haiti: the origin evolution, and extinction of West Indian rodents and their bearing on the origin of New World hystricognaths. *Natural History Museum of Los Angeles County, Contributions in Science.*

WOODS, C. A. & HERMANSON, J. W., 1985. Myology of hystricognath rodents: an analysis of form, function, and phylogeny. In W. P. Luckett & J. L. Hartenberger (Eds), *Evolutionary Relationships among Rodents:* 515–548. New York: Plenum Publishing Corporation.

WOODS, C. A. & HOWLAND, E. B., 1979. Adaptive radiation of capromyid rodents: anatomy of the masticatory apparatus. *Journal of Mammalogy, 60:* 95–116.

WOODS, C. A., OTTENWALDER, J. A. & OLIVER W. L. R., in press. *Lost mammals in the Antilles.* Dodo: Jersey Wildlife Preservation Trust.

Appendix. Species list, geographic distribution and time period of last recorded occurrence (if extinct) of West Indian non-volant mammals

| Taxon | Geographic distribution | Time period of last recorded occurrence |
|---|---|---|
| Insectivora | | |
| Solenodontidae | | |
| *Solenodon cubanus* | Cuba | extant |
| *Solenodon* large undescr. sp. | Cuba | late Pleistocene[1] |
| *Solenodon paradoxus* | Hispaniola | extant |
| *Solenodon marcanoi* | Hispaniola | post-Columbian |
| Nesophontidae | | |
| *Nesophontes major* | Cuba | Amerindian |
| *Nesophontes micrus* | Cuba | post-Columbian |
| *Nesophontes submicrus* | Cuba | Amerindian |
| *Nesophontes hypomicrus* | Hispaniola | post-Columbian |
| *Nesophontes paramicrus* | Hispaniola | post-Columbian |
| *Nesophontes zamicrus* | Hispaniola | post-Columbian |
| *Nesophontes edithae* | Puerto Rico | Amerindian |
| *Nesophontes* undescr. sp. | Cayman Islands | post-Columbian |
| Edentata | | |
| Megalonychidae | | |
| *Habanocnus paulacoutoi* | Cuba | late Pleistocene |
| *Habanocnus hoffstetteri* | Cuba | late Pleistocene |
| *Megalocnus rodens* | Cuba | late Pleistocene |
| *Mesocnus browni* | Cuba | late Pleistocene |
| *Mesocnus torrei* | Cuba | late Pleistocene |
| *Miocnus antillensis* | Cuba | late Pleistocene |
| *Neocnus gliriformis* | Cuba | late Pleistocene |
| *Neocnus major* | Cuba | late Pleistocene |
| *Neocnus minor* | Cuba | late Pleistocene |
| *Parocnus serus* | Hispaniola | Amerindian |
| *Synocnus comes* | Hispaniola | Amerindian |
| additional undescr. taxa[2]—two genera and four species | Hispaniola | — |
| *Acratocnus odontrigonus* | Puerto Rico | late Pleistocene |
| Primates | | |
| Cebidae | | |
| *Ateles anthropomorpha* | Cuba | Amerindian |
| 'Saimiri' bernensis | Hispaniola | Amerindian |
| *Xenothrix mcgregori* | Jamaica | late Pleistocene |
| Rodentia | | |
| Capromyidae[3, 4] | | |
| *Capromys acevedoi* | Cuba | late Pleistocene |
| *Capromys antiquus* | Cuba | late Pleistocene |
| *Capromys jaumei* | Cuba | late Pleistocene |
| *Capromys latus* | Cuba | late Pleistocene |
| *Capromys melanurus* | Cuba | extant |
| *Capromys nanus* | Cuba | extant |
| *Capromys pilorides* | Cuba | extant |
| *Capromys prehensilis* | Cuba | extant |
| *Capromys* undescr. sp. | Cayman Islands | post-Columbian |
| *Geocapromys columbianus* | Cuba | post-Columbian |
| *Geocapromys megas* | Cuba | late Pleistocene |
| *Geocapromys pleistocenicus* | Cuba | Amerindian |
| *Geocapromys brownii* | Jamaica | extant |
| *Geocapromys ingrahami* | Bahamas[5] | extant |
| *Geocapromys thoracatus* | Little Swan Island | recently extinct[6] |
| *Geocapromys* undescr. sp. | Cayman Islands | post-Columbian |
| *Plagiodontia aedium* | Hispaniola | extant |
| *Plagiodontia araeum* | Hispaniola | Amerindian |
| *Plagiodontia ipnaeum* | Hispaniola | late Pleistocene |
| *Plagiodontia spelaeum* | Hispaniola | late Pleistocene |

## Appendix. Continued

| Taxon | Geographic distribution | Time period of last recorded occurrence |
|---|---|---|
| *Plagiodontia velozi* | Hispaniola | post-Columbian |
| *Isolobodon montanus* | Hispaniola | Amerindian |
| *Isolobodon portoricensis* | Hispaniola[7] | post-Columbian |
| *Hexolobodon phenax* | Hispaniola | Amerindian |
| *Hexolobodon poolei* | Hispaniola | late Pleistocene |
| undescr. genus and sp. | Hispaniola | Amerindian |
| Echimyidae | | |
| *Boromys offella* | Cuba | post-Columbian |
| *Boromys torrei* | Cuba | post-Columbian |
| *Brotomys contractus* | Hispaniola | late Pleistocene |
| *Brotomys voratus* | Hispaniola | post-Columbian |
| *Heteropsomys antillensis* | Puerto Rico | late Pleistocene |
| *Heteropsomys insulans* | Puerto Rico | Amerindian |
| '*Proechimys*' *corozalus* | Puerto Rico | late Pleistocene |
| Heptaxodontidae | | |
| *Quemisia gravis* | Hispaniola | Amerindian |
| *Clidomys osborni* | Jamaica | late Pleistocene |
| *Clidomys parvus* | Jamaica | late Pleistocene |
| *Amblyrhiza inundata* | Anguilla and St. Martin | late Pleistocene |
| Cricetidae | | |
| *Oryzomys antillarum* | Jamaica | recently extinct[6] |
| *Oryzomys victus* | St. Vincent | recently extinct[6] |
| *Oryzomys* undescr. sp. | Barbados | late Pleistocene |
| *Megalomys desmaresti* | Martinique | recently extinct[6] |
| *Megalomys luciae* | St. Lucia | recently extinct[6] |
| *Megalomys audreyae* | Barbuda | late Pleistocene |
| large undescr. oryzomyine | Lesser Antilles[8] | Amerindian |
| small undescr. oryzomyine | Lesser Antilles[9] | Amerindian |

[1] Late Pleistocene includes the early Holocene as well.

[2] At least two undescribed genera and four undescribed species of extinct ground sloths are known from Hispaniola. When discussing the mammalian fauna of Hispaniola in the text, the figure of six megalonychid species is used.

[3] Five additional Recent species of *Capromys* have been described from Cuba in the last 15 years: *C. angelcabrerai*, *C. arboricolus*, *C. auritus*, *C. garridoi* and *C. sanfelipensis* (Kratochvil *et al.*, 1978; Varona, 1979). All but one of these species occur only on small offshore islands, and are probably best regarded as subspecies of already named forms until more detailed studies of geographic variation in Cuban *Capromys* are conducted.

[4] At least eight additional extinct species of *Capromys* have been described from fossil deposits in Cuba (Varona & Arredondo, 1979), but are not included here as they were described from inadequate material.

[5] *Geocapromys ingrahami* is extant only on East Plana Cay in the southeast Bahamas; however, extinct populations of this species are known from many of the Bahama Islands, including Great Abaco, Andros, New Providence, Eleuthera, Cat, San Salvador, Great Exuma, Little Exuma, Long, Crooked and Acklins.

[6] Species listed as 'recently extinct' have disappeared within the last 100 years, and were originally described from recent skins and skulls. These species are not included when discussing the living mammalian faunas of the islands on which they occurred.

[7] *Isolobodon portoricensis* is known from Amerindian archaeological sites in Puerto Rico and the Virgin Islands; however, this species was almost certainly introduced on these islands and is regarded as native only on Hispaniola.

[8] A large extinct oryzomyine rodent ("undescribed species B" of Steadman *et al.*, 1984b) is known from the Lesser Antillean islands of Antigua, Barbuda, Guadeloupe, Marie Galante and Montserrat.

[9] A small extinct oryzomyine rodent ("undescribed species A" of Steadman *et al.*, 1984b) is known from the Lesser Antillean islands of Anguilla, Montserrat, St. Eustatius, and St. Kitts.

*Biological Journal of the Linnean Society* (1986), *28:* 205–230. With 4 figures

# Genetics of insular populations of mammals, with particular reference to differentiation and founder effects in British small mammals

R. J. BERRY

*Department of Zoology, University College London,
Gower Street, London WC1E 6BT*

*Accepted for publication 19 March 1986*

Island populations are of interest for their differentiation as well as their species diversity; some of the earliest biological interest in islands was concerned with the number of 'endemics' thereon. There is dispute about the long-term evolutionary importance of island forms, but they are rich sources of data for studying the under-exploited interface of genetics, ecology and physiology. Differentiation of island populations may arise from genetic change after isolation, or from the chance collection of alleles carried by the colonizing group itself. The general reduction of genetic variance in island populations compared to continental forms of the same species suggests that founder events have played a major role in the formation of most island forms. However, there is ample evidence of adaptation in island populations despite this lower variation; this is relevant when using island biology as a base for the deriving of rules for genetic conservation.

KEY WORDS:—Evolution – islands – natural selection – small mammals.

## CONTENTS

## INTRODUCTION

*If we look to the character of the inhabitants of small islands, we shall find that those situated close to other land have a similar fauna with that land, whilst those at a considerable distance from other land often possesses an almost entirely peculiar fauna.*

Charles Darwin, *Essay* of 1844

    Two factors have impressed all biologists who have visited islands from at least the time of Darwin (Hooker, 1867; Wallace, 1880; Carlquist, 1974; Williamson, 1981): the numbers of species which are *not* represented, and the

0024–4066/86/050205 + 26 $03.00/0

differentiation of those species that are present from their relatives elsewhere. Recent interest has been overwhelmingly concerned with the first of these: refining, checking, quantifying but not substantially changing the statement made by Alfred Russel Wallace (1880) more than a century ago, that

> "the distribution of the various species and groups of living things over the earth's surface and their aggregation in definite assemblages in certain areas is the direct result and outcome of . . . firstly, the constant tendency of all organisms to increase in numbers and to occupy a wider area, and their various powers of dispersion and migration through which, when unchecked, they are enabled to spread widely over the globe; and secondly, those laws of evolution and extinction which determine the manner in which groups or organisms arise and grow, reach their maximum, and then dwindle away . . ."

The words used by Wallace in pointing out that species composition is a balance between colonization and extinction are very similar to those he (and, for that matter, Charles Darwin) used in his original paper about evolution by natural selection (Darwin & Wallace, 1858). The earlier paper, of course, linked the struggle for existence produced by colonization and extinction with variation, and showed how this could lead to evolutionary change.

MacArthur and Wilson devoted a chapter of their *Island Biogeography* (MacArthur & Wilson, 1967) to "evolutionary changes following colonization", and three pages in that chapter to the founder effect (i.e. genetic differences resulting from, rather than following, colonization), but the spate of studies stimulated by their seminal work has concentrated almost entirely on diversity. This is not to suggest that diversity has been completely neglected, but to point out that the acute reduction in gene flow which is the key element in forming island faunas, and which was so lucidly expounded in Mayr's classic paper (Mayr, 1954), has tended to be forgotten in the enthusiasm for compiling species lists, calculating species turnover, and discussing biotic equilibria. Mayr's ideas have been applied explicitly to the evolution of the Hawaiian Drosophilidae (Templeton, 1980; Williamson, 1981; Carson, 1983), but 'island theory' has come for many to mean nothing more than the equation expounded by MacArthur and Wilson (Bengston & Enckell, 1983). This paper is about differentiation in island small mammal faunas, concentrating on the British Isles but taking British forms as exemplars of processes happening generally.

## GENETICS OF ISLAND POPULATIONS

Islands may be populated by relict or colonizing populations. A relict population will be expected to have an amount of variation initially similar to the source or parental population, whereas a population founded by a finite number of colonizers will be expected to have a reduced amount of variation. In general, island races of mammals have a lower mean heterozygosity than their mainland neighbours, suggesting that their most likely origin is via a founding event (Kilpatrick, 1981; see also Nevo, 1978) (Table 1) although there are, of course, many islands where the mammal populations are likely to be survivors of a time when a landbridge existed between island and mainland. For example, the Channel and Scilly archipelagos to the south of Britain support populations

Table 1. Inherited variation (heterozygosity) in island and mainland populations of the same species (after Kilpatrick, 1981)

| | Mainland | | Island | | Reduction in heterozygosity (%) | Reference |
|---|---|---|---|---|---|---|
| | N | Mean heterozygosity per locus (range) | N | Mean heterozygosity per locus (range) | | |
| *Macrotus waterhousii* | 3 | 0.021(0–0.043) | 1 | 0.040 | — | Greenbaum & Baker, 1976 |
| *Macaca fuscata* | 13 | 0.019(0–0.035) | 5 | 0.013(0.03–0.018) | 31.6 | Nozawa et al., 1975 |
| *Spermophilus spilosoma* | 12 | 0.090(0.049–0.160) | 1 | 0.009 | 90.0 | Cothran et al., 1977 |
| *Peromyscus eremicus* | 44 | 0.040(0.006–0.079) | 2 | 0.009(0–0.022) | 77.5 | Avise et al., 1974a |
| *Peromyscus leucopus* | 3 | 0.080(0.076–0.084) | 3 | 0.071(0.052–0.078) | 11.3 | Browne, 1977 |
| *Peromyscus maniculatus* | 22 | 0.088(0.054–0.124) | 11 | 0.068(0.010–0.131) | 22.7 | Aquadro, 1978; Avise et al., 1979; Gill, 1979 |
| *Peromyscus polionotus* | 26 | 0.063(0.050–0.086) | 4 | 0.052(0.018–0.086) | 17.5 | Selander et al., 1971 |
| *Sigmodon hispidus* | 4 | 0.022(0.017–0.025) | 1 | 0.021 | 4.6 | Johnson et al., 1972 |
| *Microtus pennsylvanicus* | 4 | 0.142(0.120–0.171) | 9 | 0.056(0.023–0.114) | 60.6 | Kilpatrick & Crowell, 1985 |
| *Mus domesticus* | 16 | 0.091(0.032–0.114) | 20 | 0.041(0–0.079) | 55.0 | Berry & Peters, 1977; Selander & Yang, 1979 |
| *Rattus fuscipes* | 3 | 0.047(0.020–0.100) | 9 | 0.011(0–0.040) | 76.6 | Schmitt, 1978 |
| *Rattus rattus* | 1 | 0.031 | 11 | 0.026(0.008–0.056) | 16.1 | Patton et al., 1975 |

of long-tailed field (or wood) mice (*Apodemus sylvaticus*) indistinguishable from those on mainland Britain (Berry, 1973, 1975; Handford & Pernetta, 1974), but those on Shetland and the Hebrides to the north and west of Britain are very different from each other and from the British mainland (Berry, Evans & Sennitt, 1967; Berry, 1969). The southern island groups were not glaciated during the Pleistocene and their mouse populations could well be relics of a time when the islands were part of a Britain–European continent; in contrast, the northern groups were never connected to Britain after the Pleistocene, and must therefore have been colonized from elsewhere (apparently from Scandinavia).

Traditionally, the northern populations were interpreted as relics, initially part of a continuous mainland race, which became differentiated as the islands were separated from the mainland and their inhabitants adapted to local conditions. For example, Darling (1947) wrote of the situation in the Hebrides, "*Apodemus* is considered to be a true relic . . . it is probable that the island races of Britain form steps in a broken cline". However, when these animals are studied in detail (and Delany, summarized in 1970, has taken classical taxonomic methods as far as they can probably go), it is found that "the mice of no island group, such as the Inner Hebrides, seem uniform and consequently there is little evidence that the island populations have evolved other than from separately isolated groups of animals" (Delany & Healy, 1964); the only pattern in the genetic relationships between races is that they are all more closely related either to another island race or to Norwegian mice.

The simplest assumption about field mice in the Hebridean and Shetland groups is that commensal mice clandestinely accompanied man to the islands when he settled there. A few mice would emerge from seed crops or bedding for stock, and almost inevitably differ from their ancestors because of their small numbers. The Vikings were the first to make boats good enough for routine movement on the hazardous waters around the islands (Sawyer, 1971); it is not surprising that Shetland and Hebridean mouse populations show affinities with Norway.

Similar conclusions can be drawn from the study of other species. Orkney voles (*Microtus arvalis orcadensis*) were originally believed to be a glacial survivor on north British islands (Hinton, 1910, 1913; Beirne, 1952), but comparisons with other samples showed that their closest relatives seem to be in the Mediterranean area, rather than northern Europe (Berry & Rose, 1975). Repeatedly, island forms have been shown to be introduced rather than relict (Corbet, 1961).

There are examples which involve situations where there is no possibility of the present fauna being relict. The house mice of the Faroe Islands have been quoted as examples of spectacularly rapid evolution. Huxley (1942) reviewed evidence that subspeciation usually takes about 5000 years, but "the facts concerning rats and mice show that subspeciation may sometimes occur much more quickly. In particular the Faroe house mouse, which was introduced into the islands not much more than 250 years ago, is now so distinct that certain modern authorities have assigned full specific status to it". Matthews (1952) has argued similarly: "These island races are particularly interesting in showing the rate at which isolated wild populations can develop new genetic characteristics, for it is definitely known that their forerunners could not have been introduced into the Faroes less than 250 years or more than 1000 years ago".

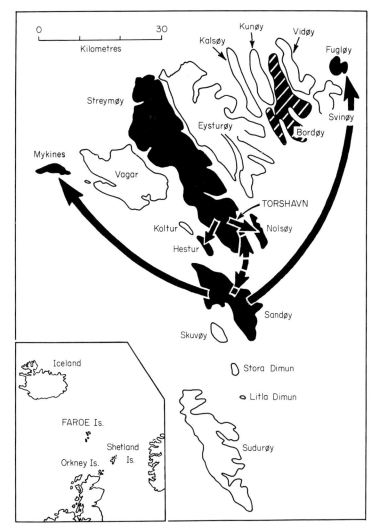

Figure 1. Possible routes of inter-island colonizations by house mice in the Faroe archipelago. Six islands (shown in black) now support house mice; Bordøy (striped) had mice within living memory, but they are now extinct (based on Berry *et al.*, 1978).

In fact, the situation is even more abrupt: of the six Faroe Islands where mice occur, Hestur seems to have acquired them since 1939, while both Fugløy and Mykines were recorded as being free from mice in 1800. Notwithstanding this, all the island races are very distinct for morphometric, non-metrical skeletal traits, and allozymic frequencies (Berry, Jakobson & Peters, 1978).

The most variable population comes from Sandøy, one of the southern Faroe Islands. The southern islands are more fertile and intensively farmed than the northern ones, and it seems plausible that the original establishment of mice in Faroe was on Sandøy, and that mice spread from there to the other islands, although on the basis of distance statistics both Hestur and Nolsøy were probably colonized from the large neighbouring island of Streymøy (Fig. 1).

An esterase variant ($Es$-$2^e$) is segregating on three of the Faroes; it also occurs in Denmark, but has only been found on the Shetland island of Yell among

British islands (including Great Britain itself). Narrowing of the mesopterygoid fossa was used as a diagnostic criterion of the Mykines race by Degerbøl (1942); this also occurs in Shetland, which suggests that both the Faroe and Shetland populations were derived from a common ancestor. On historical grounds, the most likely agents for introducing house mice to the islands were, just as for field mice, the Vikings.

It would be easy to list many similar cases where the relationship and differentiation of an island form can be reasonably attributed to the founder principle (Berry, 1979c, 1983a). One final example will suffice. Patton (1984) has studied both the 'native' and the introduced rats of the Galapagos archipelago. There are three groups of 'native' rats: the extinct genus *Megaoryzomys*, apparently derived from a thomasomyine of mainland South America (Steadman & Ray, 1982); *Nesoryzomys*, which has no close relatives among the mainland rats nearest to it, which are the highly diverse rice rats, *Oryzomys*; and a single living species of *Oryzomys*, *O. bauri*, which is morphologically and allozymically virtually identical with the mainland *O. xantheolus*. (Another island species *O. galapagoensis*, has become extinct within historical times.) This implies two successful introductions in the far distant past, and a more recent introduction of *Oryzomys*.

Allozymic, morphometric and non-metrical skeletal traits all show the same set of inter-island relationships for the 'introduced rat' *Rattus rattus*, and can be interpreted as indicating three groups of introductions, corresponding to different periods of human activity in the islands: the first in the late 1600s, the most recent during World War II. Apart from the primary introductions, gene flow between the islands seems to have been slight (Patton, Yang & Myers, 1975).

MacArthur & Wilson (1967) predicted that isolation would increase the importance of immigration and emigration as factors affecting the genetic structure of a population, and hence permit rapid evolutionary change. Although they discussed the founder effect, they were more concerned with the reduction in genetic variability resulting from it than the differentiation produced by the founder event itself.* In fact, it is impossible to separate the differentiation resulting from the stochastic gene frequency changes of the founder event from subsequent genetic changes, whatever their causes. Berry and his colleagues have shown that selection may act powerfully on island house mouse (*Mus domesticus*) populations to produce rapid adaptation, often involving major shifts in gene frequencies (Berry & Peters, 1977; Berry, Peters & van Aarde, 1978; Berry, Bonner & Peters, 1979). In particular, they have shown considerable skeletal and allozymic changes over a 15 year period in the mice on a small Welsh island (Skokholm), which is known to have gone through a founder 'bottleneck' about a century ago (Berry, 1964, 1978; Berry & Jakobson, 1975a).

In the course of an extensive survey of island mammal populations, Kilpatrick (1981) has calculated Nei's (1972) mean genetic identity (*I*) between island

---

*All genetic changes resulting from allele sampling fluctuations in small populations are formally called 'drift'. However, it is useful (following Waddington, 1957) to distinguish between continuing, random, disadaptive change in a small population (*Persistent drift*) (which seems to be extremely rare in nature), and single (or uncommon) changes produced by an ecological crisis or a colonizing (i.e. founding) event (*intermittent drift*) (Halkka *et al.*, 1974; Berry, 1983a).

Table 2. Inherited variation and number of endemic rodent species on islands compared to the related mainland species (after Kilpatrick, 1981)

| | Island species | | Mainland species | | | |
|---|---|---|---|---|---|---|
| | $N$* | Mean heterozygosity per locus (range) | | $N$ | Mean heterozygosity per locus (range) | Reference |
| Dipodomys compactus | 3 | 0.023(0–0.069) | Dipodomys spp. | 41 | 0.021(0–0.071) | Johnson & Selander, 1971 |
| Peromyscus eva | 1 | 0 | Haplomylomys spp. | 25 | 0.030(0–0.106) | Avise et al., 1974a |
| Peromyscus dickeyi | 1 | 0 | Haplomylomys spp. | 25 | 0.030(0–0.106) | Avise et al., 1974a |
| Peromyscus interparietalis | 1 | 0 | Haplomylomys spp. | 25 | 0.030(0–0.106) | Avise et al., 1974a |
| Peromyscus guardia | 1 | 0.014 | Haplomylomys spp. | 25 | 0.030(0–0.106) | Avise et al., 1974a |
| Peromyscus stephani | 1 | 0 | Peromyscus boylii spp. group | 68 | 0.032(0–0.118) | Avise et al., 1974a, b Kilpatrick & Zimmerman, 1975 |
| Peromyscus sejugis | 2 | 0.017 | Peromyscus maniculatus spp. group | 81 | 0.081(0.033–0.124) | Avise et al., 1974a; Aquadro, 1978; Avise et al., 1979; Selander et al., 1971 |
| Microtus breweri | 1 | 0.020 | Microtus spp. | 8 | 0.098(0.012–0.186) | Kilpatrick & Crowell, 1985 |

* $N$ = number of samples scored.

populations and between island and mainland populations of seven mammalian species (Table 2). Among island populations, the highest value of $I$ was between *Macaca fuscata* from the oceanic islands of southern Japan, and the lowest between *Rattus fuscipes* from continental shelf islands of southern Australia. The simplest explanation of this difference is that it is a direct consequence of the much greater mean heterozygosity of mainland *R. fuscipes* than of *M. fuscata* (4.7 and 1.9% respectively: Schmitt, 1978; Nozawa, Shotake & Okura, 1978), permitting much greater genetic changes in the founding event.

Kilpatrick went on to analyse the amount of differentiation of so-called fast and slow evolving loci (Sarich, 1977). He found that in island populations 83% more genetic variation occurred at 'fast' as compared with 'slow' evolving loci; among mainland populations this figure was 36%. This difference was largely due to increased levels of genetic differentiation at 'slow' evolving loci among insular populations. This again would seem to be a founder effect since all loci will be affected equally by a colonization bottleneck.

Kilpatrick concluded his review, "All evolutionary forces play a role in structuring insular gene pools. While accumulated evidence suggests founder effect as the major evolutionary force responsible for the reduction of genetic variation and differentiation of insular populations, additional data are needed to substantiate the relative importance of founder effect and to determine the relative importance of other evolutionary forces. Manipulations of insular populations with partially known genomes and repeated sampling of these populations prior and subsequent to manipulations should allow determination of the relative importance of founder effect, genetic drift, gene flow, and selection in determining the genetic structure of insular populations."

### *Founder events: stochastic and adaptational genetic change*

Conventional evolutionary interpretation is that genetic differences between populations living in different environments are most likely the result of adaptation; differences between populations living in similar environments are commonly attributed to drift or unperceived environmental differences which lead to different selective forces. My first involvement with the factors leading to a differentiated island form was that of the house mouse population of Skokholm, which differed from its nearest neighbour and putative closest relative in body size, ecological behaviour (such as range of movement), reproductive traits, and a number of non-metrical skeletal variant frequencies. With no further comparisons, these differences could easily be interpreted as adaptive, albeit representing very rapid evolution since mice had only been on Skokholm for about 70 years (Berry, 1964; Howells, 1968). However, comparison with mice from the Isle of May (an island in the Firth of Forth nearly 800 km from Skokholm, but apparently similar to Skokholm in the environment it provided for mice) showed that the two island populations were very different in their inherited skeletal variant pattern, although similar in more obviously ecologically important traits like body size. Both the May and Skokholm populations were most like their respective neighbours on their nearest mainland, albeit very much more distinct than the mainland populations were from each other; but the two island populations were extremely dissimilar (Fig. 2).

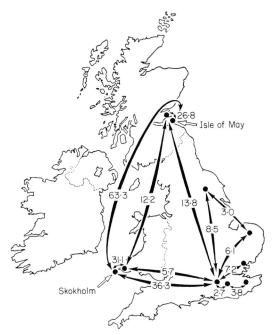

Figure 2. Genetic distances (×100) between house mouse population samples, based on non-metrical skeletal traits (see text) (from Berry, 1967).

Much of the skeletal distinctiveness of the Skokholm mice was due to the high frequency of a number of mid-line traits, despite the fact that these were largely uncorrelated with each other (Berry & Jakobson, 1975a). These traits are rare in most mouse populations, but were present in one of the neighbouring mainland populations. The simplest assumption was that the founding population had carried a high frequency of alleles affecting the mid-line traits. However, there is no way of determining how much of the Skokholm distinctiveness was the result of the founding event itself, and how much to subsequent change.

Berry & Jakobson (1975a) sampled the Skokholm population once or twice per year for a 10 year period. They found that there was a continuing and apparently progressive overall change in skeletal trait frequencies (cf. Barnett & Dickson, 1984), but the greatest change was a seasonally reversed change in frequencies. For example, the frequency of 'parted frontals' averaged 24% in spring populations (before the beginning of breeding) and 33% in autumn ones (at the end of breeding for the year); for "dys-symphysis of the 2nd thoracic vertebra" the figures were 22% and 32% respectively. It would be dangerous to put too much emphasis on this latter finding in isolation, but independent evidence of selection acting in opposite directions in different seasons (the summer breeding period from April to September, and the winter survival period when negligible breeding occurs) has come from allozyme studies. These have shown alleles at two electrophoretically scored loci fluctuating significantly in frequency between spring and autumn samples (Berry & Murphy, 1970; Berry, 1978). One of the loci involved (*Hbb*) consistently showed a disproportionate increase in heterozygotes over homozygotes during the summer, and a reciprocal decrease in winter. This locus is the structural gene for the $\beta$ chain of haemoglobin; haemoglobins produced by the two common alleles have different oxygen-binding characteristics, and hence may be expected to respond to selection (Newton & Peters, 1983).

Williamson (1981) has argued that the case for a major founder effect contribution is not fully established in producing differentiation on islands. He suggested that island populations might adapt similarly to common elements in a maritime environment. Ironically, Handford & Pernetta (1974) also argued for the importance of adaptation in differentiating island rodents, but on the opposite basis of environmental heterogeneity. Davis (1983) has tested Williamson's conclusion by carrying out similar analyses on population samples chosen specifically to distinguish between island and mainland effects. He compared mice from the mainland of Great Britain, concentrating on samples from northeast Scotland, with mice from the Orkney, Shetland and Faroe archipelagos. His null hypothesis was that the island mice would group together, separately from British mainland animals, if there was a major 'maritime island effect'. Using a discriminant factor analysis similar to that employed by Williamson, he found instead that the island mice grouped together with those of Caithness (northeast Scotland), showing a regional geographic effect rather than an island effect, thus effectively disproving his initial hypothesis. A further study which compared populations with different chromosomal (Robertsonian) fusions in Caithness and several Orkney islands showed that there was an overall genetic similarity between populations based on morphometric characters, despite the fact that some of the populations differed considerably in their chromosomal constitutions (Nash, Brooker & Davis, 1983). In other words, genetic (chromosomal) differences which in some cases must have arisen since isolation, did not obscure the general relationships between the populations in the area.

### FOUNDER EFFECTS: AN EXAMPLE

The most common form of biological sampling involves collecting from a number of different geographical or ecological localities. Only rarely is the same population sampled on different occasions, although this procedure is by far the best method of detecting genetic change (Berry, 1978; Manley, 1985). However, a considerable amount can be learnt from 'cross-sectional' sampling, if genetical traits are scored on the individuals caught (Berry & Peters, 1977). The study described in this section involved house mice caught from 13 sites in the Orkney archipelago, and seven in the Shetland one. All these sites except two represented collections from different islands; the exceptions were the large 'Mainland' island and the island of Yell in Shetland, where mice were caught at two separated sites. One island in Orkney was sampled twice (in successive years), and two Shetland islands were sampled two and three times respectively. All the mice (except the Foula I sample, which was live-trapped: Berry & Tricker, 1969) were caught by hand when cereal ricks (usually oats) were broken down for threshing (or in a few cases, for feeding directly to animals). Mice colonize ricks after harvest in the autumn, and live a sheltered life between the sheaves which constitute the rick (Southern & Laurie, 1946; Southwick, 1958; Rowe, Taylor & Chudley, 1963).

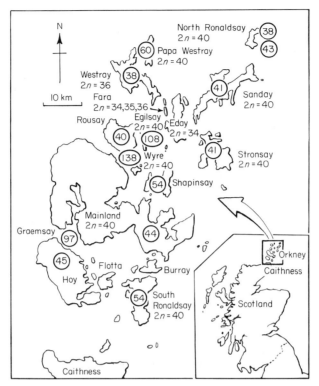

Figure 3. Estimates of uniqueness of Orkney house mouse population samples, based on non-metrical skeletal traits (from Table 5).

The mice were killed within 2–3 days of being caught, and the organs used for various purposes (Batten & Berry, 1967; Berry & Jakobson, 1975b; Berry & Peters, 1977). For the present study, skeletons were prepared by enzymatic digestion with papain, and every skeleton scored (by one person) for 26 non-metrical traits (Luther, 1949; Berry, 1963; Berry & Jakobson, 1975a). Non-metrical variants have advantages over metrical characteristics for genetical studies in that their occurrence is inherited (albeit in a complicated quasi-continuous or epigenetic fashion: Grüneberg, 1963), and is largely independent of age, size or sex (Berry, 1967, 1979a; Howe & Parsons, 1967; Sjøvold, 1973, 1984; Self & Leamy, 1978). Populations can be conveniently compared by computing a single multivariate distance statistic based on the frequencies of individual variants; this can be regarded as a 'genetic distance' because the component variants are inherited. There are many ways of calculating such a difference, all of which give broadly similar values; in this work a 'measure of divergence' (M.D.) devised by C. A. B. Smith has been used (Grewal, 1962; Berry, 1963).

The frequencies of the variants classified are set out in Tables 3 & 4, and the distance statistics in Tables 5 & 6. The final column in Tables 5 & 6 lists a 'measure of uniqueness' for each sample, which is the simple arithmetical mean of the M.D. for each sample. This provides an indication of the distinctiveness of each sample. The measures of uniqueness ($\times 100$) are the values shown on Figs 3 & 4.

Table 3. Percentage incidence of non-metrical skeletal variants in Orkney Island samples of *Mus domesticus*

| | Hoy | Graemsay | South Ronaldsay | Deerness (Mainland) | Shapinsay | Rousay | Wyre | Egilsay | Westray | Papa Westray | Stronsay | Sanday | North Ronaldsay I | North Ronaldsay II |
|---|---|---|---|---|---|---|---|---|---|---|---|---|---|---|
| 1 Preorbital foramen double | 11.5 | 3.4 | 8.3 | 1.6 | 1.4 | 3.9 | 5.7 | 7.3 | 5.5 | 10.7 | 1.1 | 2.6 | 1.0 | 2.0 |
| 2 Interfrontal present | 5.1 | 41.9 | 1.8 | 0 | 0 | 0 | 1.7 | 0 | 0 | 0 | 0 | 0 | 0 | 0 |
| 3 Parted frontals | 28.2 | 95.1 | 48.1 | 90.3 | 9.5 | 90.2 | 66.1 | 51.3 | 40.6 | 0 | 37.8 | 23.4 | 38.5 | 20.0 |
| 4 Fused frontals | 0 | 2.4 | 1.8 | 3.2 | 0 | 3.9 | 1.8 | 0 | 0 | 0 | 4.4 | 2.0 | 1.9 | 0 |
| 5 Frontal fontanelle present | 28.9 | 0 | 14.8 | 3.2 | 0 | 3.9 | 0 | 40.5 | 15.6 | 0 | 26.7 | 2.0 | 5.8 | 0 |
| 6 Frontal foramen double | 7.7 | 0 | 8.3 | 4.8 | 0 | 0 | 2.8 | 6.0 | 2.8 | 1.7 | 3.0 | 0.9 | 5.8 | 2.0 |
| 7 Maxillary foramen I double | 20.5 | 4.5 | 1.8 | 0 | 18.6 | 11.8 | 5.5 | 4.0 | 1.4 | 33.0 | 0 | 5.3 | 7.7 | 2.0 |
| 8 Maxillary foramen II double | 3.8 | 48.9 | 22.2 | 21.0 | 27.1 | 51.0 | 15.7 | 26.7 | 48.6 | 18.1 | 43.3 | 43.8 | 28.8 | 28.0 |
| 9 Foramen palatine major double | 14.1 | 3.4 | 6.5 | 0 | 7.1 | 1.0 | 0 | 14.0 | 6.2 | 10.9 | 1.9 | 16.7 | 5.8 | 2.0 |
| 10 Alae palatine present | 0 | 83.7 | 25.0 | 4.8 | 7.1 | 3.9 | 80.5 | 2.0 | 9.7 | 0 | 0 | 0.8 | 1.0 | 2.0 |
| 11 For. sphen. med. present | 87.0 | 97.7 | 38.9 | 51.6 | 31.0 | 37.2 | 59.3 | 59.4 | 63.9 | 85.1 | 63.5 | 77.0 | 73.1 | 64.0 |
| 12 For. sphen. lat. ventr. present | 60.2 | 0 | 65.7 | 53.2 | 41.4 | 17.6 | 21.3 | 55.4 | 46.5 | 53.2 | 21.1 | 61.4 | 57.7 | 20.0 |
| 13 Proc. pterygoideus absent | 0 | 4.5 | 3.7 | 9.7 | 35.7 | 27.7 | 4.6 | 33.1 | 7.1 | 9.6 | 19.2 | 0.8 | 8.6 | 4.0 |
| 14 Foramen ovale double | 21.8 | 48.9 | 67.6 | 43.5 | 22.8 | 61.8 | 33.3 | 80.3 | 37.5 | 26.9 | 36.5 | 16.7 | 26.0 | 2.0 |
| 15 Foramen infraovale double | 41.0 | 16.3 | 15.7 | 17.7 | 11.4 | 28.4 | 23.1 | 15.5 | 5.7 | 6.4 | 11.5 | 18.4 | 8.6 | 6.0 |
| 16 Foramen pterygoideum double | 7.7 | 31.8 | 32.4 | 1.6 | 11.4 | 4.9 | 13.0 | 2.7 | 7.0 | 9.6 | 21.1 | 31.6 | 2.9 | 8.0 |
| 17 Preoptic sutures present | 38.5 | 79.5 | 45.4 | 45.2 | 78.6 | 57.8 | 80.0 | 21.2 | 66.2 | 43.6 | 51.0 | 36.8 | 37.5 | 14.0 |
| 18 Foramen hypoglossi double | 30.3 | 37.5 | 55.5 | 45.6 | 60.0 | 35.3 | 51.1 | 36.5 | 30.5 | 46.8 | 73.1 | 29.0 | 17.0 | 25.5 |
| 19 Acc. mental foramen | 35.9 | 14.8 | 27.8 | 24.2 | 24.3 | 10.8 | 51.1 | 1.3 | 18.0 | 28.7 | 1.6 | 9.6 | 11.5 | 20.0 |
| 20 Mandibular foramen present | 0 | 0 | 1.0 | 0 | 0 | 0 | 1.9 | 24.5 | 1.4 | 0 | 1.0 | 0.8 | 0 | 0 |
| 21 Fossa olecrani perforata | 30.8 | 75.0 | 50.9 | 77.0 | 100.0 | 43.9 | 56.5 | 1.4 | 69.4 | 94.7 | 44.5 | 71.9 | 61.5 | 34.0 |
| 22 F.t.i. of C. VI | 0 | 2.3 | 0 | 0 | 1.4 | 0 | 0 | 1.4 | 0 | 0 | 0 | 0 | 0 | 0 |
| 23 Proc. spin. of Th. I abs. | 8.3 | 0 | 0 | 0 | 2.8 | 4.2 | 1.8 | 0 | 25.7 | 0 | 2.0 | 1.9 | 0 | 0 |
| 24 Proc. spin. of Th. II abs. | 0 | 0 | 0 | 0 | 0 | 0 | 1.8 | 0 | 0 | 0 | 0 | 4.0 | 0 | 0 |
| 25 Dys-symphysis of Th. I | 0 | 0 | 0 | 0 | 2.8 | 0 | 0 | 1.4 | 2.8 | 0 | 4.0 | 1.9 | 0 | 0 |
| 26 Dys-symphysis of Th. X | 5.4 | 2.3 | 0 | 6.4 | 0 | 0 | 1.8 | 0 | 11.1 | 0 | 5.9 | 11.5 | 0 | 0 |
| No. of specimens classified | 39 | 41 | 54 | 31 | 35 | 51 | 54 | 75 | 36 | 47 | 52 | 52 | 52 | 25 |

Table 4. Percentage incidence of non-metrical skeletal variants in Shetland Island samples of *Mus domesticus*

| | Fair Isle | Scousburgh (Mainland) | Ollaberry (Mainland) | Mid Yell | Aywick, Yell | Fetlar I | Fetlar II | Fetlar III | Unst | Foula I | Foula II |
|---|---|---|---|---|---|---|---|---|---|---|---|
| 1 Preorbital foramen double | 5.5 | 10.7 | 12.5 | 9.8 | 7.7 | 22.0 | 31.3 | 35.1 | 13.3 | 2.3 | 2.5 |
| 2 Interfrontal present | 0 | 0 | 0 | 0 | 0 | 0 | 0 | 0 | 0 | 0 | 0 |
| 3 Parted frontals | 53.8 | 83.9 | 92.8 | 54.5 | 30.4 | 96.0 | 61.0 | 82.8 | 88.2 | 49.0 | 50.0 |
| 4 Fused frontals | 3.8 | 3.6 | 3.6 | 15.1 | 8.7 | 8.0 | 11.9 | 0 | 3.7 | 0 | 0 |
| 5 Frontal fontanelle present | 0 | 8.9 | 0 | 12.1 | 26.1 | 0 | 0 | 0 | 0 | 2.3 | 0 |
| 6 Frontal foramen double | 3.7 | 7.1 | 1.8 | 5.4 | 4.1 | 6.0 | 2.5 | 6.7 | 3.4 | 10.5 | 0 |
| 7 Maxillary foramen I double | 7.4 | 25.0 | 22.3 | 24.3 | 5.8 | 8.0 | 5.9 | 16.2 | 3.3 | 12.8 | 7.5 |
| 8 Maxillary foramen II double | 0 | 0.9 | 59.8 | 74.3 | 15.4 | 18.0 | 11.9 | 75.7 | 15.0 | 31.4 | 20.0 |
| 9 Foramen palatine major double | 16.7 | 0 | 4.5 | 5.4 | 0 | 2.0 | 2.7 | 1.3 | 0 | 0 | 1.2 |
| 10 Alae palatine present | 1.8 | 13.4 | 0.9 | 40.5 | 5.8 | 0 | 5.9 | 2.7 | 5.0 | 0 | 12.5 |
| 11 For. sphen. med. present | 96.3 | 66.1 | 76.8 | 86.5 | 69.2 | 96.0 | 91.5 | 94.6 | 86.7 | 23.2 | 75.0 |
| 12 For. sphen. lat. ventr. present | 38.9 | 60.0 | 42.0 | 73.0 | 55.8 | 24.0 | 31.0 | 1.3 | 30.0 | 37.2 | 55.0 |
| 13 Proc. pterygoideus absent | 14.8 | 8.0 | 4.5 | 17.6 | 3.8 | 8.0 | 7.7 | 8.1 | 10.0 | 2.3 | 1.2 |
| 14 Foramen ovale double | 1.8 | 53.6 | 13.4 | 24.3 | 1.9 | 44.0 | 91.4 | 73.0 | 76.7 | 3.5 | 11.2 |
| 15 Foramen infraovale double | 18.5 | 3.6 | 0.9 | 4.0 | 0 | 56.0 | 40.7 | 21.6 | 33.3 | 23.2 | 12.5 |
| 16 Foramen pterygoideum double | 11.1 | 8.9 | 10.7 | 4.0 | 5.8 | 4.0 | 13.5 | 18.9 | 1.7 | 17.4 | 15.0 |
| 17 Preoptic sutures present | 35.2 | 19.6 | 14.3 | 68.9 | 44.2 | 24.0 | 53.4 | 24.3 | 26.7 | 24.4 | 36.2 |
| 18 Foramen hypoglossi double | 70.4 | 37.4 | 70.1 | 72.2 | 76.9 | 72.0 | 76.8 | 74.3 | 31.7 | 62.8 | 81.2 |
| 19 Acc. mental foramen | 29.6 | 17.0 | 36.6 | 7.0 | 48.1 | 4.0 | 13.5 | 24.3 | 21.6 | 22.1 | 7.5 |
| 20 Mandibular foramen present | 7.4 | 0 | 8.0 | 0 | 1.9 | 0 | 0 | 2.7 | 0 | 1.2 | 1.2 |
| 21 Fossa olecrani perforata | 1.9 | 61.6 | 17.0 | 64.4 | 50.0 | 6.0 | 15.4 | 12.2 | 8.3 | 70.9 | 90.0 |
| 22 F.t.i. of C. VI | 0 | 0 | 0 | 0 | 0 | 0 | 0 | 1.3 | 0 | 1.2 | 0 |
| 23 Proc. spin. of Th. I abs. | 3.8 | 1.8 | 0 | 11.1 | 0 | 0 | 3.5 | 2.8 | 0 | 0 | 0 |
| 24 Proc. spin. of Th. II abs. | 0 | 0 | 0 | 0 | 0 | 0 | 0 | 0 | 0 | 2.5 | 0 |
| 25 Dys-symphysis of Th. I | 0 | 0 | 0 | 0 | 0 | 0 | 0 | 0 | 0 | 0 | 0 |
| 26 Dys-symphysis of Th. X | 15.4 | 0 | 0 | 0 | 0 | 0 | 0 | 0 | 0 | 0 | 0 |
| No. of specimens classified | 26 | 56 | 56 | 33 | 26 | 25 | 59 | 37 | 27 | 43 | 40 |

Table 5. Measures of divergence between Orkney Island samples (standard errors of estimate in italics)

| | Graemsay | South Ronaldsay | Deerness (Mainland) | Shapinsay | Rousay | Wyre | Egilsay | Westray | Papa Westray | Stronsay | Sanday | North Ronaldsay I | North Ronaldsay II | Estimate of uniqueness |
|---|---|---|---|---|---|---|---|---|---|---|---|---|---|---|
| Hoy | 0.796 *0.077* | 0.550 *0.061* | 0.252 *0.047* | 0.456 *0.062* | 0.291 *0.045* | 1.414 *0.096* | 0.964 *0.076* | 0.175 *0.038* | 0.321 *0.048* | 0.254 *0.042* | 0.121 *0.029* | 0.104 *0.023* | 0.186 *0.045* | 0.453 |
| Graemsay | | 0.529 *0.058* | 0.620 *0.072* | 1.071 *0.092* | 0.414 *0.052* | 1.744 *0.103* | 2.040 *0.106* | 0.917 *0.084* | 1.178 *0.089* | 0.912 *0.077* | 1.007 *0.081* | 0.720 *0.068* | 0.663 *0.080* | 0.970 |
| South Ronaldsay | | | 0.479 *0.062* | 0.529 *0.058* | 0.621 *0.060* | 0.897 *0.070* | 0.685 *0.058* | 0.490 *0.059* | 0.285 *0.042* | 0.530 *0.055* | 0.413 *0.049* | 0.493 *0.053* | 0.537 *0.070* | 0.541 |
| Deerness (Mainland) | | | | 0.409 *0.062* | 0.078 *0.025* | 1.588 *0.110* | 1.141 *0.089* | 0.085 *0.028* | 0.459 *0.062* | 0.151 *0.035* | 0.228 *0.043* | 0.082 *0.025* | 0.102 *0.034* | 0.436 |
| Shapinsay | | | | | 0.204 *0.039* | 1.532 *0.104* | 1.382 *0.094* | 0.195 *0.041* | 0.229 *0.042* | 0.236 *0.042* | 0.319 *0.048* | 0.213 *0.040* | 0.283 *0.054* | 0.543 |
| Rousay | | | | | | 1.258 *0.084* | 0.939 *0.069* | 0.146 *0.033* | 0.519 *0.057* | 0.149 *0.030* | 0.253 *0.039* | 0.134 *0.028* | 0.239 *0.047* | 0.404 |
| Wyre | | | | | | | 0.583 *0.052* | 1.255 *0.093* | 1.813 *0.103* | 1.347 *0.087* | 1.218 *0.082* | 1.559 *0.093* | 1.498 *0.115* | 1.362 |
| Egilsay | | | | | | | | 0.850 *0.078* | 1.354 *0.085* | 0.945 *0.069* | 0.927 *0.068* | 1.047 *0.072* | 1.162 *0.098* | 1.078 |
| Westray | | | | | | | | | 0.301 *0.048* | 0.094 *0.026* | 0.108 *0.028* | 0.095 *0.026* | 0.174 *0.043* | 0.376 |
| Papa Westray | | | | | | | | | | 0.312 *0.044* | 0.402 *0.050* | 0.289 *0.042* | 0.378 *0.060* | 0.603 |
| Stronsay | | | | | | | | | | | 0.133 *0.028* | 0.133 *0.028* | 0.169 *0.039* | 0.413 |
| Sanday | | | | | | | | | | | | 0.075 *0.021* | 0.082 *0.027* | 0.407 |
| North Ronaldsay I | | | | | | | | | | | | | 0.059 *0.023* | 0.385 |
| North Ronaldsay II | | | | | | | | | | | | | | 0.426 |

Table 6. Measures of divergence between Shetland Island samples (standard errors of estimate in italics)

| | Scousburgh (Mainland) | Ollaberry (Mainland) | Mid Yell | Aywick, Yell | Fetlar I | Fetlar II | Fetlar III | Unst | Foula I | Foula II | Estimate of uniqueness |
|---|---|---|---|---|---|---|---|---|---|---|---|
| Fair Isle | 0.354 *0.055* | 0.271 *0.057* | 0.417 *0.064* | 0.203 *0.049* | 0.271 *0.057* | 0.457 *0.062* | 0.533 *0.067* | 0.667 *0.085* | 0.404 *0.061* | 1.270 *0.070* | 0.485 |
| Scousburgh (Mainland) | | 0.214 *0.034* | 0.344 *0.049* | 0.199 *0.042* | 0.234 *0.046* | 0.381 *0.051* | 0.151 *0.028* | 0.133 *0.032* | 0.191 *0.035* | 1.376 *0.095* | 0.358 |
| Ollaberry (Mainland) | | | 0.236 *0.040* | 0.185 *0.040* | 0.197 *0.042* | 0.158 *0.033* | 0.387 *0.046* | 0.384 *0.041* | 0.199 *0.035* | 1.487 *0.099* | 0.372 |
| Mid Yell | | | | 0.300 *0.052* | 0.393 *0.064* | 0.414 *0.059* | 0.542 *0.061* | 0.451 *0.065* | 0.330 *0.051* | 1.563 *0.112* | 0.499 |
| Aywick, Yell | | | | | 0.429 *0.072* | 0.451 *0.067* | 0.397 *0.062* | 0.408 *0.067* | 0.141 *0.037* | 1.528 *0.122* | 0.424 |
| Fetlar I | | | | | | 0.127 *0.036* | 0.328 *0.054* | 0.327 *0.061* | 0.605 *0.077* | 1.452 *0.121* | 0.436 |
| Fetlar II | | | | | | | 0.414 *0.059* | 0.424 *0.063* | 0.331 *0.051* | 1.428 *0.107* | 0.459 |
| Fetlar III | | | | | | | | 0.451 *0.065* | 0.324 *0.045* | 1.423 *0.096* | 0.495 |
| Unst | | | | | | | | | 0.194 *0.041* | 1.683 *0.123* | 0.512 |
| Foula I | | | | | | | | | | 0.294 *0.047* | 0.301 |
| Foula II | | | | | | | | | | | 1.350 |

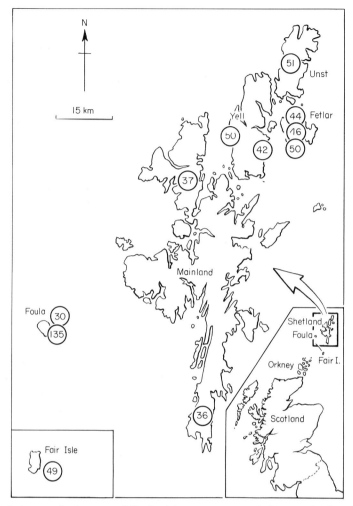

Figure 4. Estimates of uniqueness of Shetland house mouse population samples, based on non-metrical skeletal traits (from Table 6).

In a formal sense, every sample is unique even when the same island has been visited in different years, and there are many significant differences in the frequencies of individual variants. These results are similar to many others in a wide variety of organisms. Indeed, uniformity appears to be present only when the techniques used to score inherited variation are insensitive or the observations too few. Lewontin (1974) has argued that at least 100 loci are required to obtain meaningful measures of comparison with studies of allozymic variation; in the context of the study reported here, it is worth recording that 10 loci would seem to be a reasonable guess for the genetic determinants of each non-metrical trait, and thus a survey involving 26 such uncorrelated traits will probe variation over a substantial part of the genome.

The most interesting conclusions can be drawn from considering the measures of uniqueness. Most of the islands have mouse populations similarly distinct from each other. There are two main exceptions to this:

(1) In Orkney, populations on the smaller islands (Egilsay, Wyre, Graemsay and possibly Papa Westray) have much higher 'uniquenesses' than on the larger islands. There is no reason to suspect that sampling on the smaller islands is biased, so this effect could be *a priori* attributable to either 'small island' adaptation, or some random effect. However, the small island populations do not show any convergence with each other (Table 5), and it seems more realistic to assume that their distinctiveness is related to the size of the effective founding gene-pool: although any area where cereal growing has been practised for a long period will have had multiple immigrations of mice, the *effective* founders will be those which were established early enough to colonize the whole available area; later immigrants will contribute only marginally to a well-established population. The difference between a large and a small island will thus lie in the likelihood of a number of separate founding propagules being able to establish themselves in different areas in the former, with subsequent mixing and greater uniformity arising from the greater number of founders. In all cases, the populations will be based necessarily on the chromosomes (i.e. both alleles and associations) initially introduced. It must not be forgotten that a 'founder effect' influences all loci, and therefore is a much more radical force than either natural selection (which may be powerful, but affects only a finite number of genes) or conventional drift (which is a relatively weak force).

It is surprising that there is no 'small island' effect in Shetland. However, Shetland is very much less fertile and less suitable for agriculture (and mice) than Orkney (Berry, 1985a), and thus all the populations may be regarded as coming from 'small islands'. The lack of difference between large and small island populations may be the result of a general lower amount of variability in Shetland than Orkney (Berry & Peters, 1977), and a consequent reduction in the change due to founder effect.

(2) The two Foula samples differ enormously (Table 6; Fig. 4). The only viable explanation for this is that it represents a 'founder effect within a founder'. As already noted, the first Foula sample was live-trapped from sites all over the island; the second (anomalous) sample came from ricks on a single croft. Presumably it was derived from a few animals atypical of the island gene-pool (which is effectively a definition of a founder effect). The only other explanation for the difference between the two samples is that the second was derived from a recent group of immigrants. This is possible, but unlikely: Foula is 30 km from the main island of Shetland, and is served almost entirely by small boats, with little import of cargoes which might contain mice (Gear, 1983).

Assuming that the differentiation of the second Foula sample truly represents a 'founder within a founder' event, it is another example of the serial differentiation of populations described by Berry (1969) in Hebridean *Apodemus sylvaticus*, by Berry *et al.* (1978) in Faroe house mice (see above, p. 209), and by Carson (1983) in Hawaiian *Drosophila*. Such events can lead to 'instant subspeciation' (Berry, 1967), particularly if colour and/or body proportion genes are involved. Corbet (1963) described a single conifer plantation in the Scottish Highlands containing a population of *Clethrionomys glareolus* differing from its nearest neighbour (isolated by only 150 m of rough land) in the frequency of complex upper third molars (92% in the aberrant population; 29% in the neighbouring plantation and other parts of the Highlands). This character has

been used to distinguish island races of the species (Steven, 1953). Fifteen years
later bracken had grown up in the area between the two plantations allowing
voles to move about more and the atypical population had reverted to the
normal Highland situation (Corbet, 1975). House mouse populations isolated
for around 6 months in corn-ricks on a single 800 ha farm which had no obvious
cause for their differentiation (Berry, 1963), proved to be completely typical of
the southern British pattern when pooled together (Berry & Berry, 1972); once
again, differentiation arose through the simple process of isolation, with no time
for genetical changes to take place after the isolation event.

It is perhaps surprising that there is still controversy about the operation (as
distinct from the long-term importance) of the founder effect. Probably the
reason is that it reflects the long-running arguments about adaptive and random
changes in evolution, which have historically been polarized around the
respective views of R. A. Fisher and Sewall Wright (Provine, 1985). The irony
is that all the modern proponents of founder effects have emphasized the
importance of selection as well as the stochastic uncertainties of the actual
founding event (e.g. Mayr, 1954; Carson, 1971; Halkka, Raatikainen & Halkka,
1974; Berry 1983a). And as for the long-term importance of the genetic
experiments produced by the founder effects, Mayr (1963) summarized the
situation admirably:

> "Do peripheral isolates frequently (or usually) produce new species and
> evolutionary novelties? NO.
> Are new species and evolutionary novelties usually produced by peripheral
> isolates? YES—since peripheral isolates are produced fifty to five hundred
> times as frequently as a new species. Hence most peripheral isolates do *not*
> evolve into a new species, but *when* a new species evolves, it is almost
> invariably from a peripheral isolate."

### FOUNDERS, ISLANDS AND CONSERVATION

Island biogeography theory has been used to devise positive rules for
conservation practice (Diamond & May, 1976). Most of the concern has been
with the chances of species extinction, but it has been increasingly realized that
management practices may produce genetical consequences (Berry, 1971). At
first, the response of conservationists was simply to seek to preserve particular
variants or gene-pools (Rowlands, 1964), but this was soon recognized to be
only part of the problem, and that gene flow reduction and the existence of
finite populations in nature could lead to non-adaptive changes, loss of genetic
variance, and hence an increased risk of extinction. Clearly, the study of the
genetics of island populations is relevant to understanding the possible genetic
problems of conservation management (Schonewald-Cox, Chambers, MacBryde
& Thomas, 1983).

In my original discussions of the genetical consequences of conservation, I
argued that it was improper to apply uncritically simple inbreeding theory to
small populations, because there is a strong conservative effect due to gene
action and interaction, which acts to retard random genetical changes and allele
loss. I reviewed genetical work on finite (and small) populations and concluded

"the amount of variation (at least in normally outbred, diploid species) is extremely large and resistant to loss. Even in a population subjected to rigorous and long-continued directional selection, considerable variation remains unused . . . . It is extremely unlikely that any natural management procedures could significantly affect the amount of variation in a local population to the extent of making that population unable to respond to environmental change" (Berry, 1971, 1974).

Frankel & Soulé (1981) have accused me of unwarranted 'phyletic optimism'; in other words, for concluding that the genetical results of conservation may not necessarily be badly damaging; they believe that "nothing but the incisive action by *this* generation can save a large proportion of now-living species from extinction within the next few decades". They argue at length about the long-term survival hazards resulting from an erosion of genetical variance. They define conservation genetics as 'the genetics of scarcity', where the scarcity is that of population numbers:

"Whether our concern is the wild relatives of cultivated plants or wild animals, the conservationist is faced with the ultimate sampling problem—how to preserve genetic variability and evolutionary flexibility in the face of diminishing space with very limited economic resources. Inevitably we are concerned with the genetics and evolution of small populations, and with establishing practical guidelines for the practising conservation biologist."

Now it is obviously sensible to base any such guidelines on valid genetical criteria, but Frankel and Soulé adopt an extreme 'beanbag' genetics point of view (Haldane, 1964), and ignore both the consensus arising from the neutralist controversies of the 1970s which has involved a radical reappraisal of the older deterministic models of population genetics (Berry, 1982), and the effects of what may be termed 'genetic architecture' in retarding allele loss in small populations. They are, of course, aware of the problem. They quote Mayr (1970): "It is a limited number of highly successful epigenetic systems and homeostatic devices which is responsible for the severe restraints on genetic and phenotypic change displayed by every species", but they do not pursue the point. Their argument about genetic erosion is based entirely on the two 'beanbag' conclusions that the input of new variation by immigration will be negligible ("Gene flow is in most cases irrelevant when dealing with the capacity of an endangered species to respond to novel selection pressures. The reason is that endangered species are usually isolated remnants of hitherto widely distributed forms. Isolates, by definition, receive no immigration.") and that genetic drift will result in a significant loss of variation ("The conservation biologist is perforce operating with relatively small populations; he courts disaster when pretending that such populations have the same evolutionary plasticity and potential as do larger ones.").

The power of genetical architecture to protect variation cannot be measured at the present moment, but it is undeniably strong. There is abundant evidence from laboratory populations that inherited variants persist to a theoretically surprising extent under either intense selection or close inbreeding, and natural populations which have been through a bottleneck in numbers do not seem to be adversely affected (Nei, Maruyama & Chakraborty, 1975). Palaeontological observations on 'punctuated equilibria' are also pertinent: many species remain apparently unchanged for millions of years, showing the operation of strong conservative forces (Jones, 1981). There is little doubt that the next major advance in evolutionary biology will be an understanding of genetic architecture; such a better understanding should not be omitted from conservation genetics. Frankel and Soulé seem to have fallen into the error of assuming that things that cannot be currently measured must be unimportant.

The only certain principle in conservation genetics is to use every available stratagem to protect variation. Frankel and Soulé extend this to assert "the basic rule . . . [is] there is no safe amount of inbreeding for normally outbred organisms". They apply this by taking an assumption of animal breeders that natural selection for performance and fertility can balance inbreeding depression if the rate of fitness loss per generation is no more than 1%, which will result (using a formula due to Sewall Wright) if the effective breeding size of the population is less than 50. They then argue that genetic drift may be important up to a population size of around 500 (which assumes, wrongly, that natural selection is negligible), and conclude that "a genetically effective size of 500 is a satisfactory first approximation of the minimum size for the accommodation of continuing evolution". This conclusion certainly errs on the safe side, but that is the correct side on which to err.

The fine dynamic equilibrium between environmental change and genetical adaptation is not the whole of the story; a balanced assessment of the importance and value of genetics in conservation must include both 'beanbag' results and conservatism coming from genetical architecture. Further island studies will clearly be of potential benefit for practical conservation.

THE GENETICAL MOULDING OF ISLAND POPULATIONS

We can recognize four factors which contribute to the differentiation of island populations:

(1) The first factor must be isolation involving a virtual absence of immigration, coupled with a bottleneck in numbers that accompanies colonization events. It appears from Table 1 that island rodent populations tend to have about half the heterozygosity of mainland populations. However, Nei *et al.* (1975) have shown that the reduction in average heterozygosity in a population depends not only on the size of the founding group, but also on the rate of subsequent population growth; if population size increases rapidly after going through a bottleneck, the heterozygosity loss is not great, even if the bottleneck is rather small. Mayr (1954) argued that the simple fact of isolation can produce a 'genetic revolution', since "the mere change of the genetic environment may change the selective value of a gene very considerably. Isolating a few individuals (the 'founder') from a variable population which is situated in the midst of the stream of genes which flows ceaselessly through every widespread species will produce a sudden change of the genetic environment of most loci". Unfortunately we do not know enough about the effects of allele substitution to test this idea. Such evidence as we have indicates that isolated populations retain their historical characteristics rather than manifest large

amounts of post-isolation change (see above; also Larson, Wake & Yanev, 1984).

(2) Notwithstanding, a genome exposed to a new environment is likely to face new selective pressures. Chapman (1928) has compared population pressures with Ohm's Law since "it seems evident that we have in nature a system in which the potential rate of reproduction of the animal is pitted against the resistance of the environment, and that the quantity of organisms which may be found is a result of the balance between the biotic potential, or the potential rate of reproduction, and the environmental resistance". The 'environmental resistance' experienced by a form will almost certainly change following isolation. For example, the species composition of island biotas is likely to differ from that from which a colonizing form came (although not, of course, when a previously continuous habitat is divided), and a change in biological environment may well affect selection pressures (Berry, 1985b). A specific case of this was the extinction of house mice on the Hebridean island of St Kilda following the evacuation of the human population (Berry & Tricker, 1969); the island field mouse (*Apodemus sylvaticus hirtensis*) population underwent a marked genetical change, despite having been genetically unchanged for years previously (Berry, 1970). The complexity of interactions between small mammal species has been elegantly demonstrated by Dueser & Porter (1986), and their genetic consequences explored by Garten (Garten, 1976; Smith, Garten & Ramsey, 1975).

(3) Natural selection is an opportunistic, not a perfecting agency. This is often forgotten in considering the effects of adaptation. In time spans of the length measured by geologists, related populations may genetically converge towards each other in similar environments, but in 'ecological time' populations can only respond to selection according to the variation available for selection. The founder effect may be compared in some ways to the production of 'hopeful monsters'. It can produce extremely different gene frequencies and because of the complexities of gene action and interaction, those frequencies may well remain highly heterogeneous after 'founder selection' has taken place. For example, the house mouse *Hbb* locus responds rapidly and precisely to selection (Berry & Murphy, 1970; Myers, 1974; Garnett & Falconer, 1975), but *Hbb* allele frequencies vary greatly in different populations, including the fixation of alternative alleles (Berry, 1981). Population differentiation is not necessarily a sign of different selection pressures (Kohn & Tamarin, 1978).

(4) Finally, population history must not be ignored (Berry, 1978). Part of any relevant history will include genetic 'bottlenecks', but other parts will involve the colonization sequence and past species interactions. For example, pygmy shrews (*Sorex pygmaeus*) occur on many of the outlying British islands, but their larger relative, the common shrew (*S. araneus*) is less widespread; the yellow-necked mouse (*Apodemus flavicollis*) is extremely restricted in its distribution in Britain despite co-existing with its conspecific *A. sylvaticus* over large areas of continental Europe. Yalden (1982) has reviewed the history of the British mammal fauna, and drawn attention to many anomalies of distribution (cf. Berry, 1979c, 1983b). It is clear that the existing distribution (and differentiation) of many species is far from that predicted on any naive expectation of either biogeographical or genetical equilibrium (Rothschild & Clay, 1952; Connell, 1978, 1979; Berry, 1985b).

Williamson (1981) has calculated that on average only one colonization every 25 000 years leads to speciation in Hawaiian *Drosophila*. Barton & Charlesworth (1984) believe that founder effects have been unimportant in speciation, but they admit to relying on criticism of models as distinct from empirical data. One of the characteristics of island mammal populations is their heterogeneity and probable lack of long-term static equilibrium. A full assessment of the evolutionary importance of island faunas is likely to be reliable only if it comes from an accumulation of detailed species studies. The review presented here is a limited one, and I have mainly used a restricted set of examples. However, it is worth remembering that our interpretation of island faunas has undergone two radical revisions in comparatively recent time: a recognition of the distinction between introduced and relict faunas, and a breaking-down of the thrall of theoretical population genetics when electrophoresis studies showed that expectations about evolutionary rates and amounts of genetic diversity were wildly awry. The main danger we run into when investigating island populations is dogmatism. Island populations have an enormous potential for exploring the interface of genetics, ecology and physiology. It is best to concentrate here, and not lose our way by attempting over-generalization.

ements

The mouse skeletons from Orkney and Shetland were prepared and classified by Mrs Ann Mitchell. Her labours are gratefully acknowledged. The field work described in this paper was largely supported by the Medical Research Council.

## REFERENCES

AQUADRO, C. F., 1978. *Evolutionary genetics of insular* Peromyscus: *electrophoretic, morphological and chromosomal variation.* M.Sc. thesis, University of Vermont, Burlington.
AVISE, J. C., SMITH, M. H., SELANDER, R. K., LAWLOR, T. E. & RAMSAY, P. R., 1974a. Biochemical polymorphism and systematics in the genus *Peromyscus*. V. Insular and mainland species of the subgenus *Haplomylomys*. *Systematic Zoology, 23:* 226–238.
AVISE, J. C., SMITH, M. H. & SELANDER, R. K., 1974b. Biochemical polymorphism and systematics in the genus *Peromyscus*. VI. The *boylii* species group. *Journal of Mammalogy, 55:* 751–763.
AVISE, J. C., SMITH, M. H. & SELANDER, R. K., 1979. Biochemical polymorphism and systematics in the genus *Peromyscus*. VII. Geographic differentiation in members of the *truei* and *maniculatus* species groups. *Journal of Mammalogy, 60:* 177–192.
BARNETT, S. A. & DICKSON, R. G., 1984. Changes among wild House mice (*Mus musculus*) bred for ten generations in a cold environment, and their evolutionary implications. *Journal of Zoology, 203:* 163–180.
BARTON, N. H. & CHARLESWORTH, B., 1984. Genetic revolutions, founder effects and speciation. *Annual Review of Ecology and Systematics, 15:* 133–164.
BATTEN, C. A. & BERRY, R. J., 1967. Prenatal mortality in wild-caught house mice. *Journal of Animal Ecology, 36:* 453–463.
BEIRNE, B. P., 1952. *The Origin and History of the British Fauna.* London: Methuen.
BENGSTON, S.-A. & ENCKELL, P. H. (Eds), 1983. Island ecology. *Oikos, 41:* 293–547.
BERRY, A. C. & BERRY, R. J., 1972. Origins and relationships of the ancient Egyptians. *Journal of Human Evolution, 1:* 199–208.
BERRY, R. J., 1963. Epigenetic polymorphism in wild populations of *Mus musculus*. *Genetical Research, 4:* 193–220.
BERRY, R. J., 1964. The evolution of an island population of the house mouse. *Evolution, 18:* 468–483.
BERRY, R. J., 1967. Genetical changes in mice and men. *Eugenics Review, 59:* 78–96.
BERRY, R. J., 1968. The biology of non-metrical variation in mice and men. In D. R. Brothwell (Ed.), *The Skeletal Biology of Earlier Human Populations:* 103–133. London: Pergamon.
BERRY, R. J., 1969. History in the evolution of *Apodemus sylvaticus* (Mammalia) at one edge of its range. *Journal of Zoology, London 159:* 311–328.
BERRY, R. J., 1970. Covert and overt variation, as exemplified by British mouse populations. *Symposia of the Zoological Society of London, 26:* 3–26.

BERRY, R. J., 1971. Conservation aspects of the genetical constitution of populations. In E. Duffey & A. S. Watt (Eds), *The Scientific Management of Animal and Plant Communities for Conservation:* 177–206. Oxford: Blackwell.

BERRY, R. J., 1973. Chance and change in British Long-tailed Field Mice. *Journal of Zoology, London, 170:* 351–366.

BERRY, R. J., 1974. Conserving genetical variety. In A. Warren & F. B. Goldsmith (Eds), *Conservation in Practice:* 99–115. London. Wiley.

BERRY, R. J., 1975. On the nature of genetical distance and island races of *Apodemus sylvaticus. Journal of Zoology, London, 176:* 293–296.

BERRY, R. J., 1978. Genetic variation in wild house mice: where natural selection and history meet. *American Scientist, 66:* 52–60.

BERRY, R. J., 1979a. Genes and skeletons, ancient and modern. *Journal of Human Evolution, 8:* 669–677.

BERRY, R. J., 1979b. Genetical factors in animal population dynamics. In R. M. Anderson, B. D. Turner & L. R. Taylor (Eds), *Population Dynamics:* 53–80. Oxford: Blackwell.

BERRY, R. J., 1979c. The Outer Hebrides: where genes and geography meet. *Proceedings of the Royal Society of Edinburgh, 77B:* 21–43.

BERRY, R. J., 1981. Population dynamics of the house mouse. *Symposia of the Zoological Society of London, 47:* 395–425.

BERRY, R. J., 1982. *Neo-Darwinism.* London: Edward Arnold.

BERRY, R. J., 1983a. Diversity and differentiation: the importance of island biology for general theory. *Oikos, 41:* 523–529.

BERRY, R. J., 1983b. Evolution of animals and plants in the Inner Hebrides. *Proceedings of the Royal Society of Edinburgh, 83B:* 433–447.

BERRY, R. J., 1985a. *The Natural History of Orkney.* London: Collins New Naturalist.

BERRY, R. J., 1985b. The processes of pattern: genetical possibilities and constraints in coevolution. *Oikos, 44:* 222–228.

BERRY, R. J., BONNER, W. N. & PETERS, J., 1979. Natural selection in mice from South Georgia (South Atlantic Ocean). *Journal of Zoology, London, 189:* 385–398.

BERRY, R. J., CUTHBERT, A. & PETERS, J., 1982. Colonization by house mice: an experiment. *Journal of Zoology, London, 198:* 329–336.

BERRY, R. J., EVANS, I. M. & SENNITT, B. F. C., 1967. The relationships and ecology of *Apodemus sylvaticus* from the Small Isles of the Inner Hebrides, Scotland. *Journal of Zoology, London, 152:* 333–346.

BERRY, R. J. & JAKOBSON, M. E., 1975a. Ecological genetics of an island population of the house mouse. *Journal of Zoology, London, 175:* 523–540.

BERRY, R. J. & JAKOBSON, M. E., 1975b. Adaptation and adaptability in wild-living house mice. *Journal of Zoology, London, 176:* 391–402.

BERRY, R. J., JAKOBSON, M. E. & PETERS, J., 1978. The house mice of the Faroe Islands: a study in microdifferentiation. *Journal of Zoology, London, 185:* 73–92.

BERRY, R. J. & MURPHY, H. M., 1970. Biochemical genetics of an island population of the house mouse. *Proceedings of the Royal Society of London, Series B, 176:* 87–103.

BERRY, R. J. & PETERS, J., 1977. Heterogeneous heterozygosities in *Mus musculus* populations. *Proceedings of the Royal Society of London, Series B, 197:* 485–503.

BERRY, R. J., PETERS, J. & VAN AARDE, R. J., 1978. Sub-Antarctic house mice: colonization, survival and selection. *Journal of Zoology, London, 184:* 127–141.

BERRY, R. J. & ROSE, F. E. N., 1975. Islands and the evolution of *Microtus arvalis* (Microtinae). *Journal of Zoology, London, 177:* 395–409.

BERRY, R. J. & TRICKER, B. J. K., 1969. Competition and extinction: the mice of Foula, with notes on those of Fair Isle and St Kilda. *Journal of Zoology, London, 158:* 247–265.

BROWNE, R. A., 1977. Genetic variation in island and mainland populations of *Peromyscus leucopus. American Midland Naturalist, 97:* 1–9.

CARLQUIST, S., 1974. *Island Biology.* New York and London: Columbia University Press.

CARSON, H. L., 1968. The population flush and its genetic consequences. In R. C. Lewontin (Ed.), *Population Biology and Evolution.* Syracuse: New York University Press.

CARSON, H. L., 1983. Chromosomal sequences and interisland colonizations in Hawaiian *Drosophila. Genetics, 103:* 465–482.

CHAPMAN, R. N., 1928. The quantitative analysis of environmental factors. *Ecology, 9:* 111–122.

CONNELL, J. H., 1978. Diversity in tropical rain forests and coral reefs. *Science, 199:* 1302–1310.

CONNELL, J. H., 1979. Tropical rain forests and coral reefs as open non-equilibrium systems. In R. M. Anderson, B. Turner & L. R. Taylor (Eds), *Population Dynamics:* 141–163. Oxford: Blackwell.

CORBETT, G. B., 1961. Origin of the British insular races of small mammals and of the 'Lusitanian' fauna. *Nature, 191:* 1037–1040.

CORBET, G. B., 1963. An isolated population of the bank vole (*Clethrionomys glareolus*) with aberrant dental pattern. *Proceedings of the Zoological Society of London, 140:* 316–319.

CORBET, G. B., 1975. Examples of short- and long-term changes of dental pattern in Scottish voles (Rodentia; Microtinae). *Mammal Review, 5:* 17–21.

COTHRAN, E. G., ZIMMERMAN, E. G. & NADLER, C. F., 1977. Genic differentiation and evolution in the ground squirrel subgenus *Ictidomys* (genus *Spermophilus*). *Journal of Mammalogy, 58:* 610–622.

DARLING, F. F., 1947. *Natural History in the Highlands and Islands.* London: Collins New Naturalist.

DARWIN, C. & WALLACE, A. R., 1858. On the tendency of species to form varieties; and on the perpetuation of varieties and species by natural means of selection. *Journal of the Linnean Society (Zoology), 3:* 45–62.

DAVIS, S. J. M., 1983. Morphometric variation of populations of house mouse *Mus domesticus* in Britain and Faroe. *Journal of Zoology, London, 199:* 521–534.

DEGERBØL, M., 1942. *Mammalia. Zoology of the Faroes.* Part 65, 1–133.

DELANY, M. J., 1970. Variation and ecology of island populations of the Long-tailed field-mouse (*Apodemus sylvaticus* [L.]). *Symposia of the Zoological Society of London, 26:* 283–295.

DELANY, M. J. & HEALY, M. J. R., 1964. Variation in the long-tailed field-mouse (*Apodemus sylvaticus* [L.]) in north-west Scotland. II. Simultaneous examination of all characters. *Proceedings of the Royal Society of London, Series B, 161:* 200–207.

DIAMOND, J. M. & MAY, R. M., 1976. Island biogeography and the design of nature reserves. In R. M. May (Ed.), *Theoretical Ecology:* 163–186. Oxford: Blackwell.

DUESER, R. D. & PORTER, J. H., 1986. Habitat use by insular small mammals: relative effects of competition and habitat structure. *Ecology, 67:* 195–201.

FRANKEL, O. H. & SOULÉ, M. E., 1981. *Conservation and Evolution.* Cambridge: Cambridge University Press.

GARNETT, I. & FALCONER, D. S., 1975. Protein variations in strains of mice differing in body size. *Genetical Research, 25:* 45–57.

GARTEN, C. T., 1976. Relationships between aggressive behaviour and genic heterozygosity in the oldfield mouse *Peromyscus polionotus. Evolution, 30:* 59–72.

GEAR, S., 1983. *Foula. Island West of the Sun.* London: Hale.

GILL, A. E., 1977. Maintenance of polymorphism in an island population of the California vole, *Microtus californicus. Evolution, 31:* 512–525.

GREENBAUM, I. F. & BAKER, R. J., 1976. Evolutionary relationships in *Macrotus* (Mammalia: Chiroptera): biochemical variation and karyology. *Systematic Zoology, 25:* 15–25.

GREWAL, M. S., 1962. The rate of genetic divergence in the C57BL strain of mice. *Genetical Research, 3:* 226–237.

GRÜNEBERG, H., 1963. *The Pathology of Development.* Oxford: Blackwell.

HALDANE, J. B. S., 1964. A defense of beanbag genetics. *Perspectives in Biology and Medicine, 7:* 343–360.

HALKKA, O., RAATIKAINEN, M. & HALKKA, L., 1974. The founder principle, founder selection and evolutionary divergence and convergence in natural populations of *Philaenus. Hereditas, 78:* 73–84.

HANDFORD, P. T. & PERNETTA, J. C., 1974. The origin of island races of *Apodemus sylvaticus:* an alternative hypothesis. *Journal of Zoology, London, 174:* 534–537.

HINTON, M. A. C., 1910. A preliminary account of the British voles and lemmings; with some remarks on the Pleistocene climate and geography. *Proceedings of the Geological Association, 21:* 489–507.

HINTON, M. A. C., 1913. Note on the voles of the *orcadensis* group. *Annals and Magazine of Natural History, (8)12:* 452–462.

HOOKER, J. D., 1867. Insular floras. Originally published in the *Gardeners' Chronicle*; reprinted in 1984 with an introduction by M. H. Williamson. *Biological Journal of the Linnean Society, 22:* 55–77.

HOWE, W. L. & PARSONS, P. A., 1967. Genotype and environment in the determination of minor skeletal variant and body weight in mice. *Journal of Embryology and Experimental Morphology, 17:* 283–292.

HOWELLS, R., 1968. *The Sounds Between.* Llandysul: Gomerian.

HUXLEY, J. S., 1942. *Evolution, the Modern Synthesis.* London: Allen and Unwin.

JOHNSON, W. E. & SELANDER, R. K., 1971. Protein variation and systematics in kangaroo rats (genus *Dipodomys*). *Systematic Zoology, 20:* 377–405.

JOHNSON, W. E., SELANDER, R. K., SMITH, M. H. & KIM, Y. J., 1972. Biochemical genetics of sibling species of the cotton rat (*Sigmodon*). University of Texas Publication no. 7213. *Studies in Genetics, 7:* 297–305.

JONES, J. S., 1981. An uncensored page of fossil history. *Nature, 293:* 427–428.

KILPATRICK, C. W., 1981. Genetic structure of insular populations. In M. H. Smith & J. Joule (Eds), *Mammalian Population Genetics:* 28–59. Athens, Georgia: University of Georgia Press.

KILPATRICK, C. W. & CROWELL, K. L., 1985. Genetic variation of the rock vole, *Microtus chrotorrhinus. Journal of Mammalogy, 66:* 94–101.

KILPATRICK, C. W. & ZIMMERMAN, E. G., 1975. Genetic variation and systematics for four species of mice of the *Peromyscus boylii* species group. *Systematic Zoology, 24:* 143–162.

KOHN, P. H. & TAMARIN, R. H., 1978. Selection of electrophoretic loci for reproductive parameters in island and mainland voles. *Evolution, 32:* 15–28.

LARSON, A., WAKE, D. B. & YANEV, K. P., 1984. Measuring gene flow among populations having high levels of genetic fragmentation. *Genetics, 106:* 293–308.

LEWONTIN, R. C., 1974. *The Genetic Basis of Evolutionary Change.* New York and London: Columbia University Press.

LUTHER, P. G., 1949. Enzymatic maceration of skeletons. *Proceedings of the Linnean Society of London, 161:* 146.

MACARTHUR, R. H. & WILSON, E. O., 1967. *The Theory of Island Biogeography.* Princeton: Princeton University Press.

MANLY, B. F. J., 1985. *The Statistics of Natural Selection.* London and New York: Chapman and Hall.

MATTHEWS, L. H., 1952. *British Mammals.* London: Collins New Naturalist.

MAYR, E., 1954. Change of genetic environment and evolution. In J. Huxley, A. C. Hardy & E. B. Ford (Eds), *Evolution as a Process:* 157–180. London: Allen and Unwin.

MAYR, E. 1963. *Animal Species and Evolution.* London: Oxford.

MAYR, E., 1970. *Population, Species and Evolution.* Cambridge, Massachusetts: Harvard University Press.

MYERS, J. H., 1974. Genetic and social structure of feral house mouse populations on Grizzly Island, California. *Ecology, 55:* 747–759.

NASH, H. R., BROOKER, P. C. & DAVIS, S. J. M., 1983. The Robertsonian translocation house-mouse populations of north east Scotland: a study of their origin and evolution. *Heredity, 50:* 303–310.

NEI, M., 1972. Genetic distance between populations. *American Naturalist, 106:* 283–292.

NEI, M., MARUYAMA, T. & CHAKRABORTY, R., 1975. The bottleneck effect and genetic variability in populations. *Evolution, 29:* 1–10.

NEVO, E., 1978. Genetic variation in natural populations: patterns and theory. *Theoretical and Population Biology, 13:* 121–177.

NEWTON, M. F. & PETERS, J., 1983. Physiological variation of mouse haemoglobins. *Proceedings of the Royal Society of London, Series B, 218:* 443–453.

NOZAWA, K., SHOTAKE, T. & OKURA, Y., 1975. Blood protein polymorphisms and population structure of the Japanese macaque, *Macaca fuscata fuscata.* In C. L. Markert (Ed.), *Isozymes,* Vol. 4. *Genetics and Evolution:* 225–241. New York: Academic.

PATTON, J. L., 1984. Genetical processes in the Galapagos. *Biological Journal of the Linnean Society, 21:* 97–111.

PATTON, J. L., YANG, S. Y. & MYERS, P., 1975. Genetic and morphologic divergence among introduced rat populations (*Rattus rattus*) of the Galápagos Archipelago, Ecuador. *Systematic Zoology, 24:* 296–310.

PROVINE, W. B., 1985. The R. A. Fisher–Sewall Wright controversy and its influence upon modern evolutionary biology. *Oxford Surveys in Evolutionary Biology, 2:* 197–219.

ROTHSCHILD, M. & CLAY, T., 1952. *Fleas, Flukes and Cuckoos.* London: Collins New Naturalist.

ROWE, F. P., TAYLOR, E. J. & CHUDLEY, A. H. J., 1963. The numbers and movements of house mice (*Mus musculus*(L.)) in the vicinity of four corn-ricks. *Journal of Animal Ecology, 32:* 87–97.

ROWLANDS, I. W., 1964. Rare breeds of domesticated animals being preserved by the Zoological Society of London. *Nature, 202:* 131–132.

SARICH, V. M., 1977. Rates, sample sizes and the neutrality hypothesis in evolutionary studies. *Nature, 265:* 24–28.

SAWYER, P., 1971. *The Age of the Vikings,* 2nd edition. London: Edward Arnold.

SCHMITT, L. H., 1978. Genetic variation in isolated populations of the Australian bush-rat, *Rattus fuscipes. Evolution, 32:* 1–14.

SCHONEWALD–COX, C. M., CHAMBERS, S. M., MACBRYDE, B. & THOMAS, W. L. (Eds), 1983. *Genetics and Conservation.* Menlo Park, California: Benjamin/Cummings.

SELANDER, R. K., SMITH, M. H., YANG, S. Y., JOHNSON, W. E. & GENTRY, J. B., 1971. Biochemical polymorphism and systematics in the genus *Peromyscus.* I. Variation in the old-field mouse (*Peromyscus polionotus*). University of Texas Publication no. 7103. *Studies in Genetics, 6:* 49–90.

SELANDER, R. K. & YANG, S. Y., 1969. Protein polymorphism and genic heterozygosity in a wild population of the house mouse (*Mus musculus*). *Genetics, 63:* 653–667.

SELF, S. G. & LEAMY, L., 1978. Heritability of quasi-continuous skeletal traits in random-bred populations of house mice. *Genetics, 88:* 109–120.

SJØVOLD, T., 1973. The occurrence of minor non-metrical variants in the skeleton and their quantitative treatment for population comparisons. *Homo, 24:* 204–233.

SJØVOLD, T., 1984. A report on the heritability of some cranial measurements and non-metric traits. In G. N. Van Vark & W. W. Howells (Eds), *Multivariate Statistical Methods in Physical Anthropology:* 223–246. Amsterdam: Reidel.

SMITH, M. H., GARTEN, C. T. & RAMSAY, P. R., 1975. Genic heterozygosity and population dynamics in small mammals. In C. L. Markert (Ed.), *Isozymes,* Vol. 4. *Genetics and Evolution:* 85–102. New York: Academic.

SOUTHERN, H. N. & LAURIE, E. M. O., 1946. The house mouse (*Mus musculus*) in corn ricks. *Journal of Animal Ecology, 15:* 135–149.

SOUTHWICK, C. H., 1958. Population characteristics of house mice living in English corn ricks: density relationships. *Proceedings of the Zoological Society of London, 131:* 163–175.

STEADMAN, R. W. & RAY, C. E., 1982. The relationships of *Megaoryzomys curioi,* an extinct cricetine rodent (Muroidea: Muridae) from the Galapagos Islands, Ecuador. *Smithsonian Contributions in Paleobiology,* no. 51.

STEVEN, D. M., 1953. Recent evolution in the genus *Clethrionomys. Symposia of the Society for Experimental Biology, 7:* 310–319.

TEMPLETON, A. R., 1981. Mechanisms of speciation—a population genetic approach. *Annual Review of Ecology annd Systematics 12:* 23–48.

WADDINGTON, C. H., 1957. *Strategy of the Genes.* London: Allen & Unwin.

WALLACE, A. R., 1880. *Island Life*. London: Macmillan.
WILLIAMSON, M., 1981. *Island Populations*. Oxford: Oxford University Press.
YALDEN, D. W., 1982. When did the mammal fauna of the British Isles arrive? *Mammal Review, 12:* 1–57.

*Biological Journal of the Linnean Society* (1986), *28:* 231–251. With 3 figures

# Two decades of interaction between the MacArthur–Wilson model and the complexities of mammalian distributions

JAMES H. BROWN

*Department of Ecology and Evolutionary Biology, University of Arizona, Tucson, Arizona 85721, U.S.A.*

*Accepted for publication 14 February 1986*

More than two decades after its publication, MacArthur and Wilson's equilibrium model of insular biogeography continues to provide the conceptual foundation for investigating the distribution of species on islands and the composition of insular biotas. During this period, studies of the distributions of mammals among insular habitats have tested, modified, and extended MacArthur and Wilson's simple formalism to enhance greatly our understanding of the complexities of biogeographic patterns and processes. The papers in this symposium summarize many of the past contributions of mammalian biogeographers and introduce important new data and ideas. The diversity of biological characteristics and associated distributional patterns exhibited by mammals has facilitated this endeavour. Some insular mammalian faunas appear to represent approximate equilibria between opposing rates of contemporary colonization and extinction. Other faunas are currently decreasing in diversity because of extinctions, owing either to natural habitat fragmentation that has occurred since the Pleistocene or to human activities within the last few centuries. Still other faunas have been increasing in diversity (at least until recent human impacts) because limiting rates of origination, both colonization and speciation, have been extremely low. The questions and analyses of island biogeography can also be applied to continents with comparable overall results: the distributions of continental faunas reflect the consequences of similar processes of colonization, speciation and extinction. Analyses of insular distributions show unequivocally that probabilities of extinction, colonization and speciation are highly deterministic and vary in predictable ways among different taxa and archipelagos. These findings have important implications for applying the theory and data of insular biogeography to the pressing practical problems of designing natural reserves to preserve native species.

KEY WORDS:—Colonization – conservation – continental biogeography – equilibrium biogeography – extinction – island biogeography – mammals – natural reserves – speciation.

## CONTENTS

0024–4066/86/050231+21 $03.00/0

## INTRODUCTION

With the publication of their elegantly simple and intuitively appealing model, which represented insular species richness as a dynamic equilibrium between opposing rates of colonization and extinction, MacArthur & Wilson (1963, 1967) stimulated a resurgence of interest and research in biogeography. Subsequent developments—including the collection and analysis of data on insular distributions, the testing and modification of the MacArthur–Wilson model, the development of alternative, non-equilibrial hypotheses to account for insular distributions, the extension of insular concepts to continental biogeography, the application of the theory and data of insular biogeography to the design and management of natural reserves, and the investigation of other aspects of the ecology, evolution, and genetics of insular populations—have not only revitalized biogeography, they have made the integrated study of insular biotas one of the most conspicuous and successful research programmes in biology during the last two decades. The papers in this symposium attest both to the great increase in understanding of the biology of insular mammals that has resulted, and to the important contributions that studies of insular mammals have made to recent conceptual developments in biogeography.

In my attempt to evaluate and synthesize these diverse contributions, I shall develop several different but interrelated themes. First, the MacArthur–Wilson model has endured, not necessarily as the correct explanation for the vast majority of insular mammal distributions, but as a heuristic construct. It has provided the conceptual and methodological basis for evaluating the differential contributions of colonization, extinction and speciation to the composition of isolated biotas, and for understanding how these processes operate in different kinds of organisms with distinctive biologies and in different kinds of insular habitats with distinctive histories and environments. Secondly, mammals exhibit a wide variety of patterns of insular distribution. These reflect differences among mammalian taxa in dispersal ability, population structure and dynamics, and resource requirements and other niche dimensions, and differences among islands in history, size, habitat and barriers to dispersal. Thirdly, the diversity of these insular patterns does not imply that they are disordered. Although there is often some unexplained, apparently stochastic variation, many of the patterns are highly deterministic, suggesting that they are the consequences of biogeographic processes that operate in regular, predictable ways. Fourthly, mammalian biogeographers have taken advantage of the diversity of insular patterns to develop increasingly complete and rigorous interpretations of how the biological attributes of different mammalian taxa and the histories and environments of different archipelagos have influenced the composition of insular faunas through the processes of colonization, extinction and speciation. Some of these faunas represent an approximate balance between opposing rates of origination and extinction, whereas others are far from equilibrium. Fifthly, I incorporate some recent analyses by Flessa (1975, 1981) and my student, Renee Rusler (unpubl. obs.), to suggest that the concepts and data used by insular biogeographers can also be applied to the distributions of mammals among continents. Results of these analyses suggest that the spectacular large mammalian herbivores and carnivores are particularly susceptible to extinction because they require very large areas of appropriate habitat. Sixthly, the data and theories of insular mammal distributions are sufficiently precise to permit reasonably accurate predictions of the fates of island populations and faunas under alternative scenarios of natural and human-caused environmental change. It should now be possible to assess realistically the prospects for survival of many rare and endangered species and to apply sound scientific principles in the design and management of nature preserves. I shall end by considering some of the current problems and future prospects of contemporary mammalian biogeography.

## THE MACARTHUR–WILSON MODEL

It is hard to find a paper on insular biogeography, in this symposium or elsewhere in the current literature, that does not cite the equilibrium model of MacArthur & Wilson (1963, 1967; hereafter abbreviated M–W). The idea that the number of species inhabiting an island represents a dynamic equilibrium between opposing rates of colonization and extinction remains the starting point of most investigations, which usually begin by testing the predictions of the familiar, elegantly simple graphical model showing effects of island size and isolation by distance on rates of extinction and colonization, respectively. The enduring value of the M–W model is not so much that it is right, as that it provides a robust conceptual framework for understanding the patterns of insular distribution and the ecological and evolutionary processes that have produced them.

In fact, I suspect that the model has ultimately proven more valuable when its predictions have been refuted than when they have been supported. Certainly this is true in the case of my own work. It was in trying to figure out why mammals and birds on mountaintops (Brown, 1971, 1978), fishes in lakes (Barbour & Brown, 1974), and arthropods on thistle plants (Brown & Kodric-Brown, 1977) were not distributed as the model predicted that we really began to understand the processes that determined the composition of these insular biotas. These cases are hardly unique. In the last two decades we have gone far beyond MacArthur and Wilson's simple idea to document and explain many of the complexities of insular distributions.

It is an interesting commentary on the role of theory in contemporary biology that so much of this progress can be attributed directly to falsification of the M–W model. That MacArthur and Wilson recognized this role of their theory is eloquently expressed in Crowell's recollection of MacArthur saying that a model is a lie which helps you to see the truth. This point seems to have been lost on the vociferous critics of the M–W model, most notably Sauer (1969) and Gilbert (1980), who have argued that the model is so oversimplified as to be of little value in understanding the real complexities of the distributions of particular kinds of organisms on different archipelagos.

Elsewhere (Brown, 1980; Brown & Gibson, 1983), I have discussed some of the features of the M–W model that have enabled it to remain a conceptual cornerstone of insular biogeography for more than two decades, serving, as Crowell says, as a null hypothesis against which to evaluate the real world. It is worth re-emphasizing these attributes, because many are so well exemplified in the contributions to this symposium. They include the following:

(1) MacArthur and Wilson shifted the emphasis of biogeographic investigation from attempts to reconstruct the histories of particular taxa to an

effort to understand the general processes that determine the diversity and composition of biotas. Under this new perspective, similarities and differences in the distributional patterns of different taxa became the basis for studies (such as Lawlor, 1986) that have used a comparative approach to identify the underlying mechanisms.

(2) The seminal insight—that there is a theoretical equilibrium between opposing origination and extinction processes—provided the basis for a wide variety of analyses and interpretations. Results of these studies revealed that some biotas represent an approximate equilibrium between opposing rates of contemporary colonization and extinction, as the model predicts (Crowell, 1986; Hanski, 1986; Lomolino, 1986). Other biotas, however, can be viewed as still changing in response to historical perturbations, either increasing in diversity owing to very low rates of colonization (Lawlor, 1986) and speciation (Heaney, 1986), or decreasing in richness owing to extinctions (Lawlor, 1986; Morgan & Woods, 1986; Patterson & Atmar 1986).

(3) The model employs variables that are relatively easy to measure. Many of these variables, such as number of species in the taxon of interest, island area, and distance of the island from the nearest mainland, can often be obtained from the literature. Others, such as colonization and extinction rates, require much more effort, but can be measured by long-term monitoring (Crowell, 1986; Hanski, 1986; Lomolino, 1986), perturbation experiments (Crowell, 1986), and careful collection and interpretation of fossils (Morgan & Woods, 1986).

(4) The model makes robust, qualitative predictions about how species richness and turnover rate should vary with island size and isolation. These predictions can be tested rigorously with quantitative data, and they have frequently been falsified unequivocally. Now investigators are not only testing the critical predictions about turnover rates (Crowell, 1986; Hanski, 1986; Lomolino, 1986), they are also extending the theory to make and test new predictions (Lomolino, 1986; Lawlor, 1986).

(5) The basic framework of the model has provided a valuable point of departure for investigating other important issues of biogeography. Examples in the present symposium include the degree of determinism in extinction and colonization rates (Patterson & Atmar, 1986; Hanski, 1986; Lomolino, 1986), the effects of interactions among species (Crowell, 1986; Hanski, 1986), the interpretation of faunal composition and endemism in archipelagos with complex histories (Heaney, 1986; Morgan & Woods, 1986), and the effectiveness of parks in preserving endangered native biotas (Newmark, 1986).

Like Darwin, Wallace, Mayr, Darlington, and Lack before them, MacArthur and Wilson recognized the potential of islands as replicated natural experiments for studying evolution, ecology and biogeography. Their unique and lasting contribution, however, was to show the kinds of patterns that could be documented and the kinds of processes that could be modelled to make biogeography the vigorous, modern, quantitative, hypothesis-testing science that it has become.

## PATTERNS OF MAMMALS ON ISLANDS

Biogeography will always remain a discipline comprised largely of taxonomic specialists. There are several reasons for this. The basic data on distributions and phylogenetic affinities of taxa have traditionally been obtained by systematists and described in their literature. A sound knowledge of the phylogenetic affinities of insular forms is essential to frame realistic hypotheses about their geographic origins, pathways of colonization and patterns of evolutionary differentiation. A thorough knowledge of their biology is just as essential for understanding how historical events and ecological interactions have influenced their distribution.

Given the necessity of becoming a taxonomic specialist, mammals are an ideal group for a biogeographer to choose. No other taxon of comparable size has its basic biology so well known, exhibits such a wide variety of morphologies, physiologies and behaviours, and exemplifies such a diversity of distributional patterns and processes. As the papers in this symposium show, mammals provide excellent systems for investigating all kinds of biogeographic problems, from those attempting to reconstruct the history of colonization and speciation (Heaney, 1986) to those trying to understand the ecological dynamics of insular populations (Crowell, 1986; Hanski, 1986; Lomolino, 1986). That the diversity of mammalian form, function and distribution is expressed within the constraints imposed by a common evolutionary history and similar body plan, greatly facilitates comparative studies, such as Lawlor's (1986) tests of alternative hypotheses using comparisons of bats and small terrestrial mammals.

A survey of the papers in this symposium and in the recent literature illustrates the amazing diversity of insular distribution patterns exhibited by mammals. Colonizing abilities differ greatly among the taxa. As might be expected from their capacity for flight, bats are the most widely dispersed insular mammals. They have managed to reach such distant outposts as New Zealand and Hawaii and are well represented on larger, less isolated archipelagos such as the Philippines and West Indies (Darlington, 1957; Koopman, 1968, 1975; Lawlor, 1986; Heaney, 1986; Morgan & Woods, 1986). Other patterns of colonization are not so straightforward. Small mammals, especially rodents and insectivores, are reasonably good colonists, presumably in part because their habits facilitate rafting and other kinds of migration, and in part because there are so many individuals and species that begin to disperse that, just by chance, some manage to make long-distance journeys. Both taxa have managed to cross substantial water gaps, so that rodents inhabit the Galapagos, New Guinea and Australia and both taxa are found on Celebes, Madagascar and the West Indies (Darlington, 1957). But even these small mammals can surprise us. On the one hand, they readily cross 1 km or so of water, especially if they do not hibernate and can cross on ice in winter (Crowell, 1986; Hanski, 1986; Lomolino, 1986; see also Lomolino, 1982, 1984a, b). On the other hand larger water gaps and a few kilometres of unsuitable terrestrial habitat constitute such severe barriers that successful dispersal is extremely infrequent (Brown, 1971, 1978; Patterson, 1980; Lawlor, 1986; Heaney, 1986; Morgan & Woods, 1986). Many larger mammals, such as carnivores and ungulates, can disperse substantial distances by swimming or by travelling over ice or inhospitable land (Crowell, 1986).

Patterns of extinction are becoming increasingly well documented. The occurrence of extinctions no longer must be inferred from indirect distributional evidence, as it usually was in the past. Now, extinctions are increasingly well documented by direct observations of faunal turnover (Crowell, 1986; Hanski,

1986; Lomolino, 1986) and by the discovery of fossils (Morgan & Woods, 1986; see also Grayson, 1981; Thompson & Meade, 1982). Since extinction is typically regarded as a highly stochastic process, it is surprising how deterministic the extinctions of species on archipelagos have been. This is particularly apparent in the faunas of landbridge islands, which have been reduced by extinctions from once diverse continental biotas. The predictability of extinctions is evidenced by the tendencies of most species to be found only on islands above some threshold size (Lomolino, 1986), by the fact that certain insular faunas constitute highly non-random nested subsets of species (Patterson & Atmar, 1986; see also Diamond & May, 1976; Brown & Gibson, 1983), and by the infrequent occurrence of species that would have low population sizes because of attributes of large body size, carnivorous diet, or specialized habitat requirements (Heaney, 1986; see also Brown, 1971, 1978; Patterson, 1984; Heaney, 1984). These patterns of extinction have important implications for conservation and the design of natural reserves (Newmark, 1986), especially as it becomes apparent that some of them are true for spatial scales up to entire continents (see p. 240).

Because mammals, aside from bats, are such poor long-distance dispersers, the relatively few populations that have managed to reach distant islands and to persist there have been isolated from genetic exchange with related populations on other land masses or habitat patches. Such isolation, depending on the time and selective pressures involved, has led to genetic differentiation of insular races, species, and higher taxa. At its most extreme, insular differentiation has resulted in extensive adaptive radiation by the descendants of a single propagule. Mammals require lots of space, however, and such radiations have occurred only on large islands and archipelagos. The best known examples are the spectacular radiations that occurred on continent-sized islands: marsupials on Australia, several groups of both marsupials and placentals on South America (before its connection to North America; see Simpson, 1980), and lemurs on Madagascar. Less well known radiations of solenodontid insectivores in the West Indies (MacFadden, 1980) and of murid rodents in the islands of the Sunda Shelf (Heaney, 1986; see also Musser, 1977; Musser, Heaney & Rabor, 1985) are of particular interest because they involved repeated episodes of inter-island colonization followed by differentiation.

Despite several centuries of collecting and systematic work, the various levels of insular endemism remain incompletely documented and understood. Excellent case studies of patterns of differentiation and endemism within archipelagos (e.g. Lawlor's work in the Gulf of California, and Heaney's and Musser's studies in the Malaysian region) show the importance of basing biogeographic inferences on a sound knowledge of geological and climatic history, but accurate reconstructions of past land forms and climates are still undergoing extensive revision for most regions of the world. Endemic taxa are so numerous and diverse that there has as yet been no major effort to sort through the mass of data in search of general patterns. The kind of comparative approach that Lawlor (1986) has applied to species–area relationships seems to offer considerable promise for the analysis of endemism.

Trends in insular evolution, such as flightlessness, tameness, gigantism and dwarfism have long fascinated island biogeographers. Mammals have contributed most of the data for discussions of insular trends in the evolution of body size. The general pattern seems to be a 'central tendency': that is, small forms (especially rodents and insectivores) typically evolve giant forms on islands, whereas large mammals (carnivores and ungulates) usually evolve dwarfed races. Although it has not been a major topic of this symposium, the basis of these trends has been the subject of much discussion, most recently by Lomolino (1985, and references therein). Loss of flight and degeneration of wings is such a pervasive pattern in the evolution of many groups of insular birds and insects, that I wonder why there have apparently been no flightless bats and why this non-phenomenon has not received more discussion.

No discussion of insular evolution would be complete without an analysis of patterns of genetic differentiation. Most of the recent research on genetics of insular mammalian populations (and of continental ones) has focused on isozymic and karyotypic evolution (Berry, 1986). Epigenetic morphological traits may offer a valuable alternative to direct genic and chromosomal markers for assessing the roles of founder events, immigration, genetic drift, inbreeding and selection in the evolution of insular populations (Hanski, 1986; Berry, 1986). A particular benefit of morphological markers is that they can be assayed on museum specimens and even on fossils, providing invaluable information on the evolutionary history of insular populations, including those that are extinct or so endangered that additional collecting is impossible. The relationship between variation in these kinds of easily scored markers (whether they are genic, chromosomal or epigenetic) and those kinds of genetic changes that cause major, functionally significant modifications of the phenotype remains one of the most challenging problems of population biology. The kinds of advances discussed by Berry (1986) suggest that islands may prove to be excellent systems to investigate these genetic mechanisms, just as they have for studying other features of the evolutionary process.

## CONCEPTUAL CONTRIBUTIONS OF MAMMALIAN STUDIES

Ever since Wallace's original work in the Malay Archipelago, many of the seminal contributions to biogeography have come from studies of mammals. And ever since the M–W model provided a theoretical perspective for investigating insular distributions, analyses of the diverse patterns exhibited by mammals on islands have contributed importantly to understanding the processes that determine the composition of insular biotas.

Some of the most significant contributions of mammalian studies have been methodological ones. It is easy to underestimate the importance of methodology. At least in these cases, methodological innovations have led to major conceptual advances and helped to resolve important questions.

### Deterministic or random?

A nagging question raised by the M–W model is the extent to which insular distributions are deterministic or stochastic. MacArthur and Wilson themselves were unclear and almost contradictory on this point. On the one hand, the equilibrium model presents a very stochastic view of essentially random colonization and extinction events determining the richness of an insular biota; the names, taxonomic affinities and ecologies of the species are not considered to be important variables. Yet, MacArthur and Wilson clearly recognized that this was an oversimplification, and they studied cases in which differences among species in such attributes as mechanisms of dispersal, demography and competitive ability profoundly influenced the composition of insular biotas (MacArthur & Wilson, 1967; see also Wilson, 1959, 1961; MacArthur, 1972; MacArthur et al., 1972, 1973).

Trying to distinguish between random and deterministic patterns and processes has continued to provide one of the major challenges in understanding insular distributions. A major contribution was made by Simberloff and his associates (e.g. Simberloff, 1978, 1980; Connor & Simberloff, 1978, 1979; Connor & McCoy, 1979), who advocated the development and testing of null or random hypotheses that assume a minimum of deterministic mechanism. Their analyses have tended to support a highly stochastic view of insular biogeography. In contrast, several of the contributions to this symposium (Patterson & Atmar, 1986; Lomolino, 1986; Lawlor, 1986; Crowell, 1986) advocate just the opposite viewpoint: that many of the differences among individual islands and entire archipelagos and among individual species and higher taxa can be explained, and hence predicted, in terms of measurable variation in the attributes of islands and organisms.

Although MacArthur & Wilson (1967) performed some simulations to show how probability of extinction could depend on population size and other demographic variables, extinction has long been regarded as a highly stochastic process. Certainly there is a significant element of chance, both in the fluctuations of any small population and in the environment, that may cause some of the variations. Nevertheless, the *relative* susceptibility to extinction of populations of different species or on different islands may be highly predictable. This is convincingly demonstrated by the analyses of Patterson & Atmar (1986), who have developed statistical techniques for determining whether the species compositions of islands within archipelagos differ from random assemblages. They find that landbridge islands, which are presumed to have biotas derived primarily by extinction from a common set of once widespread, continental species, exhibit non-random, nested subsets of species: i.e. each island with a successively smaller biota tends to have a subset of the species on more species-rich islands. Patterson & Atmar (1986) imply that the extinction process may be just as predictable in other situations, but its effect may be more difficult to detect when colonization as well as extinction has played a major role in determining the composition of the biota.

This latter problem is addressed by Lomolino (1986; see also Hanski, 1986), who has developed elegant techniques for determining the extent to which the occurrence of a species among the islands of an archipelago can be attributed to island size, distance from a source of species, or an interaction between these two variables. Like MacArthur and Wilson, Lomolino assumes that island size influences population size and hence extinction probability, and that distance from source affects colonization probability. Then, by analysing the incidence of each species as a function of these two variables, Lomolino is able to distinguish between species whose distributions are affected primarily by their capacities to immigrate from those whose distributions reflect mostly their ability to maintain viable populations on islands. That these assessments correspond well to our knowledge of the biology of the species supports the assumptions of the M–W model and the validity of Lomolino's analyses.

## *Equilibrium or non-equilibrium?*

The issues addressed by the M–W model remain the fundamental problems of insular biogeography: does the biota of an individual island or an entire archipelago represent an equilibrium between origination and extinction processes, and what are the processes that determine the number, taxonomic relationships and ecological characteristics of the species? Several papers in this symposium address these questions. As mentioned above, the analyses of Patterson & Atmar (1986) and Lomolino (1986) provide valuable insights into the processes of extinction and colonization. Both studies lend additional support to my conclusion (Brown, 1971; see also Findley, 1969; Patterson, 1980, 1984; Grayson, 1981; Thompson & Mead, 1982) that the boreal mammal faunas inhabiting the isolated mountain ranges in the southwestern United States are not in equilibrium, but are relicts, derived by extinctions from a set of species that colonized when appropriate habitat connections existed in the Pleistocene. Lawlor's (1986) analysis supports a similar interpretation for the non-volant mammal faunas of continental islands that were connected to the mainland by landbridges during the Pleistocene.

On the other hand, the studies of Crowell (1986), Hanski (1986) and Lomolino (1986) on real islands in the Gulf of Maine, lakes of Finland, and St. Lawrence River, respectively, indicate that the mammalian faunas of these archipelagos are approximately in equilibrium between opposing rates of colonization and extinction. These studies (see also Crowell, 1973, 1983; Lomolino, 1982, 1984a, b) largely agree, not only in adducing evidence for ongoing colonization (from an inverse relationship between species richness and distance to a source of species and from observations of turnover in species composition over time), but also in the specific mechanisms of colonization (dispersal across ice in winter) and extinction (small population size owing to limited resources, interspecific competition and predation).

Yet another contrast is provided by Lawlor's conclusion that some oceanic islands and archipelagos are not in equilibrium, because colonization rate has been insufficient to achieve an equilibrium with the relatively low extinction rate, especially on large and distant islands. Lawlor's evidence is based primarily on systematic differences in the slopes of species–area curves between bats and non-volant mammals and between oceanic and landbridge islands. Although there is precedence for such comparisons (e.g. MacArthur & Wilson, 1967; Brown, 1971, 1978; Barbour & Brown, 1974), the biological meaning of species–area relationships and the kinds of inferences that can be drawn from differences in slopes have been questioned (Schoener, 1974; Connor & McCoy, 1979; but see Sugihara, 1981). The fact that Lawlor (1986) can make *a priori* predictions that are supported by subsequent analyses of data suggests that species–area relationships can embody important biogeographic information, especially when specific comparative hypotheses are carefully framed and tested so as to control for the effects of extraneous variables.

Another perspective on the problem of equilibrium is provided by Heaney (1980), who emphasizes the importance of speciation as well as colonization in contributing to the origination of insular species. In his paper, Heaney synthesizes a large body of primarily descriptive work (but see Musser, 1977; Musser *et al.*, 1985; Heaney, 1984, 1985) to understand the composition of the mammal faunas of the islands of the Philippines and Sunda Shelf. This region has been the scene of much tectonic and volcanic activity, and it has a complex history of land connections among islands and to the mainland of SE Asia during the Pleistocene. Not surprisingly, the relationships among the non-volant mammals are also complex and reflect the influences of these historical events on the processes of colonization, differentiation, speciation and extinction. Perhaps the most important contribution of Heaney's work is his analysis of patterns of endemism and taxonomic affinity, which permits convincing reconstructions of dispersal (over both landbridges and water gaps) and of differentiation and speciation of isolated populations. The composition of the fauna can be visualized as approaching an equilibrial species richness through repeated episodes of colonization and speciation opposed by episodic extinctions. Perhaps more realistically, the fauna can be viewed as being in a perpetual state of perturbation, because geological and ecological changes occur so rapidly relative to some of the origination and extinction processes that the hypothetical equilibrium is never attained. This sort of general model can probably be applied to other archipelagos (i.e. the West Indies; see below), large islands (i.e. Madagascar and New Guinea), and even to continents.

Heaney's (1986) and Berry's (1986) studies indicate the importance of obtaining a much better understanding of the process of speciation. In particular, when speciation occurs by geographic isolation, it is essential to know whether allopatry resulted from long-distance colonization by a few individuals or from a vicariance event that isolated large populations. Resolution of this question is crucial for resolving the role of founder effects and other evolutionary forces in the speciation process. Berry and Heaney show that for some islands it is possible to identify populations that have been isolated by each mechanism, to estimate the date of separation and to assess the direction and rate of genetic and phenotypic differentiation.

A final insight into the problems of trying to understand the dynamics of insular biotas comes from the synthesis of Morgan & Woods (1986) of the present and past distributions of West Indian mammals. Although they place much more emphasis on the unique evidence provided by an excellent fossil record, Morgan & Woods (1986) develop a general scenario that is remarkably similar to that of Heaney (1986) for the islands of SE Asia. The non-volant mammal fauna of the archipelago reflects a complex history of: colonization across water gaps, interisland connections during periods of low sea level, and ancient landbridges to the mainland; differentiation and speciation of populations isolated on different islands or in different regions within single large islands; and highly episodic extinction. Perhaps the most important and sobering lesson of their work, however, is the enormous number of extinctions that can apparently be attributed to the direct and indirect effects of humans, both aboriginal and modern. So many species have been lost since humans colonized these islands, that the present faunas (especially of the large islands, which once supported diverse species including many well-differentiated endemics) bear little resemblance to their late-Pleistocene antecedents. These findings (see also Crowell, 1986) illustrate the potential pitfalls of assuming that the biota of any island that has ever been settled or otherwise substantially affected by humans reflects 'natural' processes of origination and extinction, let alone some kind of equilibrium! Perhaps we can take some consolation from the fact that some of the general patterns of insular biogeography, such as species–area relationships and Lawlor's contrast between bats and non-volant forms, appear to persist in the West Indian mammals despite this enormous effect of human-caused extinctions.

### Continents as islands?

The complexity of patterns and processes exhibited by the mammalian faunas of the SE Asian and West Indian archipelagos raises the question of whether and how the conceptual approach pioneered by MacArthur and Wilson can be applied to continental biogeography. This question has not been addressed comprehensively by any of the contributors to this symposium, but it is relevant here for several reasons. It represents a logical extension of ideas presented in several of the papers, but especially in those of Heaney (1986) and Morgan & Woods (1986). In fact, it offers the logical opportunity to generalize the entire approach of M–W, because from a biogeographic perspective continents are nothing more than very large islands with complex histories of climatic and geological change. Their faunas must reflect equally complex histories of colonization over both land and water, allochthonous and autochthonous differentiation, speciation and radiation, and highly episodic extinction owing to both natural causes and the effects of human beings. Any general theory of biogeography should apply to continents (and oceans) as well as to islands, and the same kinds of quantitative data are available to show patterns and test hypotheses.

Credit for first applying the M–W model to continents must go to my colleague Karl Flessa (1975, 1981), who analysed data on the distribution of mammalian genera from Walker (1968). Flessa's analyses demonstrated patterns of generic richness and affinities that suggested underlying mechanisms of colonization and extinction similar to those predicted by the M–W model. A positive relationship between number of genera and area of continent was closely fitted by a power curve and suggested that increasing extinction rates play a major role in limiting diversity on progressively smaller land masses. Flessa (1975) analysed data for all living mammals except marine forms. My plotting of genera– and species–area relationships for non-volant terrestrial mammals (Fig. 1) shows a similar pattern. Interestingly, as Lawlor predicts, the slope of the species–area relationship for non-volant mammals is very steep ($z$ value $= 0.48$) and diversity–area relationships are much steeper for non-volant mammals than for bats (e.g. $z$ values for genera–area curves $= 0.39$ and $0.18$ for non-volant mammals and bats, respectively).

Flessa (1981) used measures of generic similarity (Jaccard coefficients) to assess colonization and interchange among continents. This analysis, performed for both the non-volant mammals and the entire terrestrial mammal fauna including bats, revealed that in both cases similarity in faunal composition at the generic level was closely and inversely correlated with the overland distance separating the continents. This suggests that there has been and probably still is substantial interchange among continental faunas, and that such colonization occurs primarily over land connections at a rate inversely proportional to the distance that must be travelled by dispersing individuals. Interestingly, Flessa obtained a closer inverse correlation between faunal similarity and overland distance when bats were included than when they were omitted. This does not

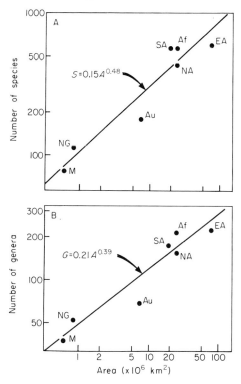

Figure 1. Plots on logarithmic axes of number of species (A) and genera (B) of non-volant terrestrial mammals inhabiting continents and large islands. The regression line and equation are shown. Land masses are identified as follows: New Guinea, NG; Madagascar, M; Australia, Au; South America, SA; North America, NA; Africa, Af; Eurasia, EA. Note the good fit of both regressions and the steep slope of the species–area relationship. (Species data from D. H. Wright, unpubl. obs.; genetic data from Nowak & Paradiso, 1983.)

indicate that bats are unable to colonize across large water gaps, because we know they have done so (e.g. Lawlor's analysis). Rather, it suggests that bats are excellent colonists that disperse over land even better than over water. Although Flessa does not emphasize this point, the overall magnitude of faunal dissimilarity among continents should be related to the degree of endemism, and hence reflect the extent to which the faunas have acted as isolated units, giving rise to distinctive taxa by speciation and evolutionary differentiation. Marshall and colleagues (Marshall *et al.*, 1982, Marshall, 1985) provide an excellent example of how these kinds of analyses and arguments can be applied to a particular case study. They account for the present composition of the South American mammal fauna in terms of colonization from other land masses (both over water gaps and the inter-American landbridge), autochthonous speciation, and extinction.

My student, Renee Rusler (unpubl. obs.), has analysed data obtained principally from Nowak & Paradiso (1983) on the body sizes of non-volant mammals in relation to their distribution among continents. Two patterns are of particular interest here. First, the relative number of large forms in the fauna, measured as the proportion of genera with median body mass exceeding some arbitrary threshold, increases directly with the area of the land mass (Fig. 2).

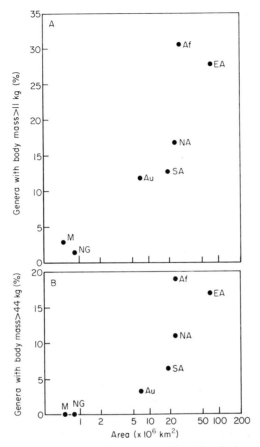

Figure 2. Plots of the percentage of mammalian genera with median body masses greater than two arbitrary values (11 and 44 kg) as a function of area of land mass on a logarithmic scale. Note that the proportion of genera of large body size in the fauna increases consistently with the size of the continent (data and analysis from R. Rusler, unpubl. obs.).

Secondly, the extent to which genera tend to be endemic to single land masses decreases with increasing body size, with the striking exception of the seven heaviest genera, which are without exception endemic to a single large continent (Fig. 3). Taken together, these patterns suggest that probability of extinction varies inversely with body size and hence with population density. Consequently, increasing land areas are required to support progressively larger mammals, and areas as large as the largest continents are necessary to maintain the largest living mammals over the time spans required for differentiation and radiation at the generic level. Since, in the last stages before its extinction, a taxon will tend to be restricted to a single region, we take the endemism of the largest mammals to single continents as evidence of high probabilities of extinction. Thus, this analysis complements that of Patterson & Atmar (1986) in providing independent evidence that variation in probability of extinction between taxa can be highly deterministic and can be attributed to biological variables that affect ecological attributes such as population size.

Taken together, the analyses of Flessa and Rusler suggest that the conceptual framework developed by MacArthur & Wilson (1963, 1967) for islands can

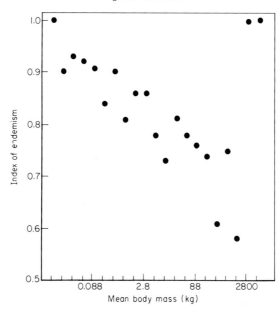

Figure 3. Plot of an index of endemism (1/the average number of continents inhabited) for genera of non-volant terrestrial mammals as a function of body size. Median body masses of genera were lumped into $\log_2$ categories for analysis. Note that endemism decreases regularly with increasing size, except for the very largest genera which are all endemic to single continents (data and analysis from R. Rusler, unpubl. obs).

productively be applied to continents. As in the case of island biogeography, however, considerable modification of the original M–W model is necessary to deal with the complexity of patterns and processes that are exhibited at a continental scale. For example, it should be emphasized that the analyses of both Flessa and Rusler are based on the mammalian genera and species that survived into historical times and are documented in museum collections of contemporary forms. Thus, they do not include the numerous forms known to have disappeared in the late Pleistocene and/or early Holocene. Like the extinction of the West Indian island faunas documented by Morgan & Woods (1986), the demise of these mammals has been attributed in large part to the impact of humans (e.g. Martin & Klein, 1984).

### APPLIED BIOGEOGRAPHY AND THE DESIGN OF NATURAL RESERVES

Applications of the M–W model of island biogeography to the design of natural reserves represent some of the first concerted efforts to apply theories of modern population biology to practical problems of ecosystem management. These efforts are now more than a decade old, and they have increased in sophistication with the theoretical and empirical advances of the field. These applications must be intensified if we are to preserve not only individual endangered species, such as the spectacular large mammalian carnivores and herbivores, but also entire habitats and ecosystems that support both human and non-human populations. Is the theory of biogeography and related areas of ecology and evolution up to this formidable task?

I do not think we know the answer to this question, and one could argue that we will know the answer only when it is negative and it is too late. On the other hand, I believe we are making progress rapidly, and that many beneficial results could be obtained by synthesizing and applying the kind of information contained in this symposium.

In particular, one of the important issues that has thus far been the subject of much controversy can now be largely resolved. There has been a long-standing debate about whether or not a single large reserve is preferable to several small ones of the same total area and habitat diversity, i.e. SLOSS: (e.g. Diamond, 1975; Terborgh, 1975; Wilson & Willis, 1975; Diamond & May, 1976; Forman, Galli & Leck, 1976; Galli, Lech & Forman, 1976; Simberloff & Abele, 1976, 1982; Whitcomb et al., 1976; Simberloff, 1978; Kitchener et al., 1980; Higgs, 1981; Reed, 1983; Lynch & Wigham, 1984; Wilcox, 1985). This problem is addressed cogently by Patterson & Atmar (1986). The nestedness expected in the distribution matrix (occurrence of species by islands) provides a rigorous theoretical basis for choosing the appropriate reserve design, but application of the theory requires detailed data on the variation in the environment and the requirements of the species.

In the absence of sufficient data (which is usually the case), the appropriate general model for reserve design is the biota of an archipelago of islands that were once interconnected but now are isolated by virtually absolute barriers. Mammals on isolated desert mountaintops (Brown, 1971, 1978; Patterson, 1980, 1984) or on continental shelf, landbridge islands (Lawlor, 1983, 1986) that have been isolated since the end of the Pleistocene provide excellent examples. Patterson & Atmar's (1986) demonstration that these faunas comprise highly nested subsets of species indicates the deterministic nature of extinction, and shows that species that are near the threshold of their area requirements (see also Lomolino, 1986; and data of R. Rusler presented above) should have a high probability of becoming extinct in all patches if the habitat is fragmented. The tendency of relictual faunas to occur as nested sets, together with their steep-sloped species–area relationships (Lawlor, 1986; see also Brown, 1971, 1978; Lawlor, 1983), means that a single large island preserves substantially more species of mammals than almost any combination of similar, but smaller islands. Such a large preserve will have to include the habitat types required by all species, however, or else it will have to be supplemented by other, presumably smaller, reserves that are designed specifically to preserve particular habitats and species.

From the perspective of conservation, the mammalian diversity supported by existing reserves can be misleading. For example, it is not surprising that Newmark (1986) reports many more species and a much lower slope for the species–area relationship for the mammals currently inhabiting National Parks in the western United States than Lawlor (1986) and I find for post-Pleistocene relictual insular faunas in islands of comparable habitat. This difference can be attributed to the fact many of the species that inhabit the parks also have substantial contiguous populations living outside the reserves, so that the persistence of these species cannot be attributed to the parks serving as the sole refuges. If all of the matrix between the parks were converted into uninhabitable terrain, the parks would be unable to preserve their present mammalian diversity (for an instructive mammalian example see Kitchener et al., 1980). In fact, the diversity of relictual mammals on desert mountain tops would suggest that reserves of less than about 500 km² should lose more than half of their species in a few thousand years!

Furthermore, the loss of species would not be random. Species that maintain small populations because of large body size, carnivorous diet, specialized habitat requirements, or other constraints would be differentially lost by extinction from all preserves. In fact, Renee Rusler's analyses suggest that the largest mammalian carnivores and herbivores require continent-sized areas in order to persist, so even the largest reserves in the world will not be sufficient to prevent the inevitable extinction of these species if present trends of human population growth and habitat alteration continue. This raises the disturbing spectre of a future world mammal fauna of drastically reduced diversity, comprised primarily of small herbivorous and insectivorous species that can persist in the reserves, and of commensals and other forms that can live in the drastically man-modified habitats outside the parks. Clearly, to avert such a future we require increasing attention to problems of applied biogeography.

## CRITIQUE AND PROSPECT

It would be easy to find some basis for criticizing all of the papers in this collection. Biogeography is such a large, diverse field that none of us can really master all of its many facets. I believe that one of the great strengths of mammalian biogeography during the last two decades has been its ability to produce empirically sound, conceptually important contributions without becoming embroiled in the often bitter, counterproductive ideological disputes that have dominated some parts of the discipline. It is easier to be a critic than a creator; it is easier to find fault with previous work than to evaluate its original contributions. In my role as commentator on this symposium, I have deliberately emphasized the positive. I have tried to synthesize the important data and ideas in the individual papers in order to assess the progress of the last twenty years and to point out the contributions of mammalian biogeographers to these advances.

But some general criticism of the subdiscipline of mammalian biogeography as represented by this symposium and the recent literature is warranted lest we become complacent. There are limitations and deficiencies in our present knowledge and approaches that require attention if mammalian biogeography is to maintain its position of prominence and leadership.

For one thing, we must avoid becoming too parochial and specialized. This symposium abundantly demonstrates that distributional patterns and processes are complex. To understand them accurately and completely requires that one know the geological and climatic history of the regions as well as their current geography and environments, and the past distribution and phylogenetic relationships of the organisms as well as their present ranges and ecological relationships. One must manage to keep abreast of the latest theory and statistical techniques, and still maintain the first-hand field experience with the regions and organisms that is essential to evaluate current ideas in a realistic context. One must know the distributional patterns of other groups in the same region and of the same group in other regions, because the similarities and differences offer valuable clues to the underlying processes. None of us can do all of these things really well, but we must do the best we can, admit our limitations and seek help to overcome them.

I suspect so many of us have chosen to study islands not just because islands are inherently interesting, but because, like Darwin & Wallace and MacArthur & Wilson before us, we believe that islands offer simplified, replicated, model systems for investigating more complex ecological, evolutionary and biogeographic problems. Up to a point, this perspective is justified, but we should question the extent to which islands provide good models for the more complex phenomena that are probably characteristic of continental and oceanic systems. Compare the satisfyingly simple patterns and processes invoked by Crowell (1986), Hanski (1986), and Lomolino (1986) to explain the distributions of a relatively few species on tiny islands, with the much more complex and tentative explanations advanced by Heaney (1986) and Morgan & Woods (1986) to account for the distribution and diversity of the mammalian faunas of the islands of SE Asia and the West Indies. Then imagine the problems of trying to explain the entire biogeography of South American or Eurasian mammals!

It is unfortunate that the kind of 'ecological' biogeography pioneered by MacArthur & Wilson (1963, 1967) and pursued by most of the contributors to this symposium, and the kind of 'historical' or 'vicariance' biogeography pioneered by Croizat (1958) and developed recently by Nelson, Platnick, Rosen and others (e.g. Nelson & Platnick, 1981; Nelson & Rosen, 1981), have developed as alternative, competing research programs. Although it is true that the former emphasizes dispersal and its role in the colonization of small islands, whereas the latter focuses on speciation and its effects on the distribution and diversification of biotas of large archipelagos and continents, the two approaches need not be mutually exclusive. In fact, as the studies of Heaney (1986), and Morgan & Woods (1986) clearly show, an integration of ecological and historical explanations is absolutely essential for understanding any reasonably complex distributional pattern. I predict that some of the greatest advances in biogeography in the next two decades will be made by those who have the breadth of knowledge and the courage to try to understand the distributions of organisms in terms of the influences of both ecological factors and historical events on the dynamics of colonization, speciation and extinction processes.

Perhaps one of the most important lessons of this symposium is that it is extremely difficult to account for the contemporary distribution of mammals on either islands or continents in terms of 'natural' patterns and processes that ignore or deliberately exclude the effects of human beings. Man has been an increasingly important part of the environment of mammals and other organisms for more than a million years. The distributions of all species of living mammals have been influenced by human activities. As shown by the studies of Crowell (1986), Heaney (1986), and Morgan & Woods (1986), it is virtually impossible to separate the effects of humans from 'natural' processes. It makes neither good sense nor good science to try. We must understand the world as it is, with man as an integral part of it. Basic as well as applied biogeographers must come to terms with this reality.

CONCLUSIONS

Two decades after its publication, the equilibrium model of MacArthur & Wilson (1963) continues to have enormous influence on the field of biogeography. This is not because the model itself provides an adequate explanation for the diverse patterns of insular distributions. The model, like most good models, is a deliberately oversimplified characterization of a much more complex reality. Often its assumptions have been shown to be incorrect and its predictions have been falsified. Nevertheless, the model continues to provide the conceptual foundation for an extremely successful research program that is largely responsible for the emergence of biogeography as a vigorous, modern, quantitative, hypothesis-testing science. As exemplified by the contributions to this symposium, the last two decades have seen real progress in understanding the distribution of organisms, especially among islands and other isolated patches of habitat.

This progress has occurred not so much because MacArthur and Wilson gave us the answers, but because they showed us how to ask the questions. The M–W model retains its influence because it still provides a conceptual framework that suggests interesting questions to ask, data sets to assemble, analyses to perform and alternative explanations to evaluate. This conceptual foundation, together with the numerous corrections, modifications, and extensions developed in the last two decades, provides the basis for interpreting the composition of biotas in terms of the interaction between the biological processes of colonization, extinction, and evolutionary differentiation and the historical and ecological settings in which these processes have occurred.

Studies of mammals have made major contributions to this endeavour. Mammals are amazingly diverse and this is reflected in a wide variety of distributional patterns. Bats are almost as vagile as birds, whereas terrestrial mammals are more sedentary than reptiles. Commensal murid rodents are currently colonizing and differentiating rapidly as they follow modern man around the world, whereas elephants have lost ground and diversity as they appear to be following the titanotheres and glyptodonts to extinction. The analysis of such diverse distributional patterns has enabled investigators working on mammals, from A. R. Wallace to G. G. Simpson to M. V. Lomolino, to make some of the most important conceptual contributions to biogeography.

This symposium suggests that the future of mammalian biogeography should be as bright as its past. There has been much progress in explaining the distribution of mammals, but much exciting work remains to be done. For good reason, we have tackled the easier problems first. Like Darwin & Wallace and MacArthur & Wilson, we have focused on islands because they provide small, replicated systems that facilitate analysis. The distributions of species and higher taxa within continents are more complex and for the most part remain to be deciphered. I believe it will require a combination of the approaches of MacArthur & Wilson, the recent promising developments in vicariance biogeography, and still additional conceptual advances of this magnitude before some of these continental distributions are well understood. In the meantime, we cannot delay applying our flawed and incomplete knowledge to the pressing problems of preserving natural ecosystems and their endangered native species, of which our nearest relatives, the mammals, comprise a distressingly large proportion.

## ACKNOWLEDGEMENTS

I am grateful to the numerous students and colleagues who have maintained my interest and knowledge of biogeography through their probing questions and stimulating discussions. I thank the other participants in this symposium for providing the basis for this synthesis, and for their herculean efforts to send me their manuscripts in time for me to prepare this one. I thank R. Rusler and D. H. Wright for generously allowing me to use the results of their unpublished analyses, and B. A. Harney, L. R. Heaney, M. Kurzius and B. D. Patterson for helpful comments on the manuscript.

## REFERENCES

BARBOUR, C. D. & BROWN, J. H., 1974. Fish species diversity in lakes. *American Naturalist, 108:* 473–489.

BERRY, R. J., 1986. Genetics of insular populations of mammals, with particular reference to differentiation and founder effects in British small mammals. *Biological Journal of the Linnean Society, 28:* 205–229.

BROWN, J. H., 1971. Mammals on mountaintops: nonequilibrium insular biogeography. *American Naturalist, 105:* 467–478.

BROWN, J. H., 1978. The theory of insular biogeography and the distribution of boreal birds and mammals. *Great Basin Naturalist Memoirs, 2:* 209–227.

BROWN, J. H., 1980. Two decades of homage to Santa Rosalia: toward a general theory of diversity. *American Zoologist, 21:* 877–888.

BROWN, J. H. & GIBSON, A. C., 1983. *Biogeography.* St. Louis: Mosby.

BROWN, J. H. & KODRIC-BROWN, A., 1977. Turnover rates in insular biogeography: effect of immigration on extinction. *Ecology, 58:* 445–449.

CONNOR, E. F. & McCOY, E. D., 1979. The statistics and biology of the species–area relationship. *American Naturalist, 113:* 791–833.

CONNOR, E. F. & SIMBERLOFF, D., 1978. Species number and compositional similarity of the Galapagos flora and fauna. *Ecological Monographs, 48:* 219–248.

CONNOR, E. F. & SIMBERLOFF, D., 1979. The assembly of species communities: chance or competition? *Ecology, 60:* 1132–1140.

CROIZAT, L., 1958. *Panbiogeography,* 2 Volumes. Caracas; published by the author.

CROWELL, K. L., 1973. Experimental zoogeography: introduction of mice onto small islands. *American Naturalist, 107:* 535–558.

CROWELL, K. L., 1983. Islands—insight or artifact?: population dynamics and habitat utilization in insular rodents. *Oikos, 41:* 442–454.

CROWELL, K. L., 1986. A comparison of relict versus equilibrium models for insular mammals of the Gulf of Maine. *Biological Journal of the Linnean Society, 28:* 37–64.

DARLINGTON, P. J., 1957. *Zoogeography: the Geographical Distribution of Animals.* New York: Wiley.

DIAMOND, J. M., 1975. The island dilemma: lessons of modern geographic studies for the design of natural reserves. *Biological Conservation, 7:* 129–146.

DIAMOND, J. M. & MAY, R. M., 1976. Island biogeography and the design of natural preserves. In R. M. May (Ed.), *Theoretical Ecology: Principles and Applications:* 163–186. Philadelphia: W. B. Saunders.

FINDLEY, J. S., 1969. Biogeography of Southwestern boreal and desert mammals. In J. K. Jones (Ed.), *Contributions in Mammalogy:* 113–128. *Miscellaneous Publications of the University of Kansas Museum of Natural History, 51:* 1–428.

FLESSA, K. W., 1975. Area, continental drift and mammalian diversity. *Paleobiology, 1:* 189–194.

FLESSA, K. W., 1981. The regulation of mammalian faunal similarity among continents. *Journal of Biogeography, 8:* 427–438.

FORMAN, R. T. T., GALLI, A. E. & LECK, C. F., 1976. Forest size and avian diversity in New Jersey woodlots with some land use implications. *Oecologia, 26:* 1–9.

GALLI, A. E., LECK, C. F. & FORMAN, R. T. T., 1976. Avian distribution patterns in New Jersey woodlots with some land-use implications. *Auk, 93:* 356–364.

GILBERT, F. S., 1980. The equilibrium theory of island biogeography: fact or fiction? *Journal of Biogeography, 7:* 209–235.

GRAYSON, D. K., 1981. A mid-Holocene record for the heather vole, *Phenacomys* cf. *intermedius,* in the central Great Basin and its biogeographic significance. *Journal of Mammalogy, 62:* 115–121.

HANSKI, I., 1986. Population dynamics of shrews on small islands accord with the equilibrium model. *Biological Journal of the Linnean Society, 28:* 23–36.

HEANEY, L. R., 1984. Mammalian species richness on islands of the Sunda Shelf, Southeast Asia. *Oecologia, 61:* 11–17.

HEANEY, L. R., 1985. Zoogeographic evidence for Middle and Late Pleistocene land bridges to the Philippine Islands. *Modern Quaternary Research in SE Asia, 9:* 127–143.

HEANEY, L. R., 1986. Biogeography of SE Asian mammals: estimates of rates of colonization, extinction and speciation. *Biological Journal of the Linnean Society, 28:* 127–165.

HIGGS, A. J., 1981. Island biogeography and nature reserve design. *Journal of Biogeography, 8:* 117–124.

KITCHENER, D. J., CHAPMAN, A., MUIR, B. G. & PALMER, M., 1980. The conservation value for mammals of reserves in the Western Australian wheatbelt. *Biological Conservation, 18:* 179–207.

KOOPMAN, K. F., 1968. Taxonomic and distributional notes on Lesser Antillean bats. *American Museum Novitates, 2333:* 1–13.

KOOPMAN, K. F., 1975. Bats of the Virgin Islands in relation to those of the Greater and Lesser Antilles. *American Museum Novitates, 2581:* 1–7.

LAWLOR, T. E., 1983. The mammals. In T. J. Case & M. L. Cody (Eds.), *Island Biogeography in the Sea of Cortéz:* 265–289, 482–500. Berkeley: University of California Press.

LAWLOR, T. E., 1986. Comparative biogeography of mammals on islands. *Biological Journal of the Linnean Society, 28:* 99–125.

LOMOLINO, M. V., 1982. Species–area and species–distance relationships of terrestrial mammals in the Thousand Island region. *Oecologia, 54:* 72–75.

LOMOLINO, M. V., 1984a. Mammalian island biogeography: effects of area, isolation, and vagility. *Oecologia, 61:* 367–382.

LOMOLINO, M. V., 1984b. Immigrant selection, predation and the distributions of *Microtus pennsylvanicus* and *Blarina brevicauda* on islands. *American Naturalist, 123:* 468–483.

LOMOLINO, M. V., 1985. Body size of mammals on islands: the island rule reexamined. *American Naturalist, 125:* 310–316.

LOMOLINO, M. V., 1986. Mammalian community structure on islands: the importance of immigration, extinction and interactive effects. *Biological Journal of the Linnean Society 28:* 1–21.

LYNCH, J. F. & WIGHAM, D. F., 1984. Effects of forest fragmentation on breeding bird communities in Maryland, USA. *Biological Conservation, 28:* 287–324.

MACARTHUR, R. H., 1972. *Geographical Ecology: Patterns in the distributions of species.* New York: Harper and Row.

MACARTHUR, R. H., DIAMOND, J. M. & KARR, J., 1972. Density compensation in island faunas. *Ecology, 53:* 330–342.

MACARTHUR, R. H., MACARTHUR, J., MACARTHUR, D. & MACARTHUR, A., 1973. The effect of island area on population densities. *Ecology, 54:* 657–658.

MACARTHUR, R. H. & WILSON, E. O., 1963. An equilibrium theory of insular zoogeography. *Evolution, 17:* 373–387.

MACARTHUR, R. H. & WILSON, E. O., 1967. *The Theory of Island Biogeography.* Monographs in Population Biology, Princeton University Press, *1.*

MACFADDEN, B. J., 1980. Rafting mammals or drifting islands?: Antillean insectivores *Nesophontes* and *Solenodon. Journal of Biogeography, 7:* 11–22.

MARSHALL, L. G., 1985. Geochronology and land mammal biochronology of the transAmerican faunal interchange. In F. G. Stehli & S. D. Webb (Eds.), *The Great American Biotic Interchange:* 49–85. New York. Plenum Press.

MARSHALL, L. G., WEBB, S. D., SEPKOSKI, J. J. & RAUP, D. M., 1982. Mammalian evolution and the Great American Interchange, *Science, 215:* 1351–1357.

MARTIN, P. S. & KLEIN, R. G. (Eds), 1984. *Quaternary Extinctions: a Prehistoric Revolution.* Tucson: University of Arizona Press.

MORGAN, G. S. & WOODS, C. A., 1986. Extinction and the zoogeography of West Indian land mammals. *Biological Journal of the Linnean Society, 28:* 167–203.

MUSSER, G. G., 1977. *Epimys benguetensis,* a composite, and one zoogeographic view of the rat and mouse faunas in the Philippines and Celebes. *American Museum Novitates, 2624:* 1–15.

MUSSER, G. G., HEANEY, L. R. & RABOR, D. S., 1985. Philippine rats: a new species of *Crateromys* from Dinagal Island. *American Museum Novitates, 2821:* 1–25.

NELSON, G. & PLATNICK, N., 1981. *Systematics and Biogeography. Cladistics and Vicariance.* New York: Columbia University Press.

NELSON, G. & ROSEN, D. E., 1981. *Vicariance Biogeography: a Critique.* New York: Columbia University Press.

NEWMARK, W. D., 1986. Species–area relationship and its determinants for mammals in western North American national parks. *Biological Journal of the Linnean Society, 28:* 83–98.

NOWAK, R. M. & PARADISO, J. L., 1983. *Walker's Mammals of the World,* 4th edition. Baltimore: Johns Hopkins University Press.

PATTERSON, B. D., 1980. Montane mammalian biogeography in New Mexico. *Southwestern Naturalist, 25:* 33–40.

PATTERSON, B. D., 1984. Mammalian extinction and biogeography in the southern Rocky Mountains. In M. H. Nitecki (Ed.), *Extinctions.* 247–293. Chicago: University of Chicago Press.

PATTERSON, B. D. & ATMAR, W., 1986. Nested subsets and the structure of insular mammalian faunas and archipelagos. *Biological Journal of the Linnean Society, 28:* 65–82.

REED, T. M., 1983. The role of species–area relationships in reserve choice: a British example. *Biological Conservation, 25:* 263–271.

SAUER, J., 1969. Oceanic islands and biogeographic theory: a review. *Geographic Review, 59:* 582–593.

SCHOENER, T. W., 1974. The species–area relationship within archipelagos: models and evidence from island land birds. In H. J. Firth & J. H. Calaby (Eds), *Proceedings of the 16th International Ornithological Congress:* 629–642. Canberra: Australian Academy of Science.

SIMBERLOFF, D. S., 1978. Using biogeographic distributions to determine if colonization is stochastic. *American Naturalist, 112:* 713–726.

SIMBERLOFF, D., 1980. Dynamic equilibrium island biogeography: the second stage. In R. Nohring (Ed.), *Acta XVII Congressus Internationalis Ornithologici, 2:* 1289–1295. Verlag der Deutschen Ornithologen-Gesellschaft.

SIMBERLOFF, D. S. & ABELE, L. G., 1976. Island biogeography theory and conservation practice. *Science, 191:* 285–286.

SIMBERLOFF, D. S. & ABELE, L. G., 1982. Refuge design and island biogeographic theory: effects of fragmentation. *American Naturalist, 120:* 41–50.

SIMPSON, G. G., 1980. *Splendid Isolation; the Curious History of Mammals in South America.* New Haven: Yale University Press.

SUGIHARA, G., 1981. $S = CA^Z$, $Z = 1/4$: a reply to Connor and McCoy. *American Naturalist, 117:* 790–793.

TERBORGH, J., 1975. Faunal equilibria and the design of wildlife preserves. In F. B. Golley & E. Medina (Eds), *Tropical Ecological Systems, Trends in Terrestrial and Aquatic Research:* 369–380. New York: Springer-Verlag.

THOMPSON, R. S. & MEAD, J. I., 1982. Late Quaternary environments and biogeography in the Great Basin. *Quaternary Research, 17:* 39–55.

WALKER, E. P., 1968. *Mammals of the World,* 2nd edition. Baltimore: Johns Hopkins University Press.

WHITCOMB, R. F., LYNCH, J. F., OPLER, P. A. & ROBBINS, C. S., 1976. Island biogeography and conservation: strategy and limitations. *Science, 193:* 1030–1032.

WILCOX, B. A. & MURPHY, D. D., 1985. Conservation strategy: the effects of fragmentation on extinction. *American Naturalist, 125:* 879–887.

WILSON, E. O., 1959. Adaptive shift and dispersal in a tropical ant fauna. *Evolution, 13:* 122–144.

WILSON, E. O., 1961. The nature of the taxon cycle in the Melanesian ant fauna. *American Naturalist, 95:* 169–193.

WILSON, E. O. & WILLIS, E. O., 1975. Applied biogeography. 534. In M. L. Cody & J. M. Diamond (Eds), *Ecology and Evolution of Communities:* 522–534. Cambridge: Harvard University Press.

# INDEX

Compiled by A. S. Thorley F.L.S.

*denotes a key word
App.—Appendix
Fig.—Figure
n.—note
Tab.—Table